How to Repair Lift Trucks

Other TAB books by the author

No. 967
$19.95

How to Repair Lift Trucks

By Paul Dempsey

TAB BOOKS

BLUE RIDGE SUMMIT, PA. 17214

FIRST EDITION

FIRST PRINTING—JULY 1978

Copyright © 1978 by TAB BOOKS

Printed in the United States
of America

Library of Congress Cataloging in Publication Data

Dempsey, Paul.
    How to repair lift trucks.

    Includes index.
    1. Industrial power trucks—Maintenance and repair. 2. Fork
lift trucks—Maintenance and repair. I. Title.
TL296.D45   621.8'63   77-22805
ISBN 0-8306-7967-7

Preface

Lift trucks are expensive to operate. According to Eaton Corporation computers, the owner of an LPG-fueled truck can expect to spend 61 cents per hour on maintenance during the first year of operation. This cost goes up to a whopping $2.46 per hour during the 10th year!

This book can save the owner some of these repair bills, and can also serve as a guide for auto mechanics who want to enter this lucrative field. While the focus is on internal combustion trucks, much of the technology applies to electric vehicles as well. Each system is described in careful detail, with the emphasis upon the unique aspects of lift trucks. For example, not many auto mechanics are familiar with diesel engines, and more and more lift trucks are diesel powered. One chapter covers diesel fuel systems—the major difference between these and gasoline engines. Another chapter is about the LPG fuel systems found on many trucks. You will learn how to handle this fuel safely, how to set up an engine to accept LPG, to troubleshoot, and how to perform component overhaul. Two chapters are devoted to hydraulics. The first explains how pumps, valves, motors, cylinders, and accumulators work—in enough detail so that you could build your own system from off-the-shelf components. The second hydraulics chapter details troubleshooting for the system at large and for individual components, and describes how to overhaul pumps, cylinders, and control valves. Since most failures involve the hoses, conventional braided and the new elastomer hoses are discussed in depth.

Engine overhaul and test procedures have a chapter of their own, as do the electrical and cooling systems. Another chapter covers steering, brake, wheel, clutch, and transmission repair.

I want to thank Messrs. John Alsentzer and Ronald T. Stewart of the Eaton Corporation for their help during the preparation of this book. Also, I wish to thank the firms acknowledged in the courtesy lines appending most illustrations. I owe a special debt to a mechanic named Joe Kinlaw, employed at Magnolia Compress in Galveston, Texas. Joe taught me more than this book could teach him.

Paul Dempsey

Contents

Maintenance Costs

Few truck owners understand the real cost of maintenance. And it's not their fault. These costs are hidden by inadequate records and are usually understated in the books. Accountants tend to include many maintenance related costs as overhead—when in fact these costs are the direct result of operating lift trucks.

LIFT TRUCKS AND MONEY

The Industrial Truck Division of the Eaton Corporation has this information, and it is an eyeopener. Eaton, the maker of Yale machines, keeps detailed records on 96,000 trucks in the field. These machines include all types from stand-up electrics for light warehouse duties to rugged diesels for the construction industry.

The size of the fleet (and it is surely the largest collection of lift trucks ever monitored) lends impressiveness to the study. One or two or even a thousand trucks might give atypical results. But with nearly 100,000 vehicles in the sample, Eaton's data is as convincing as insurance companies' actuary tables.

This backlog of data made possible computer projections into future costs. This service, known as Programmed Equipment Replacement (PER), is available free of charge to Eaton customers. The standard PER approach is to organize cost projections under five headings:

- Acquisition—the original purchase price.
- Capital—the cost of money used in the purchase.

Table 1-1. Typical PER Projection. (Courtesy Industrial Truck Div., Eaton Corp.)

YEAR	RUNNING TIME (HR)	MAINTENANCE AMOUNT (DOLLARS)	COST/HR (DOLLARS)	OWNERSHIP AMOUNT (DOLLARS)	COST/HR (DOLLARS)	DOWN TIME COST (DOLLARS)	OBSOLESCENCE COST (DOLLARS)	TOTAL COST AMOUNT (DOLLARS)	COST/HR (DOLLARS)	REPLACEMENT SAVINGS (DOLLARS)
1	2,000	962	0.48	4,913	2.46	480	1	6,356	3.178	....
2	4,000	2,157	0.54	5,538	1.38	1,075	1	8,771	2.193	....
3	6,000	3,400	0.57	6,163	1.03	1,700	1	11,264	1.877	....
4	8,000	5,907	0.74	6,613	0.83	2,950	1	15,471	1.934	....
5	10,000	7,245	0.72	7,063	0.71	3,620	1	17,929	1.793	....
6	12,000	8,447	0.70	7,313	0.61	4,220	1	19,981	1.665	....
7	14,000	11,198	0.80	7,513	0.54	5,595	1	24,307	1.736	994
8	16,000	13,781	0.86	7,713	0.48	6,890	1	28,385	1.774	1,744
9	18,000	16,538	0.92	7,813	0.43	8,265	1	32,617	1.812	2,646
10	20,000	19,613	0.98	7,913	0.40	9,805	1	37,332	1.867	4,040

[1]Based on 4000-lb capacity, cushion-tired gas truck with automatic transmission and single-stage mast; purchase price, $8913. Operates two shift on good floors in clean environment under normal duty conditions.

- Downtime—the cost incurred by production when a truck goes out of service.
- Obsolescence—the cost of using an old truck when a new, improved model would be more productive.
- Maintenance—the cost of repair.

This approach is detailed enough for most lifttruck owners. However, PER is quite flexible—any cost item can be isolated. Projections have been made on tire wear, fuel consumption, the cost of changing points and condensers. The last showed that a solid state ignition system, a system that does away with these troublesome parts, saves $0.04 an hour.

"Tell me what sort of truck you have, how you use it," says Mr. John Alsentzer, Manager of the Industrial Truck Division, "and I'll tell you your costs for the next year or the next ten years to the tenth of the penny."

One recurring theme in these computer projections is the high cost of maintenance. If the machine described in Table 1-1 were traded in at its optimum economic life, it would have accumulated 12,000 running hours. Maintenance would have cost $0.70 an hour and would have totaled $8447 or 98% of the acquisition cost. If the machine were operated 2000 hours longer, maintenance costs jump to $11,198 or 125% of the original cost.

Why is maintenance so expensive?

LABOR COSTS

Labor costs are high in any industry. Even if the mechanic works for sweat-shop wages, the true wage rate is two, three, or even four times the mechanic's rate. True wage rates may not be of much comfort to the mechanic, since he does not see the money. But true wages plus the burden costs (benefits, overhead, etc.) are part of the cost of maintenance.

Benefits include hospitalization, unemployment insurance and Social Security. These programs add another 22% (the industry average) to the nominal wage rate. Of course, firms that offer retirement programs, recreational facilities, and other worker benefits incur higher true wage costs.

There are 260 working days in the year. But the mechanic's wages (typically) continue through ten holidays and three days of sick leave. At least 13 days out of the 260 available are nonproductive and amount to a 5% bonus.

It is assumed that the mechanic works a full eight hour day. But this is not the case. He must have coffee breaks and time must be allotted in the work schedule for cleanup and other miscellaneous duties associated with the shop and its equipment. If we suppose that a half-hour a day is used in this manner, then the true wage rate jumps another 6%.

The press of work is rarely so insistent that mechanics cannot take an occasional breather. Indeed, the rhythm of mechanical work is one of its attractions. You see a job through to its completion and have a moment or so to relax before the next one. (Foremen have been known to keep their men looking busy with make-work, but this approach merely disguises true costs.)

Shop situations vary and it is difficult to generalize about how much time the mechanics stand idle. From experience it appears that the typical mechanic spends 10–15% of his time talking, smoking, and puttering between jobs. Hourly wages, already inflated by taxes, holidays, sick leaves, and authorized rest periods, go up accordingly.

Everyone makes mistakes and mechanics are no exception. Even the most experienced mechanics occasionally have a call back.

Call backs are expensive. In commercial shops the costs are painfully obvious since the shop must make the work good. In-house shops—those shops that service the firm's own equipment—do not boast of their mistakes and can usually correct them without management's knowledge. But recognized or not, the costs are there and can account for 5% of the mechanic's productive time.

OVERHEAD COSTS

Shop overhead is another matter. Accountants keep a separate tally of overhead but overhead is another maintenance expense. And to figure the true costs of a particular bit of maintenance, the overhead has to be added to the mechanic's wages.

Overhead costs are very difficult to make generalizations about. First echelon maintenance on gasoline and LPG machines is relatively simple and few shop tools are needed. Serious diesel work requires a heavy investment in test equipment, and these costs are part of the overhead.

Other shop expenses include parts inventory (or more exactly the cost of the money used to purchase parts, since parts cost for each machine is not included under labor), heating, lighting, insurance, and shop maintenance. Many of these costs are inflexible. For example, the investment in parts is not as much a function of the number of mechanics hired as it is of the equipment. Parts inventory is determined by the number of trucks in service and their use. A one- or two-man shop may burden their rates with overhead costs two or three times greater than their nominal wages.

If a supervisor is employed—and one usually is when there are four or more mechanics in the crew—his wages are pure overhead. The rare exception is a supervisor who actually works on the trucks. His supervisory functions would not exist were it not for the mechanics under him. Therefore his wages are added to the shop rates. If the supervisor is paid the same as the mechanics, and four mechanics were hired, the cost of supervision adds 25% on top of mechanic's real wages.

The wages of a parts man are added to the mechanics like those of a supervisor, and is also an overhead expense. Without someone at the counter, it has been observed that mechanics spend 10% of their working day looking up parts.

Once the true wage rate is determined, the true cost of service operations is easy to calculate. One merely multiplies man-hours spent on the job by the true wage rate and adds the cost of parts. The results are a bit disconcerting. Eaton has service contracts on twenty-five million dollars worth of equipment in the Philadelphia area. An oil and crankcase filter change costs Eaton $25, plus parts, with the machine in the shop. If the mechanic has to travel, he can ring up another $25 before he opens his tool box.

TRUCK ENVIRONMENTAL LIFE

Automobile leasing companies consider 24 months or 55,000 miles to be the economic life of a passenger car. If they keep the vehicle longer, maintenance and depreciation skyrockets. Under extremely favorable operating conditions, the economical life of a lift truck is seven or eight years. Table 1-2 details the costs of such a vehicle. During this period it will have operated for 16,000 hours or more. If we assume that one hour of engine time translates as 35

Table 1-2. Costs—Clean Environment. (Courtesy Industrial Truck Div., Eaton Corp.)

YEAR	RUNNING TIME (HR)	MAINTENANCE AMOUNT (DOLLARS)	MAINTENANCE COST/HR (DOLLARS)	OWNERSHIP AMOUNT (DOLLARS)	OWNERSHIP COST/HR (DOLLARS)	DOWNTIME COST (DOLLARS)	OBSOLESCENCE COST** (DOLLARS)	TOTAL COST AMOUNT (DOLLARS)	TOTAL COST COST/HR (DOLLARS)	REPLACEMENT SAVINGS (DOLLARS)
1	2,000	732	0.36	4,955	2.47	366	1	6,055	2.03	
2	4,000	1,717	0.42	5,889	1.47	859	1	8,467	2.12	
3	6,000	4,025	0.67	6,605	1.10	2,013	1	12,644	2.11	
4	8,000	4,898	0.61	7,102	0.88	2,449	1	14,449	1.81	
5	10,000	6,108	0.61	7,380	0.73	3,054	1	16,542	1.65	
6	12,000	8,532	0.71	7,575	0.63	4,266	1	20,375	1.70	
7	14,000	9,485	0.67	7,770	0.55	4,743	1	21,999	1.57	
8	16,000	10,876	0.67	7,965	0.49	5,438	1	24,280	1.52	
9	18,000	13,621	0.75	8,160	0.45	6,810	1	28,592	1.59	1,278
10	20,000	15,304	0.76	8,355	0.41	7,652	1	31,311	1.57	980

YEAR	RUNNING TIME (HR)	DOWNTIME (HR)	PREVENTIVE MAINTENANCE (DOLLARS)	ENGINE OVERHAUL (DOLLARS)	MINOR REPAIRS (DOLLARS)	MAJOR REPAIRS (DOLLARS)	TIRES (DOLLARS)	MAINTENANCE AMOUNT (DOLLARS)	MAINTENANCE COST/HR (DOLLARS)
1	2,000	73	330	0	402	0	0	732	0.36
2	4,000	172	660	0	805	113	140	1,717	0.42
3	6,000	403	990	1,210	1,207	338	280	4,025	0.67
4	8,000	490	1,320	1,210	1,610	338	420	4,898	0.61
5	10,000	611	1,650	1,210	2,012	675	560	6,108	0.61
6	12,000	853	1,980	2,420	2,447	1,125	560	8,532	0.71
7	14,000	949	2,310	2,420	2,930	1,125	700	9,485	0.67
8	16,000	1,088	2,640	2,420	3,490	1,485	840	10,876	0.67
9	18,000	1,362	2,790	3,630	4,116	1,924	980	13,621	0.75
10	20,000	1,530	3,300	3,630	4,812	2,442	1,120	15,304	0.76

*Acquisition price = $9355.
**Obsolescence cost assigned $1.00 value since the product to be handled will not change.

miles (some builders would put the figure at 45 miles), the truck will have clocked the equivalent of 560,000 miles.

And the truck will have worked hard during this 560,000 miles. Its engine will have been started some 100 times more frequently than a typical auto engine for the same mileage, its chassis subjected to severe road shocks acting through its primitive suspension. The number of times the steering axle will have been turned from lock to lock is beyond calculation. And if the truck has been used productively, it will have been loaded.

The cost profile in Table 1-2 assumes a clean environment. Few trucks are so lucky. And those that operate in severe environments assume lower trade-in values and skyrocketing maintenance costs. For example, Table 1-3 profiles a truck in a foundry situation. The vehicle is identical to the one in Table 1-2; it does not benefit from special adaptive equipment.

A foundry is one of the most unhealthy environments for machines (and people). Dust is everywhere and seeps past ordinary filters and seals. The floor is rough and dirty. Engines, hydraulic components, tires, and chassis parts wear quickly.

The table tells the story. This truck has an economic life of five years or 10,000 hours (compared to eight years and 16,000 hours in a clean environment). If the owner keeps the truck for two years past its economical life, he will incur expenses of $1708 that he cannot recoup by trading off, rebuilding, or any other means. The longer he keeps it the more expensive it becomes. At the end of five years, tires will have cost $840 (in the clean environment the same tire cost stretches out over eight years). The engine will require overhaul at 4000 hours (as opposed to 6000 hours for the clean environment). And on and on.

Operating hours—the hours the engine runs, whether or not the machine is moving—and environment are the big variables. Cut operating hours, or upgrade the environment, and the maintenance costs drop.

CUTTING MAINTENANCE COSTS

Operating hours and the environment are pretty well fixed. A truck is purchased to do a job, and there are definite limits on how far the job can be tailored to suit the truck.

Table 1-3. Costs—Dirty Environment. (Courtesy Industrial Truck Div., Eaton Corp.)

YEAR	RUNNING TIME (HR)	MAINTENANCE AMOUNT (DOLLARS)	MAINTENANCE COST/HR (DOLLARS)	OWNERSHIP AMOUNT (DOLLARS)	OWNERSHIP COST/HR (DOLLARS)	DOWN TIME COST (DOLLARS)	OBSOLESCENCE COST (DOLLARS)	TOTAL COST AMOUNT (DOLLARS)	TOTAL COST COST/HR (DOLLARS)	REPLACEMENT SAVINGS (DOLLARS)
1	2,000	1,458	0.72	4,955	2.47	729	1	7,142	3.57	
2	4,000	4,318	1.07	6,280	1.57	2,159	1	12,758	3.19	
3	6,000	6,001	1.00	7,205	1.20	3,000	1	16,207	2.70	
4	8,000	9,216	1.15	7,730	0.96	4,608	1	21,555	2.69	
5	10,000	11,860	1.18	7,855	0.78	5,930	1	25,646	2.56	
6	12,000	15,402	1.28	8,105	0.67	7,701	1	31,209	2.60	432
7	14,000	19,511	1.39	8,355	0.59	9,756	1	37,623	2.69	1,708
8	16,000	23,493	1.46	8,605	0.53	11,747	1	43,846	2.74	2,800
9	18,000	28,399	1.57	8,855	0.49	14,200	1	51,455	2.86	5,292
10	20,000	33,172	1.65	9,105	0.45	16,586	1	58,864	2.94	7,560

YEAR	RUNNING TIME (HR)	DOWNTIME (HR)	PREVENTIVE MAINTENANCE (DOLLARS)	ENGINE OVERHAUL (DOLLARS)	MINOR REPAIRS (DOLLARS)	MAJOR REPAIRS (DOLLARS)	TIRES (DOLLARS)	MAINTENANCE AMOUNT (DOLLARS)	MAINTENANCE COST/HR (DOLLARS)
1	2,000	146	561	0	644	113	140	1,458	0.72
2	4,000	432	1,122	1,210	1,368	338	280	4,318	1.07
3	6,000	600	1,683	1,210	2,012	675	420	6,001	1.00
4	8,000	922	2,277	2,420	2,833	1,125	560	9,216	1.15
5	10,000	1,186	2,838	2,420	3,838	1,924	840	11,860	1.18
6	12,000	1,540	3,399	3,630	4,951	2,442	980	15,402	1.28
7	14,000	1,951	3,993	4,840	6,520	3,038	1,120	19,511	1.39
8	16,000	2,349	4,554	4,840	8,443	4,397	1,260	23,493	1.46
9	18,000	2,840	5,115	6,050	10,558	5,277	1,400	28,399	1.57
10	20,000	3,317	5,709	6,050	13,442	6,290	1,680	33,172	1.65

*Acquisition price = $9355.

**Obsolescence cost assigned $1.00 value on the basis that the nature of the product to be handled will not change for the foreseeable life of the equipment

18

Special Equipment

The truck can be adapted to the environment at relatively little expense. For example, the truck intended for foundry duties could be modified with a factory-installed kit at purchase. A prefilter in front of the air cleaner, boots on the hydraulic cylinders, and detailed work on the oil and grease seals adds about $450 to the price. But the results are more than worth the investment.

Table 1-4 is a projection of costs for this truck so modified. Notice that the economical life of the vehicle will stretch 4000 hours or two operating years. At this point total maintenance cost is nothing to sneeze at—$15,775. But the maintenance cost per running hour drops from $2.56 for an unprotected truck to $2.32 for a protected truck.

All the major truck manufacturers supply kits for dust protection, temperature extremes, and corrosive environments. But there are environments that are so extreme that the truck has to be engineered for them alone. Some of these environments are found in otherwise quite ordinary places. For example, a Kosher packing house is one of the most chemically corrosive environments known. Ordinary chromeplated piston rods survive 30 days before pitting into uselessness. Special hard-chroming doubles the life of the rods, but the ultimate solution requires an underlay of copper and nickel. Even then piston-rod life is measured in days rather than years.

Preventive Maintenance

PER and similar programs have not, to my knowledge, tabulated the effectiveness of preventive maintenance (PM). One reason is that Eaton holds service contracts on the vehicles under study and feels no obligation to experiment with neglect. Another reason is that the value of preventive maintenance is a well-proved way of reducing maintenance. Its effectiveness was demonstrated during the Second World War, and the day-to-day experience of industry underscores its importance.

The maintenance schedule provided with each machine is the one the manufacturer follows in his own service contract work. It has been pared down to a minimum, since each maintenance step costs money. The schedule is based on lab tests and field reports. Lab tests are reliable since vehicle components are stressed under

Table 1-4. Costs—Machine Modified for Dirty Environments. (Courtesy Industrial Truck Div., Eaton Corp.)

YEAR	RUNNING TIME (HR)	MAINTENANCE AMOUNT (DOLLARS)	MAINTENANCE COST/HR (DOLLARS)	OWNERSHIP AMOUNT (DOLLARS)	OWNERSHIP COST/HR (DOLLARS)	DOWNTIME COST (DOLLARS)	OBSOLESCENCE COST** (DOLLARS)	TOTAL COST AMOUNT (DOLLARS)	TOTAL COST COST/HR (DOLLARS)	REPLACEMENT SAVINGS (DOLLARS)
1	2,000	1,198	0.59	5,391	2.69	599	1	7,190	3.59	
2	4,000	4,025	1.00	6,716	1.67	2,013	1	12,755	3.19	
3	6,000	5,561	0.92	7,641	1.27	2,781	1	15,984	2.66	
4	8,000	8,532	1.06	8,166	1.02	4,266	1	20,966	2.62	
5	10,000	10,363	1.03	8,291	0.82	5,181	1	23,836	2.38	
6	12,000	13,621	1.13	8,541	0.71	6,810	1	28,973	2.41	
7	**14,000**	**15,775**	**1.12**	**8,791**	0.62	7,887	1	**32,454**	**2.32**	
8	16,000	19,618	1.22	9,041	0.56	9,809	1	38,469	2.40	1,376
9	18,000	22,308	1.23	9,291	0.51	11,154	1	42,753	2.37	1,026
10	20,000	27,938	1.39	9,541	0.47	13,969	1	51,448	2.57	5,080

YEAR	RUNNING TIME (HR)	DOWNTIME (HR)	PREVENTIVE MAINTENANCE (DOLLARS)	ENGINE OVERHAUL (DOLLARS)	MINOR REPAIRS (DOLLARS)	MAJOR REPAIRS (DOLLARS)	TIRES (DOLLARS)	MAINTENANCE AMOUNT (DOLLARS)	MAINTENANCE COST/HR (DOLLARS)
1	2,000	120	495	0	563	0	140	1,198	0.59
2	4,000	403	990	1,210	1,207	338	280	4,025	1.00
3	6,000	556	1,485	1,210	1,771	675	420	5,561	0.92
4	8,000	853	1,980	2,420	2,447	1,125	560	8,532	1.06
5	10,000	1,036	2,475	2,420	3,143	1,485	840	10,363	1.03
6	12,000	1,362	2,970	3,630	4,116	1,924	980	13,621	1.13
7	14,000	1,577	3,465	3,630	5,118	2,442	1,120	15,775	1.12
8	16,000	1,962	3,960	4,840	6,520	3,038	1,260	19,618	1.22
9	18,000	2,231	4,455	4,840	7,962	3,650	1,400	22,308	1.23
10	20,000	2,794	4,950	6,050	9,981	5,277	1,680	27,938	1.39

* Acquisition price = $9791.
** Obsolescence cost assigned $1.00 value on the basis that the product to be handled will not change.

20

controlled conditions. These tests show when a part will probably fail.

In other words, the maintenance schedule is not something dreamed up by engineers with their heads in the clouds. If hose replacement is called for at 4000 hours, change the hoses even though they might look good. You can be almost dead certain that if you don't, the originals are going to fail and dump hydraulic fluid all over the place. If the PCV valve is supposed to be replaced, do not try to save money by cleaning it. Replace the valve. It will more than pay for itself in fuel savings and in extended cylinder-bore life.

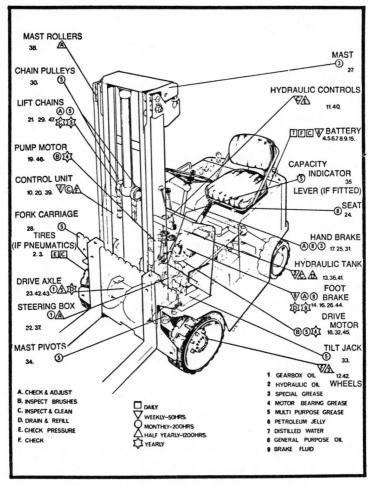

Fig. 1-1. Maintenance schedule for the Lansing Bagnall FOER 9.

PM schedules for Yale gasoline and electric trucks are shown in Figs. 1-1 and 1-2, and they cover all the lift trucks that Yale builds. While these schedules have been developed for the products of a single manufacturer, trucks built by other manufacturers do not differ markedly, and these schedules apply. LPG-powered machines require frequent inspections of the vaporizer, and diesel trucks need fuel-filter changes every 400 hours.

Maintenance Logs

OSHA (Occupational Safety and Health Administration) regulations have the force of law under the Williams-Steiger Act of 1970. The purpose of the act is to promote safety in the workplace. Necessarily, the regulations are complex and under more or less constant revision as new data and new technologies appear. But the broad outlines are clear.

OSHA requires that trucks be inspected daily. The regulation reads:

> Industrial trucks shall be examined before being placed in service, and shall not be placed in service if the examination shows any condition adversely affecting the safety of the vehicle. Such examination shall be made at least daily.

> Where industrial trucks are used on a round-the-clock basis, they shall be examined after each shift. Defects when found shall be immediately reported and corrected.

OSHA is primarily interested in those components that have a direct bearing on the vehicle's safety. Nameplates must be intact and legible; overhead guards and load backrest extensions must be secure; lighting systems must function and be adequate for conditions in the plant; fuel lines and the electrical system are to be fire safe.

If it can be shown that a truck has been cleared for service with a safety defect, the owner is liable. As a practical matter this means that a daily operator checkoff list must be filled out and filed. The list should show the data, model number of the truck, hour meter readings, and must be signed by the operator. Figure 1-3 illustrates checkoff lists for internal combustion and electric machines.

Gas Truck
Recommended Schedule of Maintenance

Gas Trucks Only

Legend:
- A—Every 8 Hours — O—Indicates Drain and Refill
- B—Every 200 Hours — √—Indicates Visual Inspection, Testing, Adjusting as Required.
- C—Every 400 Hours
- D—Every 1200 Hours — X—Indicates Replacement
- E—Every 2400 Hours — CO—Complete Overhaul

*Note: To comply with Engine Manufacturer's recommendations, oil and filter must be changed every 100 hours during warranty period.

Safety & Operational Check (To Be Performed By Operator)	A	B	C	D	E
Fuel	√				
Engine Oil Level	√				
Water Or Anti-Freeze	√				
LP Gas Odor Present ?	√				
Tires	√				
Engine Oil Pressure	√				
Ammeter Operating	√				
Lights	√				

Mast-Carriage-Platform Attachments Check:	A	B	C	D	E
Mast Safety Stops					
Mast Flange Wear			√		
Mast Rollers — Thrust Buttons			√		
Carriage Rollers — Thrust Buttons			√		
Tension Rod(s) Adjustment/Locknuts		√			
Chain Anchors		√			
Chain — Wear-Cracks (Use Wear Scale)			√		
Forks-Pallet-Platform (Visual)		√			
Forks — Use Magnaglo or Equivalent Fatigue Crack Detector					√
Attachments — Check Wear on sliding, rotating parts, Torque all Bolts			√		

Drive Unit Check:	A	B	C	D	E
Radiator Coolant check					O
Blow-off Radiator					
Radiator Leaks		√			
Radiator Pressure Cap		√			
Radiator Hoses		√			
LPG System Water Hoses		√			
LPG System Gas Pressure Hoses		√			

Fig. 1-2. Maintenance schedule with check-off. While quite detailed, these schedules are general enough to apply to all Yale (A) gasoline and (B) electric trucks. (Courtesy Industrial Truck Div., Eaton Corp.)

(Continued on following page.)

(Continued from previous page.)

Item	A	B	C	D	E
Horn	✓				
Hoist—Lower Controls	✓				
Tilt Control	✓				
Attachment Operation	✓				
Drive Control/Trans.	✓				
Steering	✓				
Service Brakes	✓				
Parking Brake	✓				
Hydraulic Leaks—Cylinders, Hoses, Valves, Etc.	✓				
Overhead Guard	✓				
Load Backrest	✓				
Lubrication Check:	A	B	C	D	E
Steam Clean or Blow-off Truck as required		✓			
Lubricate — Chassis (All Fittings)		✓			
All Linkage		✓			
Friction surfaces on Mast. and Attachments		✓			
Clean & Lub. Lift Chains		✓			
Clean/repack Wheel Bearings				✓	
CHECK:					
Engine Oil *		O			
Engine Oil Filter (Cartridge) *		X		X	
Clean Crankcase Breather/PC valve		✓			
Clean Engine Air Filter		✓			
Master Cylinder Fluid		✓			O
Hydraulic Oil		✓		O	
Hydraulic Oil Filter				X	
Power Steer Oil		✓		O	

Item	A	B	C	D	E
Fan, Pump, Alt. Drive Belts	✓	✓			
Water Pump		✓	✓		
Muffler for Leaks			✓		
Generator or Alternator Brushes, blow-out, check			✓		
Starter Brushes, blow-out, check			✓		
Fuel Pump					
Fuel Solenoid		✓			
Oil Pressure or Vacuum Switch		✓			
Carburetor Clean-Adjust			✓		
Governor setting			✓		
Spark plugs			X		
Engine Compression: Cylinder #1___, #2___ #3___, #4___, #5___, #6___, #7___, #8___					✓
Distributor Points		✓	X		
Ignition Timing			✓		
Starter/Ignition Switch		✓			
Instruments (Operational)		✓			
Foot Brake Adjustment		✓			
Clutch, Inching Pedal Adjustment		✓			
Parking and/or Dead Man Brake		✓			
Brake Drums and Linings				✓	
Engine Shock Absorbers					
Engine Mounting Bolts			✓		
Engine & Dr. Axle to Transmission Bolts			✓		
Wheel Bolts — Torque to Specs.			✓		
Brake Backing Plate/Slave Cyl. Bolts-Torque			✓		
Trunnion Cap Bolts — Torque to Specs.			✓		
Torque Transmission — Check-Adjust Hyd. Press.				✓	
General Check:	A	B	C	D	E

Item	A	B	C	D	E	CO
Transmission Oil		√		O		
Steering Gear Oil			√			
Differential Oil			√	O		
Fluid Coupling Oil			√	O		
Hydraulic Tank Breather		√		X		
Clean Transmission Screen/or				√		
Replace Filter Cartridge				X		
Gear Oil in Wheels — Check Level (Only on G5, K410, and similar models)			√	O		
Wet Clutch Oil Level			√	O		
Lub. Engine Heat Control Valve			√			
Hydraulic System Check:						
Hoist Cylinder for Leaks	√	√				
Tilt Cylinder for Leaks	√	√				
Tilt Cylinder Rod End Adjustment		√				
Main Hyd. Pump for Noise & Operation		√				
Main Control Valve for Leaks & Operation	√			√		
Relief Valve Setting				√		
All Hoses — Tubing-Fittings		√				
Auxiliary — Power Steer Pump		√				
Attachment Operation		√				
Attachment Cylinder for Leaks		√				
For General Leaks		√				
Steering — King Pin					√	
Drag Links					√	
Ring or Caster Bearing					√	
Ball Joints					√	
Bell Cranks, Steer Chain					√	
All Bolts, Nuts, Cotter pins, Etc.						
Tires				√		
Road Test Truck: General Condition					√	
Brakes					√	
Clutch					√	
Transmission Operation					√	
Acceleration					√	
Inching					√	
Hoist — Full Load					√	
Check drift ½" per minute max.						
Tilt — Full Load					√	
Check drift (at rod) 5/16" per minute max. (oil at 70° F.)						
Attachment — Check Operation				√		
Check Clamp Slippage				√		
Steering — Manual Operation				√		
— or — Power Operation				√		
Unusual Noises				√		

The Schedule shown is for normal, clean operation.

For abnormal temperatures, contamination, or moisture conditions, more frequent servicing will be required.

160—5839

Rev. May 1973

(Continued on following page.)

(Continued from previous page.)

26

Legend: Electric Truck Only

A—Every 8 Hours	O—Indicates Drain & Refill
B—Every 200 Hours	√—Indicates Visual Inspection, Testing, Adjusting as Required
C—Every 400 Hours	X—Indicates Replacement
D—Every 1200 Hours	CO—Complete Overhaul
E—Every 2400 Hours	

Safety & Operational	A	B	C	D	E
Check (to be performed by Operator)					
Battery Charge Specific Gravity	√				
Tires	√				
Lights	√				
Horn	√				
Hoist—Lower Controls	√				
Tilt Control	√				
Attachment Operation	√				
Drive Control	√				
Steering	√				
Service Brakes	√				
Parking Brake	√				
Hydraulic Leaks, Cylinders, Valves, Hoses, Etc.		√			
Overhead Guard	√				
Load Backrest	√				

Lubrication Check:	A	B	C	D	E
Steam Clean or Blow-off Truck as Required		√			
Lubricate Chassis (All Fittings)		√			
Lubricate All Linkage		√			
Lubricate Friction Surfaces On Mast And Attachments		√			
Clean & Lubricate Lift Chains		√			

	A	B	C	D	E
Forks-Pallet-Platform (Visual)		√			
Forks-Use Magnaglo or Equivalent Fatigue Crack Detector					√
Attachments — Check Wear on sliding, Rotating Parts, Torque All Bolts			√		

Drive Unit Check:	A	B	C	D	E
Foot Brake Adjustment		√			
Parking and/or Dead Man Brake		√			
Brake Linkage Adjustment				√	
Brake Drums and Linings				√	
Electric Motor Mounting Bolts			√		
Elec. Motor & Dr. Axle to Transmission Bolts			√		
Wheel Bolts — Torque to Specs.			√		
Brake Backing Plate / Slave Cyl. Bolts—Torque			√		
Trunnion Cap Bolts — Torque to Specs.			√		

Check:	A	B	C	D	E
Clean — Blow-out all Controls		√			
Contact Tips		√			
Interlock Switches		√			
Accelerator Switch		√			
Time Delay		√			
Direction Switch		√			
Dead Man Switch		√			
Drive Resistor or Carbon Pile (If Used)		√			
Valve Hoist/Tilt Switch		√			
All motors — Clean – Blow-out		√			
Drive Motor — Commutator		√			
Brushes		√			
Brush Springs		√			
Hoist Motor Commutator		√			
Brushes		√			

Left Section

Item	A	B	C	D	E
Clean/Repack Wheel Bearings			✓		
Check:					
Master Cylinder Fluid		✓			
Hydraulic Oil		✓		O	
Hydraulic Oil Filter				X	
Power Steer Oil		✓		O	
Transmission Oil		✓		O	
Steering Gear Oil			✓		
Differential Oil			✓	O	
Hydraulic Tank Breather				X	
Gear Oil In Wheels — Check Level (Only On K410 An_ Similar Models)		✓		O	
Hydraulic System	A	B	C	D	E
Check:					CO
Hoist Cylinder For Leaks		✓	✓		
Tilt Cylinder For Leaks		✓			
Tilt Cylinder Rod End Adjustment		✓			
Main Hyd. Pump For Noise & Operation		✓			
Main Control Valve For Leaks & Operation		✓			
Relief Valve Setting				✓	
All Hoses — Tubing — Fittings		✓			
Auxiliary–Power Steer Pump		✓			
Attachment Operation		✓			
Attachment Cylinder For Leaks		✓			
For General Leaks		✓			
Mast-Carriage-Platform-Attachments	A	B	C	D	E
Check:					
Mast Safety Stops			✓		
Mast Flange Wear			✓		
Mast Rollers — Thrust Buttons			✓		
Carriage Rollers — Thrust Buttons			✓		
Tension Rod(s) Adjustmen./Locknuts		✓			
Chain Anchors		✓			
Chain — Wear-Cracks (Use Wear Scale)			✓		

Right Section

Item	A	B	C	D	E
Aux. Pump Motor — Commutator	✓	✓			
Brushes	✓	✓			
Brush Springs	✓	✓			
Battery Connectors	✓	✓			
Battery Condition	✓	✓			
Charger Operation	✓	✓		✓	
All Wire Connections		✓			
General					
Check:	A	B	C	D	E
Steering — King Pins			✓		
Drag Links			✓		
Ring or Caster Bearing			✓		
Ball Joints			✓		
Bell Cranks, Steer Chain			✓		
All Bolts, Nuts, Cotter Pins, Etc.			✓		
Tires		✓			
Road-Test Truck:					
General Condition		✓			
Brakes		✓			
Gear Noise		✓			
Acceleration		✓			
Inching		✓			
Hoist — Full Load		✓			
check drift ½" per minute max.					
Tilt — Full Load		✓			
check drift (at rod) 5/16" per minute max. (oil at 70° F.)					
Attachment — Check Operation		✓			
Check Clamp Slippage			✓		
Steering — Manual Operation		✓			
— or — Power Operation		✓			
Unusual Noises		✓			

The Schedule shown is for normal, clean operation.

For abnormal temperatures, contamination, or moisture conditions, more frequent servicing will be required.

A checkoff list can be constructed to be a work order. It is not prima facie evidence that the work was actually performed. For his own legal protection the owner should keep a detailed maintenance log on each vehicle.

The maintenance log shown in Fig. 1-4 is the most comprehensive and, at the same time, the easiest to use that I have seen. Developed by Eaton, this log covers just about every conceivable repair and is coded so any mechanic can fill it out.

But even if OSHA inspectors don't come knocking at your door, a detailed maintenance log can save you money. In the first place a log, or a collection of them, shows how the mechanics are spending their time. Speed is not of the essence in repair work, but there is some relation between how long it takes a mechanic to perform a job and how proficient he is. Inexperienced mechanics spend a lot of time making false starts before they solve the repair problem. And over a period of months, the quality of the repair work shows up in the log. In some cases, repairs that have to be repeated at short intervals are the fault of the mechanic. In other cases, these chronic problems point to the driver or to the manufacturer.

A record of parts failures is helpful when deciding upon a parts inventory. Lightning can always strike, but most parts have an uneventful life that can be calculated almost to the hour. If crosshead bearings have failed at 7500 hours and the truck's use remains the same, you can expect the replacements to fail at 15,000 hours, right on schedule. Figure 1-5 shows many of the components needed for PM and failure repair.

DESIGN FACTORS

Lift trucks were to be practical during WWII and soon became indispensable to industry. The immediate post-war period was characterized by overdesign—that is, the traditional engineering practices were applied to these machines with a vengeance. Valve bodies were machined out of steel billets, parts were made deliberately stronger than necessary, and the engines' maximum life was underrated. While these trucks were undeniably reliable, they were also heavy and expensive.

The next period was characterized by attempts to rationalize production. Earlier trucks had been designed by engineers, but the

Date _____ Operator _____
Truck No. _____ Model No. _____
Dept. _____ Shift _____
Hour Mtr. Reading _____

Check	O.K. (✓)	Amount Added
Fuel		
Engine Oil Level		
Water Or Anti-Freeze		

Check	O.K. (✓) NO—	Need Maintenance YES—
LP Gas Odor Present?		
Tires		
Engine Oil Pressure		
Ammeter Operating		
Lights		
Horn		
Hoist—Lower Controls		
Tilt Control		
Attachment Operation		
Drive Control/Trans.		
Steering		
Service Brakes		
Parking Brake		
Hydraulic Leaks—Cylinders, Hoses, Valves, Etc.		
Overhead Guard		
Load Backrest		

Date _____ Operator _____
Truck No. _____ Model No. _____
Dept. _____ Shift _____
Hour Meter Reading—Drive _____ Hoist _____

Check	O.K. (✓)	Need Maintenance
Battery Charge Specific Gravity _____		
Tires		
Lights		
Horn		
Hoist—Lower Controls		
Tilt Control		
Attachment Operation		
Drive Control		
Steering		
Service Brakes		
Parking Brake		
Hydraulic Leaks, Cylinders, Valves, Hoses, Etc.		
Overhead Guard		
Load Backrest		

Fig. 1-3. Daily operator check-off lists. A applies to gasoline, LPG, and diesel trucks. B is for electrics. (Courtesy Industrial Truck Div., Eaton Corp.)

Truck No. _____ Dept. _____ Model _____ S/N _____

Attachments _____ Installation Date _____

Instructions:

Under "Service, Work Description, Component Codes" column below:

1. Enter type of service code from work order. Example—2
2. Add to it the work description code that applies method of servicing best. Example—2F
3. Then add the code for the component being serviced. Example—2F-0405-2 which means replaced spark plugs during routine maintenance.
4. If several repairs are made on the same date, be sure to list them all in the space provided or use the "Remarks" column or next line below if necessary.

Type of Service Code
1. Oil
2. Routine
3. Emergency
4. Overhaul
5. Accident/abuse
6. Warranty*

Work Description Code
A. Check fluid level
B. Drain & refill
C. Lubricate
D. Free up
E. Adjust
F. Replace
G. Repair
H. Rebuild
J. Repack
K. Tighten
L. Straighten
M. Weld

Note: *Warranty cost should not be entered into total cost to date.

Component Service Code

Brake system
0201 Wheel brake
0202 Cylinder brake
0203 Drums
0204 Fittings
0205 Linkage
0208 Brake shoes
0209 Wheel cylinder
0210 Master cylinder
0211 Brake spring
0220 Other

Wheels
1201-1 Wheels-drive
1201-2 Wheels-trail
1201-3 Wheels-caster
1202-1 Tires-drive
1202-2 Tires-trail
1202-3 Tires-caster
1204-1 Bearings-drive
1204-2 Bearings-trail
1204-3 Bearings-caster
1205 Seals
1206 Bolts
1220 Other

1008 Handle
1020

Trail assembly
1101 Axle
1102 Bell crank
1103 Knuckles
1104 Articulating shaft
1105 Platforms
1107 Pallet forks
1108 Outriggers
1109 Bearings, bushings
1110 Casters
1120 Other

Hydraulic
0601 Accumulator
0602 Mounting, etc.
0603 Hoist cylinder
0604 Steer cylinder
0605 Tilt cylinder
0606 Extend cylinder
0608 Filter
0609 Linkage
0610-1 Fittings
0610-2 Lines
0610-3 Hoses
0611 Bolts
0611-1 Hydraulic pump
0611-2 Trans. pump
0620 Other

Mast assembly
0301 Chain anchor
0302 Channel weldment
0303 Fork carriage
0304 Header (mast)
0305 Roller (mast)
0305-1 Roller (carriage)
0306 Cylinder guide
0307 Stops
0320 Other

Instruments/accessories
0701 Discharge indicator
0702 Horn
0702-1 Horn wiring
0702-2 Amp gauge
0703-1 Fuel gauge
0703-2 Temp. gauge
0703-3 Trans. pressure gauge
0703-5 Oil pressure gauge
0704 Hour meter
0705 Overhead guard
0706 Fork extension
0707 Cab
0708 Back rest
0709 Charger
0710 Head light
0711

Drive power
0401 Accelerator link
0402 Battery
0402-1 Battery cable
0402-2 Cable ends
0403 Engine block
0403-1 Head
0403-2 Head gasket
0404 Radiator
0404-2 Radiator hose
0404-3 Water pump
0404-4 Radiator cap
0404-5 Thermostat
0404-6 Fan belt
0405-1 Ignition wires

0805 Seat
0805-1 Seat cushion
0806 Battery box
0807 Cover, hood, sheet metal
0808 Motor oil
0809 Hydraulic Oil
0810 Gear oil
0811 Transmission fluid
0812 Brake fluid
0813 Fluid coupling oil
0814 Anti-freeze
0815 Water
0820 Other

0408-5 Fuel filter
0409-1 Sheave
0409-2 Belts
0409-3 Fan
0411-1 Solenoid valve
0411-2 Primary regulator
0411-3 Secondary regulator
0411-6 LPG lines
0411-7 LPG fittings
0411-7 Carburetor (LPG)
0411-8 LPG tank brkt.
0412 Primer switch
0412 Distributor
0412-1 Points
0412-2 Condenser
0412-3 Rotor
0412-4 Tune up kit
0412-5 Cap
0413-1 Generator/alternator
0413-2 Volt reg.
0414 Starter
0415 SCR diode
0416-1 SCR card
0416-2 Pack (electronic)
0420 Other

0913 Ring gear & pinion, diff
0914 Axle
0920 Other

Electrical
0501 Accelerator switch
0502 Connector
0503 Contactor
0503-1 Contact tip
0.03-2 Coil
0503-3 Armature
0503-4 Spring
0504 Directional switch
0505 Resistor
0506 Switch
0507-1 Primary wiring
0507-2 Secondary wiring
0507-3 Handle wiring
0509-1 SCR thermo relay
0509-3 SCR transformer
0509-4 SCR capacitor
0509-5 SCR misc.
0511 Fuse
0520 Other

1302-1 Hoist-brushes
1302-2 Hoist-springs
1302-3 Hoist-bearings
1302-4 Hoist-Armature
1303 Steer-
1303-1 Steer-brushes
1303-2 Steer-springs
1303-3 Steer-bearings
1303-4 Steer-armature
1304 Blower
1304-1 Blower-brushes
1304-2 Blower-springs
1304-3 Blower-bearings
1304-4 Blower-armature
1305 Extend
1305-1 Extend-brushes
1305-2 Extend-springs
1305-3 Extend-bearings
1305-4 Extend-armature
1320 Other

Attachment
0108 Attachment parts
0109 Electrical parts
0110 Hose take up
0110-1 Hose take up hose
0110-2 Hose take up bar
0110-3 Hose take up reel
0111 Fittings
0111-1 Lines

Steering
1001 Steer. gear assem.
1002 Power hyd. except pump, valve, cyl.
1003 Linkage
1004 Wheel or tiller
1005 Ring brg. or brkt.
1006 Bushing
1007 Shaft or column

0611-3 Power steer. pump
0612-1 Hoist & tilt valve
0612-2 Steer valve
0612-3 Lowering valve
0612-4 Check valve
0612-5 Solenoid valve
0613 Tanks
0614 Coupling
0620 Other

0405-2 Plugs
0405-3 Coil
0405-4 Ignition switch
0406-1 Muffler
0406-2 Clamps
0408-1 Carburetor
0408-2 Fuel pump
0408-3 Governor
0408-4 Fuel lines

0712 Tail light
0713 Rotating light
0720 Other

Miscellaneous
0602 Counterweight
0603 Forks
0804 Frame

Power transfer
0901 Clutches
0902 Shafts
0903 Gearing
0904 Housing
0905 Hyd. components
0906 Torque converter
0907 Flywheel
0908 Linkage
0909 Bearings
0910 Seals, gaskets
0911 Fluid coupling

Motors
1301 Drive-brushes
1301-1 Drive-springs
1301-2 Drive-bearings
1301-3 Drive-armature
1302 Hoist

0111-2 Hoses
0111-3 Cable
0112 Cylinder
0113 Arms
0114 Pads
0115 Motor
0116 Linkage
0117 Wear strips
0120 Other

Date	Work Order	Hour Meter Reading	Parts Cost	Labor Cost	Labor Hours	Total Cost	Total Cost to Date	Service, Work Description, Component Codes	Remarks

Fig. 1-4. Maintenance log. Each class of repair—e.g., warranty, routine, emergency—is given a code number. An additional four-number digit indentifies the repair area and an alphabetical code describes the nature of the work. Beautiful. (Courtesy Industrial Truck Div., Eaton Corp.)

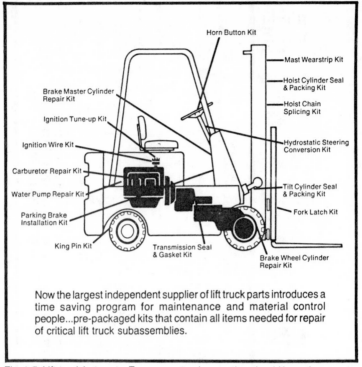

Now the largest independent supplier of lift truck parts introduces a time saving program for maintenance and material control people...pre-packaged kits that contain all items needed for repair of critical lift truck subassemblies.

Fig. 1-5. Lift-truck hot spots. Even a one-truck operation should have these parts on hand. (Courtesy List Parts Mfg. Co., a division of Echlin Mfg. Co.)

next designs looked like the creations of cost accountants. This generation cost less to build, but they also tended to be less reliable than their predecessors. Consequently, the money the customer saved in the purchase was spent many times over in maintenance.

At the same time the cost accountants have been able to reduce, or at least stabilize, production costs. Wherever possible, parts are cast rather than machined. Large parts—parts that would call for expensive foundry work—are made up of weldments. Some lift trucks use commercial-grade I-beams for chassis members. Nearly all hydraulic components are purchased "off the shelf," from general suppliers. With the exceptions of Continental and Perkins, engines are basically automobile power plants. Trucks are also built in families that share common parts, which decreases manufacturing and inventory costs.

While it may not be intentional, production efficiencies also reduce maintenance costs. Since fewer special parts are in each machine, dealers can also reduce inventories. And since many parts are borrowed from the automotive and hydraulic industries at large, a knowledgeable owner can purchase replacements directly. The operative word in the last sentence is "knowledgeable." You have to know what you're doing in order to get the correct part. In some instances, the manufacturer has specified special parts for his particular application.

While a prospective truck buyer can do little about these design factors, he should realize their importance. The enlightened members of the lift-truck industry no longer sell only hardware—they sell a working package. The vehicle itself is still important, but it is just a part (albeit a major part) of that package. Most trucks are capable of doing their designated work. The real difference between makes is the cost of maintenance. Assuming that the owner keeps his part of the bargain—hires reputable mechanics, follows a rigorous PM schedule, keeps records—the cost of maintenance is dependent upon the manufacturer's continuing evaluation of his product and his willingness to act on this knowledge.

POWER CHOICES

Gasoline? LPG? Diesel? Electric? The choice can be difficult, even if we confine ourselves to the area of maintenance.

Gasoline

Gasoline powered trucks have been popular in this country because of the availability of industrial and automotive engines and because of relatively low fuel costs. These engines are well understood by mechanics and parts problems are manageable. But gasoline engines require more routine maintenance than the others and have a relatively short operating time between overhauls. Air pollution is another problem, and one that will become more severe if OSHA sets hydrocarbon, carbon monoxide, and oxides of nitrogen standards for industrial trucks. Kits are available to make the exhaust more breathable, but as yet lift truck manufacturers have not been required to meet Clean Air Act standards. If, or more realistically, when they are forced to do so, the engines will be burdened with the same sort of smog gear that one finds on automobiles. Maintenance hours and fuel consumption will increase.

Fig. 1-6. This Yale is offered with three powerplant options—gasoline, LPG, or diesel. All engines are built by Ford. The gasoline version is rated at 78 hp at 2600 rpm; the diesel develops 65 hp at 2400 rpm. The carburetor on the gasoline engine has been modified to meet California emissions standards.

LPG

A standard gasoline engine can be adapted to burn LPG (liquified petroleum gas) quite easily. The conversion involves a pressure vessel to store the liquified gas, a regulator/converter to boil off the liquid, and a special carburetor. With a few additional modifications, the machine can be adapted to burn natural gas.

LPG is clean. Engine life is extended and the exhaust is relatively sanitary. While LPG costs have been historically lower than those associated with gasoline, the price differential between the two varies with demand. LPG is primarily a heating fuel, and truck users represent a very small segment of the market. When shortages develop, truck users have last call.

The quality of the fuel can reflect its primary role. Recently a number of lift trucks in the northeast were stalled by oil-flooded regulators. Analysis showed the oil was compressor oil that had entered the gas during manufacture. Trace quantities of oil have little effect on heating systems, and the industry had ignored the problem until alerted by lift-truck users.

Assuming that the price remains below that of gasoline and that the fuel is usable (LPG manufacturers insist that compressor oil can be virtually eliminated from the product), savings depend upon careful adjustment of the regulator. Few mechanics realize the importance of the adjustment and, if anything, tend to run their machines rich.

Diesel

Diesel power is popular in England and promises to become increasingly so here. The reason is operating economy. Diesel fuel is less costly than gasoline on a per gallon basis and each gallon of diesel oil contains some 16,000 Btus of heat energy as opposed to 12,000

Fig. 1-7. A Lansing Bagnall electric on duty with the British Ministry of Defense. This particular model—a FRER 5—features solid-state control circuits, long-range batteries, and an electrically powered pantograph to extend the forks.

Btus for gasoline. The compression-ignition engine burns fuel more efficiently, achieving thermal efficiency of nearly 40% as opposed to 30% or so for spark ignition.

In general, diesel maintenance costs are lower. The tuneup concept has very little relevance to a compression-ignition engine. The only periodic maintenance required are fuel filter changes and occasional checks of the fuel timing. And these engines are designed to run longer between overhauls. Parts are understressed and oiling systems can become quite sophisticated, with jets of oil directed at the undersides of the piston crowns, two-stage filtration, fully chamfered oil ports, and oversized pumps. In intracity bus service the Detroit Diesel two-cycle is warranted for 100,000 miles. A million miles is not unusual between major overhauls.

Diesel engines are the cleanest internal combustion engines known. The inherent efficiency of the engine coupled with fuel injection almost eliminates hydrocarbons and carbon monoxide in the exhaust. Some oxides of nitrogen are present, but well under 1975 Clean Air Act limits. Indeed, the Mercedes-Benz four-cylinder diesel was the first passenger car to meet these standards. The only emissions control equipment fitted was a PCV valve.

The weight and bulk of diesels are part of the penalty of compression-ignition. Compression ratios are on the order of 20:1 and pistons, rods, crankshafts, and cylinder heads must be sturdy enough to withstand these pressures. Although this has handicapped the diesel in passenger car and aircraft applications, it is of little significance to lift truck designers. As in the case of Japanese sumo wrestlers, weight is a virtue.

Also, diesel engines are expensive to purchase and expensive to repair. The cost differential over a gasoline engine of the same performance can be as high as $4000. Parts are not always available (particularly for imported and obsolete engines) and are always more expensive than those for automotive and high-production industrial gasoline engines. Repair requires some special training and a very high level of workmanship. Diesel precision demands the highest respect.

The rising cost of diesel oil is a matter of concern. In most areas of the world diesel fuel is cheaper than gasoline. There has been less demand for it and taxes were lower. But this may not be always the case. Taxes in British Columbia have pushed the cost of diesel fuel to 70c per gallon. And demand for diesel and allied oils is increasing.

Diesel fuel supplies are limited. A barrel of crude oil is a mixture of thousands of different hydrocarbons. The group that yields diesel oil amounts to only about 15% of the total. And this same group of hydrocarbons supplies kerosene, jet fuel, and No. 2 heating oil, as well as other products. In contrast, gasoline can be extracted from a family of hydrocarbons that accounts for some 40% of the barrel. If diesels become as numerous as gasoline engines, refinery capacity will have to be more than doubled to stay abreast of demand.

Electric

Battery-powered trucks were once thought of as light-duty, limited capacity vehicles. This is no longer true. Improvements in storage-battery technology have enabled current trucks to operate for a full eight-hour shift without a battery change. And performance is comparable to that given by gas trucks. For example, a 4000 pound electric has a top speed of seven mph which is close to that of a comparable gas truck. In many jobs, acceleration time is as important as top speed, and here the electric has a clear advantage. The electric truck accelerates through 100 feet in 11 seconds—half a second faster than the gas truck. The electric falls down in free (unloaded) lift speed. The electric truck has a lift speed of 108 ft-sec compared to 118 ft-sec for the gasoline type.

Maintenance costs have been slashed. In the old days electric trucks were assembled from a shopping list of individual components. Troubleshooting required a real understanding of the circuitry and unusual skills to make detailed repairs. This kind of ability is expensive and maintenance costs reflected it. Today, while it is still generally agreed that an electric-truck mechanic needs more training than a gas-truck mechanic, the situation has eased. Plug-in circuit boards and integral solid-state controllers have eliminated many of the skills required. The mechanic no longer needs to troubleshoot individual circuits. Instead he replaces whole circuit sections.

The mechanical simplicity of these trucks is also reflected in reduced maintenance costs. Gasoline trucks are a jumble of parts, packed closely together and on top of one another. Electrics are

Table 1-5. PER Projection—LPG. (Courtesy Industrial Truck Div., Eaton Corp.)

EATON CORP.   MODEL L83C060SBT083   BOXCAR SPECIAL   JULY 31, 1975
AXLE DIV.   CAPACITY 0060   CAPACITY LIMITER
CLEVELAND   ATTACHMENT
OHIO 44110   TOTAL PRICE 15,908

TOTAL COST SUMMARY WITH ESCALATION   LPG = 0.3450/GAL

ANNUAL ESCALATION (PCT) 10.00 0.00 0.00 0.00 0.00 0.00 0.00

YEAR	RUNNING HOURS	MAINTENANCE AMOUNT ($)	MAINTENANCE COST/HR ($)	OWNERSHIP AMOUNT ($)	OWNERSHIP COST/HR	DOWN TIME COST ($)	FUEL COST ($)	OBSOL COST ($)	TOTAL COST AMOUNT ($)	TOTAL COST COST/HR ($)	REPLACEMENT SAVINGS
1	3,000	1,835	0.61	8,408	2.80	917	1,345	1	12,507	4.169	
2	6,000	6,217	1.04	9,789	1.63	2,909	2,691	1	21,608	3.601	
3	9,000	9,192	1.02	10,908	1.21	4,139	4,036	1	28,277	3.142	
4	12,000	15,241	1.27	11,764	0.98	6,411	5,382	1	38,800	3.233	
5	15,000	19,188	1.28	12,358	0.82	7,759	6,727	1	46,033	3.069	
6	18,000	26,691	1.48	12,628	0.70	10,088	8,073	1	57,482	3.193	2,232
7	21,000	33,325	1.59	12,898	0.61	11,961	9,418	1	67,603	3.219	3,150
8	24,000	44,206	1.84	13,168	0.55	14,753	10,764	1	82,892	3.454	9,240
9	27,000	53,351	1.98	13,438	0.50	16,886	12,109	1	95,786	3.548	12,933
10	30,000	73,877	2.46	13,708	0.46	21,238	13,455	1	122,279	4.076	30,210

simple in comparison. The parts are mounted with plenty of space between them and in such a way that many can be serviced without disturbing the others. One study has shown that the cost of gas-truck maintenance is 60% labor and 40% parts. Electric-truck maintenance costs split 50–50.

Electric trucks shine in hostile environments. According to the Eaton Corporation, a 4000-pound gas truck operating in a clean plant will have an economical life of eight years. During this period it will require $10,876 in maintenance and will be down for an average of 136 hours a year. The same vehicle operated in a foundry will incur $11,860 in maintenance costs during its economic life of five years. It will be out of service for 237 hours a year.

An equivalent electric in a clean plant and operated for the same 2000 hours a year will incur $10,767 in maintenance over an economic life of 10 years. The truck will last two years or 4000 operating hours longer than its gasoline-powered cousin for about the same maintenance outlay. In a foundry, the electric will have an economic life of eight years—three years longer than the gasoline truck—for a maintenance bill of $16,557. Average annual downtime will be 207 hours or 30 hours a year less than the gasoline-powered machine.

Electricity is clean. The only pollution generated by an electric truck is ozone generated by sparks on the brushes.

And electricity is still the most inexpensive fuel. Tables 1-5 and 1-6 are PER projections of two closely matched trucks. One is fueled by LPG and the other is electric. Both are 6000-pound capacity machines with short ("boxcar special") wheelbases for maneuverability. And both have capacity limiters. This device has recently been introduced by Yale and amounts to a sophisticated hydraulic pressure-sensing circuit that prevents overload, regardless of how far the load is out on the forks or how much the mast is tilted.

LPG is pegged at $0.345 a gallon for the duration of the study and electricity at $0.035 per kilowatt hour. Both trucks do the same work, but running time for the LPG version is 3000 hours a year, or 500 hours a year more than the electric. This discrepancy can be explained because engine-powered trucks continue to run when idle. Electrics are shut down between jobs and on breaks.

Table 1-6. PER Projection—Electric. (Courtesy Industrial Truck Div., Eaton Corp.)

EATON CORP
AXLE DIV.
CLEVELAND
OHIO 44110

MODEL K70C060G36T083
CAPACITY 0060
ATTACHMENT
TOTAL PRICE 22,619
27,447

CAPACITY LIMITER

JULY 31, 1975

ELECTRIC = 0.0350/KWH

0.00

TOTAL COST SUMMARY WITH ESCALATION
ANNUAL ESCALATION (PCT) 10.00   0.00   0.00   0.00   0.00

YEAR	RUNNING HOURS	MAINTENANCE AMOUNT ($)	MAINTENANCE COST/HR ($)	OWNERSHIP AMOUNT ($)	OWNERSHIP COST/HR ($)	DOWN TIME COST ($)	COST OF CHARGING	OBSOL COST ($)	TOTAL COST AMOUNT ($)	TOTAL COST COST/HR ($)	REPLACEMENT SAVINGS
1	2,500	1,588	0.64	11,194	4.48	749	441	1	13,973	5.569	
2	5,000	3,491	0.70	13,442	2.69	1,569	883	1	19,386	3.877	
3	7,500	5,668	0.76	14,989	2.00	2,424	1,324	1	24,397	3.253	
4	10,000	8,297	0.83	16,204	1.62	3,366	1,766	1	29,635	2.963	
5	12,500	11,209	0.90	17,114	1.37	4,316	2,207	1	34,847	2.788	
6	15,000	15,224	1.01	17,840	1.19	5,517	2,649	1	41,231	2.749	
7	17,500	20,807	1.19	18,566	1.06	7,048	3,090	1	49,513	2.829	1,400
8	20,000	26,186	1.31	21,072	1.05	8,383	3,532	1	59,173	2.959	4,200
9	22,500	32,995	1.47	22,436	1.00	9,926	3,973	1	69,332	3.081	7,470
10	25,000	41,415	1.66	23,228	0.93	11,667	4,415	1	80,726	3.229	12,000

The economic life of the LPG truck is five years or 15,000 hours. Additional shutdown time of the electric adds a year to its economic life. During this period, the LPG incurs $19,188 in maintenance costs and $7,759 in downtime. The electric costs nearly $2000 less to maintain and, in this particular application, saves $2242 in downtime while operating a year longer.

But the message is in the fuel costs. The LPG truck is expected to consume $7749 in fuel while the cost of recharging is only $2649. This is why Eaton has opted for electrics on this job.

But electric trucks are not a panacea. They cannot solve all problems. No electric is capable of negotiating really rough terrain (manufacturers tacitly admit this shortcoming by their refusal to fit pneumatic tires to electrics). And while direct operating expenses are low, some consideration of the cost of the charging room is in order. The room must be built and maintained to OSHA standards. Briefly these standards mandate:

- The charging area must be distinct from the rest of the plant and used only for battery charging.
- It must be remote from fire, sparks, or from smoking areas.
- Provision must be made for ventilation, fire protection, neutralization of spilled electrolyte, and for physical protection of the charging apparatus from damage by the trucks.
- Batteries are to be transported by a conveyor, overhead crane, or equivalent. Mechanics are forbidden to manhandle batteries on and off the trucks.
- If racks are used to store the batteries, they must be made of nonconductive material.

2

Hydraulics

Sometimes a sweat-stained, oil-soaked lift truck mechanic will ask himself, "Why hydraulics? Why use a system that depends upon pressurized oil, restrained only by flexible seals and woven hoses, to exert force? Aren't there better ways of doing the job?"

The answer is no.

No other transmission system has all the advantages of hydraulics. These advantages are:

- Extreme simplicity.
- Absolute control.
- Flexibility of parts layout.
- Reduction of wear because of the absence of vibration, the control given over acceleration and deceleration, automatic pressure release should the system overload, and automatic lubrication.
- Input-output efficiency.
- Silence of operation.

But hydraulic systems are, as our mechanic knows, far from perfect. Pressures are high and a great deal of care is required to keep fittings, hoses, and seals operational. The system is as strong as its weakest point. And, because of the precision fit of parts, water, dirt, gum, and other impurities in the oil hamper efficiency.

BASICS

Hydraulic systems are based on a law formulated some three hundred years ago by Blaise Pascal. Pascal's law states: "Pressure exerted on a confined liquid is transmitted undiminished in all directions and acts with equal force on all equal areas." If you apply pressure to any part of the system, the same pressure will be exerted throughout the system because hydraulic oil is fluid and is essentially incompressible. In actual fact, some compression does take place, but it is negligible, accounting for a loss of approximately one-half quart of oil in a ten-gallon system pressurized to 3000 psi.

Figure 2-1 illustrates the first half of Pascal's law: "Pressure exerted on a confined liquid is transmitted undiminished in all directions...." If we exert a force of one pound on a piston with a cross-sectional area of one inch, the fluid is under a pressure of one pound per square inch. No matter where the gauge is inserted in the cylinder, the pressure will be the same.

But nobody builds a hydraulic system just for the sake of exerting pressure on a confined fluid. The purpose of hydraulic machines is to use pressure to exert force and thereby perform work. Force is defined as area times pressure and is expressed in pounds (or some other unit of weight). Work, in the circumspect way engineers use the term, means force acting through a distance. A

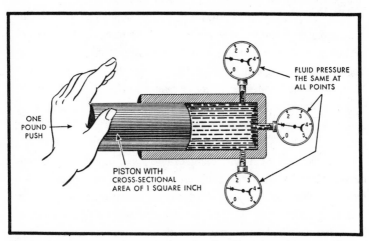

Fig. 2-1. Pressure exerted on a confined liquid is everywhere the same. (Courtesy Sun Oil Co.)

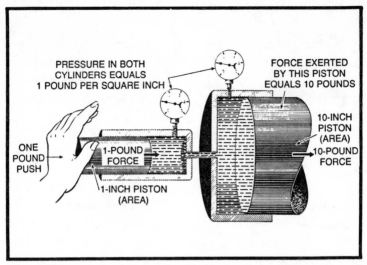

Fig. 2-2. Pressure exerted on a confined liquid acts with equal force on all equal areas. (Courtesy Sun Oil Co.)

machine that lifts 1000 pounds one foot does 1000 (foot-pounds) of work.

The second part of Pascal's law says that pressure exerted on a confined liquid "…acts with equal force on all equal areas." Pascal seems to be saying the obvious. But his statement helped change the world. The operative term is *equal*. If the areas upon which the fluid reacts are unequal, the level of force is also unequal.

Figure 2-2 illustrates how force is a function of piston area. The master piston is the same as in the first illustration—it has a cross-sectional area of one square inch. The slave piston is ten times as large with ten square inches of piston area exposed to the fluid. The pressure in the system remains at one psi. But the force on the second piston is ten times the input force of ten pounds. There is one psi on each square inch of the piston; ten square inches adds up to ten pounds.

But we do not get something for nothing. The slave piston only moves 1/10 the distance of the master piston. For its bore is ten times greater and requires ten times as much fluid to fill as the master-cylinder bore. In the real world there would be parasitic losses imposed by friction of the pistons on their bores, and frictional losses in the plumbing.

44

BASIC HYDRAULIC CIRCUITS

The circuit shown in Fig. 2-2 is too primitive to be of much practical use. The next drawing (Fig. 2-3) illustrates a slightly more practical circuit. For the master cylinder we substitute a hand pump and we add a spring to the slave piston, so the piston will have something to react against. (A free-floating piston would bleed all pressure from the system.) Several strokes of the hand pump are required to fill the slave system, and this means that we must tap a reservoir into the pump barrel. Two one-way or check valves control the direction of fluid flow. On the suction stroke, the reservoir check valve opens allowing fluid to enter the pump bore. At the same time the output valve closes to trap fluid in the slave cylinder. On the exhaust stroke, the check valve at the reservoir closes and the valve to the cylinder opens.

This system will cycle once. Nothing can happen after the slave cylinder fills unless we can figure out a way to release the trapped fluid.

Figure 2-4 represents a decided improvement. A directional control valve has been added to the circuit. When the valve is in the position shown by the dotted lines, the spring moves the piston up and the oil is shunted back to the reservoir. Another improvement is

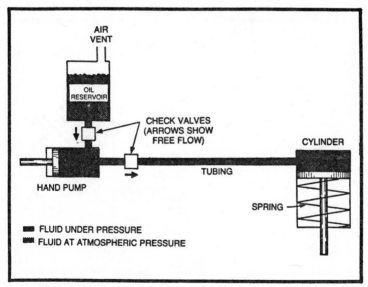

Fig. 2-3. An elementary hydraulic circuit. (Courtesy Texaco, Inc.)

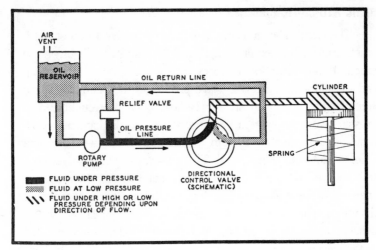

Fig. 2-4. This circuit includes a directional valve and a mechanical pump. (Courtesy Texaco, Inc.)

the rotary pump that has been substituted for the hand lever. Because pumps of this kind supply a steady flow of oil in one direction, no check valves are needed. But we do need a relief valve situated between the reservoir and the pump discharge line. Without one, we would have to stop the pump the instant the piston reached its downward limit of travel. For the pump is discharging into a

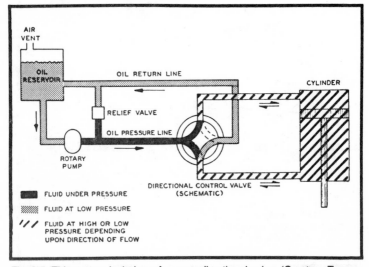

Fig. 2-5. This system includes a four-way directional valve. (Courtesy Texaco, Inc.)

closed cylinder and (since pressure is a function of resistance) will deliver all the pressure that it can. The relief valve is calibrated to "blow off" before the system damages itself.

Figure 2-5 is the next step in sophistication. The circuit shown here is perfectly practical and is only a trifle simpler than those used on lift truck tilt cylinders. The return spring has been abandoned and fluid pressure can be applied to either side of the piston. Other than a shaft seal, the only modification is the substitution of a four-way control valve in place of the two-way valve used previously. As drawn, pressure is applied above the piston and the fluid under it is routed back to the reservoir. If the valve were positioned as indicated by the dotted lines, the lower face of the piston would be pressurized.

Regardless of their seeming complexity, all hydraulic systems have these basic components (see Fig. 2-6):

- A reservoir.
- A pump to impart energy to the fluid.
- One or more control valves.
- A "hydraulic motor"—linear (as in the examples shown) or rotary, to convert hydraulic energy to mechanical power.

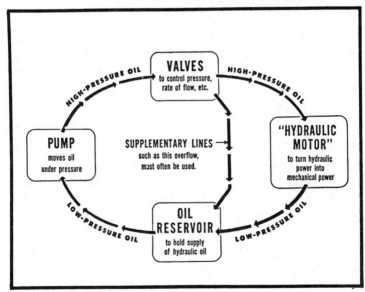

Fig. 2-6. A block diagram showing components found on all typical hydraulic circuits. (Courtesy Texaco, Inc.)

- Enough plumbing in the form of fixed lines and flexible hoses to complete the circuit between the pump and "motor."

COMPONENTS

Now that we have an understanding of how the parts work together, we'll look more closely at the individual components.

Reservoir

The reservoir is a very important part of the system. Besides holding enough oil to maintain a reasonable level when the lift cylinder is extended, the reservoir acts as a holding tank. Oil flow pauses temporarily in the reservoir to promote cooling, and to allow air bubbles and sediment to separate. Sediment will cause trouble throughout the system, and air bubbles are a mechanic's nightmare. Air compresses, resulting in jerky hydraulic action and, at the same time, heats and raises the oil temperatures.

On fixed installations the rule of thumb is to make the reservoir 2 1/2 times greater than pump flow per minute. Thus, a 25 gallons-per-minute (gpm) pump would be fed by a 62.5 gallon reservoir. This is difficult to arrange on a vehicle. The typical lift truck has a reservoir capacity of about 75% of pump capacity.

To some extent, limited tankage can be compensated for by careful design. A baffle that runs about 3/4 of the way across the tank reduces turbulence and encourages cooling, particularly if it is situated in such a way as to force the flow along the sidewalls. The center of the tank should be relatively calm to encourage sedimentation and air escape.

The shape of the reservoir is also important. A relatively deep tank offers more wall area for cooling—a consideration that is limited only by the need for some surface area for air separation.

The reservoir can, at least indirectly, have some bearing on the cleanliness of the system. The ability of the tank to promote sedimentation is of little long-term use, unless the mechanic is able to easily remove the fallout. All but the most inexpensive machines have a removable top cover, bolted and gasketed into place, and a drain cock. The access plate should be large enough so that there is ample working room on both sides of the baffle. While the fluid level on fixed installations is usually established by means of a sight glass, mobile installations generally require that the air filter be removed (ancient Towmotor practice) or, better, come equipped with a dipstick (a nice feature of Taylor's Big Red machines). Trucks intended for rough work generally have the reservoir under cover. While this approach protects the reservoir from collision damage and helps to keep it externally clean, it is trade-off purchased by less cooling. Dash-mounted reservoirs have the advantage of conventional cooling as the machine moves.

A mesh-type air filter is generally used. It must be large enough to vent the tank when the lift cylinder retracts, and readily accessible for service.

Pumps

Pumps are classified into two broad categories. By performance, pumps are either *fixed* or *variable* delivery when operated at a fixed rpm and pressure. (Pump capacity is generally taken at 1000 rpm and at 0 psi.) In terms of their construction, most pumps fall into three categories—*gear, vane,* and *piston.* These categories can be further subdivided, and a few pumps resist categorization altogether. Gear, vane, and piston pumps may be fixed-delivery types while vane and piston pumps lend themselves (with proper modification) to variable delivery.

Gear Pumps. Figure 2-7 illustrates a very typical external-gear pump of the kind used on most lift trucks. Either gear can be driven by the engine while the other idles. Oil is trapped between the outer diameters of the gears and the casing and is swept into the discharge port. The mesh of the gears discourages internal leakage between the high- and low-pressure sides of the pump. Pressure is controlled by a relief valve that shunts excess output back to the reservoir.

Most of these pumps use simple, straight-cut (spur) gears. Spiral or helical gears (shown in the illustration) promise better efficiency and, if it makes any difference, are quiet. But the sliding tooth action loads the edges of the gears and demands more input power. Herringbone gears are cut like chevrons and eliminate side thrust at the cost of additional machinework.

Internal-gear pumps are sometimes found on hydraulic systems but are more often used to supply oil to the engine. Two types are

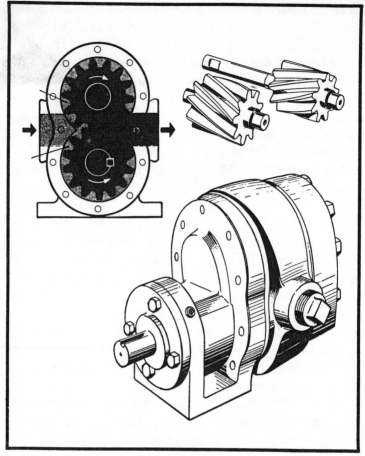

Fig. 2-7. External gear pump. (Courtesy Mobile Oil Corp.)

available. Figure 2-8 illustrates the Gerotor pump of the type favored by International. The star-shaped eccentric gear is driven and turns the large internal gear. Oil enters via a port in the pump cover at the point of tooth separation. As the inner gear marches along the inner circumference of the large gear, the oil cavity grows smaller. The outlet port accepts the spillover and the cycle repeats itself.

The classic internal-gear pump is shown in Fig. 2-9. Both gears rotate and are separated by a fixed crescent. In the example shown, oil is drawn in at the top as the spaces between the gear teeth enlarge. Oil is carried around the right side of the pump by both gears and discharged to the left as the teeth again come into mesh.

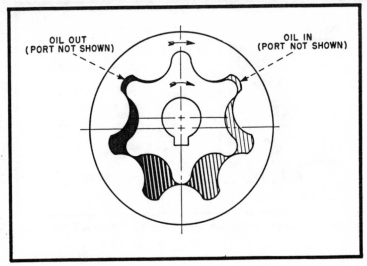

Fig. 2-8. Gerotor pump. (Courtesy Double A Products Co.)

Internal-gear pumps of either type are limited by capacity, rpm, and efficiency. External-gear designs are generally more efficient, tolerate higher rotational speeds, and can be made in a wide range of capacities. Gear pumps have good (almost nonpulsating) flow

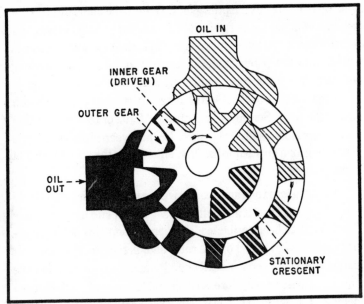

Fig. 2-9. Internal gear pump. (Courtesy Texaco, Inc.)

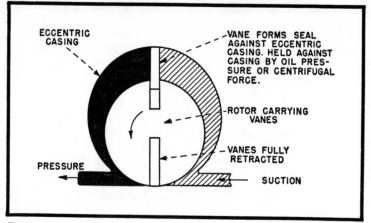

Fig. 2-10. A simplified drawing of a vane-type pump. (Courtesy Texaco, Inc.)

characteristics, but tend to churn the oil. Besides costing power, churning heats the oil and assures good circulation of any contaminants that may be present. Nor do gear pumps compensate for wear. Pump efficiency gradually falls off as pump clearances open.

Vane Pumps. Vane pumps are increasingly popular, particularly on the smaller trucks. The rotor is fitted with a number of sliding radial vanes, and turns inside an eccentric pump casing. Figure 2-10 illustrates the principle. Oil enters the pump through the suction port under the attraction of vacuum and (usually) gravity. As the rotor turns, the vanes move outward in their slots and remain in contact with the pump casing. Discharge occurs as the working surface between the rotor and casing narrows.

The vanes are made of softer material than the casing to absorb most of the wear. Sealing is by centrifugal force or by a combination of centrifugal force and oil pressure. Normal wear of the kind that is devastating for a gear pump has little effect since the vanes move out to compensate.

Nevertheless vane and bearing wear cannot be ignored. Quality pumps have paired inlet and outlet passages cast into the pump body (Fig. 2-11A) to balance the loads in opposition. This approach reduces radial (side) thrust on the rotor and, in the process, prolongs bearing life while reducing friction. Pumping losses through the convoluted passageways are an acceptable trade-off. Another refinement is shown in Fig. 2-11B. This particular design is covered by

52

Sperry Vickers patents, although other manufacturers achieve the same result with slightly different hardware. The purpose of the trailing ports in the rotor and the second vane (known as the intravane) at the base of the first is to control tip loads. Otherwise these loads would be entirely at the mercy of line pressure and centrifugal force. Oil enters through the drilled ports and collects in the space between the intravane and the main vane. Pressure varies as the main vane moves from the inlet side of the pump housing to the outlet side in proportion to the pressure against the vane tip. For a given pressure, the force pushing the vane upwards is a function of the area of the cutout above the intravane, and is easy to control during manufacture.

Vane and gear pumps may be mounted in tandem and driven from a single shaft. If one circuit is to be powered—the usual case in lift trucks—the pumps are connected internally in parallel and feed and discharge through single external fittings. The result is a relatively simple-to-service package with a minimum of leak points.

While the pumps illustrated in Fig. 2-11 are fixed delivery types it is simple enough to vary the delivery by varying the eccentricity of the casing relative to the rotor. If the casing is moved so it shares a common axis with the rotor, there will be fluctuation in the size of the

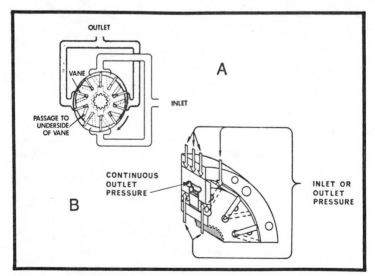

Fig. 2-11. Balanced porting prolongs bearing and vane life (A); while pressure compensation reduces vane tip loads (B). (Courtesy Sperry Vickers).

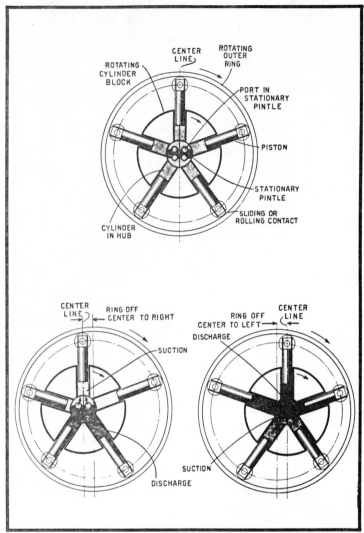

Fig. 2-12. A variable-discharge radial piston pump. (Courtesy Mobile Oil Corp.)

working spaces and no delivery—regardless of the pump's rpm. If the casing is moved further off-center, capacity will increase as the working spaces expand and shrink.

Piston Pumps. Figure 2-12 illustrates a variable-discharge, radial-piston pump. The piston block rotates around a stationary pintle. As the block turns the pistons spin with it and remain in contact with a rotating outer ring, because of the combined effects of centrifugal force and oil pressure. When the outer ring is concentric, as shown in the leftmost drawing, the pistons remain stationary in their bores and no oil is circulated. The outer ring can be moved off center. The middle drawing shows the ring displaced to the right. The pistons must follow the shape of the eccentric and so reciprocate in their bores. The bores are filled on the outbound stroke and emptied on the discharge stroke. The further the ring is moved to the right, the longer the strokes and the greater the output per revolution. If the ring is moved to the left, oil flow is reversed. The intake ports become discharge ports and vice versa.

A variable-volume, axial piston pump is shown in Fig. 2-13. In the design under discussion, the piston rods terminate in ball ends socketed to the face of the driving flange. Both the flange and the cylinder block rotate, but the block can be angled relative to the driving flange by means of a yoke.

When the block and flange are at zero angle, that is, when they are parallel, the pistons remain stationary in their rotating bores. No oil is pumped. But as the block is deflected downward, the pistons

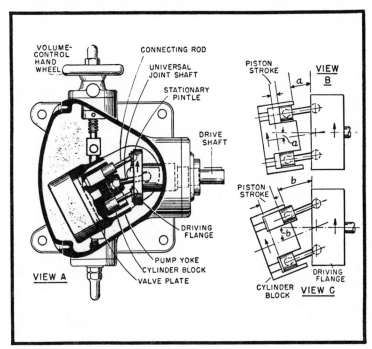

Fig. 2-13. A variable-discharge axial piston pump. (Courtesy Mobile Oil Corp.)

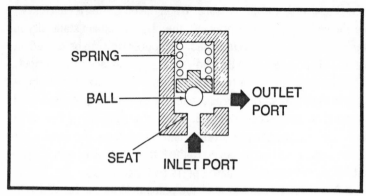

Fig. 2-14. Ball-type, right-angle check valve. (Courtesy Sperry Rand Corp.)

reciprocate. Oil passes through the valve plate and into the piston bores. The greater the offset between the cylinder block and the drive flange, the longer the stroke. When the cylinder block is arced upward, the direction of oil flow reverses.

Piston pumps are high-efficiency devices, but suffer from high initial and overhaul costs and are extremely sensitive to contaminated oil. Efficiency drops rapidly with wear.

Valves

Valves are used to control the operation of the actuators. Their function is regulating pressure, determining flow, or varying the direction of flow. They are rated by their size, pressure tolerances, and pressure drop.

Pressure-Control Valves. These valves have the function of limiting pressure in the system (to protect the pump and other components), regulating the pressure in a secondary circuit, or causing operations to follow a certain sequence. Generally these valves operate in terms of a pre-established balance. The spring or hydraulic pressure on one side of an element is balanced by working pressure. When working pressure exceeds valve pressure, the valve responds. Most pressure control valves are normally closed—the flow through the outlet port is blocked unless there is a pressure unbalance.

Check Valves. Check valves may be classified as pressure valves, as directional control valves, or both. To control pressure, the valve is put into series with the line and spring-loaded. The amount of spring load determines the pressure at which the valve will open or close. A directional control check valve is shown in Fig. 2-14. It has an inlet port and an outlet port. Flow into the valve from the inlet port unseats the ball and passes out through the outlet port. Flow in the reverse direction, or a pressure drop at the inlet port, allows the spring pressure to overcome the hydraulic pressure, thus dropping the ball and its follower, closing the ports.

The valve illustrated in Fig. 2-14 is known as a right-angle valve. Flow across the valve seat is diverted 90 degrees. Figure 2-15 shows the action of an in-line check valve. This particular valve differs from the first in that it employs a poppet rather than a simple check ball. The geometry is such that a poppet offers better flow response, but at the cost of some reliability. A ball valve is failsafe—should it bind, pressure against the face of the ball will force it open. Poppet valves can stick because of varnish and sludge accumulations on the barrel.

Check valves are sometimes *back-mounted*. That is, all ports are on the same face for mounting against a port plate. The connections for modern valves are almost always sealed by individual

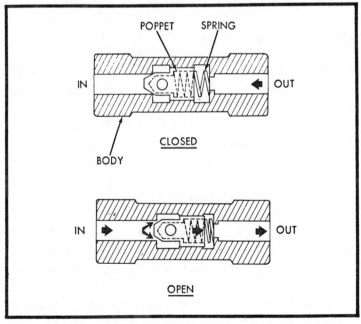

Fig. 2-15. Poppet-type in-line check valve. (Courtesy Sperry Rand Corp.)

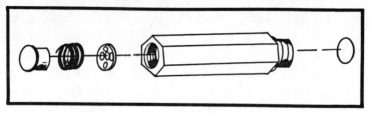

Fig. 2-16. Restrictor (pressure-reducing) check valve.

grooves and o-rings; earlier types mounted flush against gaskets. Some mechanics still call back-mounted valves *gasketed* valves.

Check Valve With Fixed Restriction. Figure 2-16 is a check-valve variant often used with lift cylinders. The valve opens to all oil entry with a minimum restriction. During back flow—when the cylinder is retracted—the valve seats and oil is diverted through the ports in the restrictor. The pressure drop slows the descent of the cylinder and to some extent compensates for load differences.

Relief Valves. Figure 2-17 depicts a *simple* relief valve of the type found on various small lift trucks. When pump pressure on the face of the ball exceeds spring compression pressure, the valve opens and shunts the circuit to the reservoir. Variations of this valve may have a tapered element or a sliding spool. If we overlook the external provision for spring adjustment, the structure of a simple relief valve is very similar to that of a check valve.

Unfortunately, the simple relief valve gives very poor pressure regulation. Cracking pressure, the pressure at which the valve unseats but is not fully opened, is lower than full-flow pressure. When working from a fair-sized pump, a simple relief valve can override several hundred psi and may chatter. Both of these conditions are objectionable. Oil spilled through the valve heats up, and chatter accelerates seat wear.

Compound relief valves employ a pilot to sense pressure inequalities on both sides of the element. Figure 2-18 shows the operation of the Vickers RM series valve with integral pilot. The pilot stage is a spring-loaded poppet built into the main valve spool. Both it and the main valve spool are spring loaded and both are normally closed.

Look at the drawings carefully. At less than relief pressure (A) the spool and the pilot stage poppet are closed. Pressure appears on

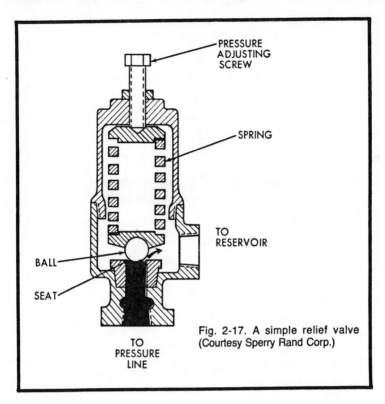

Fig. 2-17. A simple relief valve (Courtesy Sperry Rand Corp.)

both sides of the spool; it is directly applied to the left-hand face and appears on the right-hand face because of an orifice drilled through the spool. Since pressure is equal on both faces, the only effective pressure is that generated by the spool spring. It holds the valve seated across the tank port.

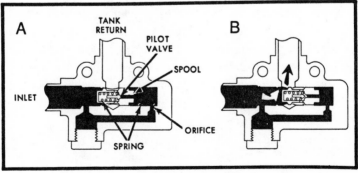

Fig. 2-18. A Vickers RM series compound relief valve. (Courtesy Sperry Rand Corp.)

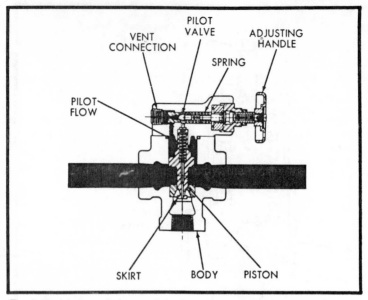

Fig. 2-19. A balanced piston relief valve with external adjustment. (Courtesy Sperry Rand Corp.)

The poppet valve opens at a preset pressure (B). Fluid pressure on its face compresses its spring. This is the cracking pressure for the whole valve assembly. Now, with the poppet unseated, oil behind the piston has a route to the tank. The routing is only roughly indicated in the drawing, but it consists of an orifice in the side of the spool connecting the poppet-valve chamber with the tank port.

Pressure on the right-hand face of the spool drops as oil behind it is shunted to the reservoir. The spool is free to slide to and fro in its bore and almost immediately moves to the right to reestablish a pressure equilibrium between its faces. Movement stops when fluid pressure on the left equals fluid pressure on the right plus spring pressure. As the spring moves to the right, it uncovers the main return port to the tank. Pump pressure dissipates through this port.

Full-flow pressure is determined by the strength of the spool spring. Since the spring is very light, this pressure is only slightly higher than cracking pressure.

Valves on the RM pattern are limited in capacity and cannot be adjusted in the field (a mixed blessing). A balanced-piston valve is adjustable, and in commercially available sizes can handle a flow of several hundred gallons a minute (Fig. 2-19).

In the normally closed position both faces of the piston are pressurized. The poppet in the pilot stage unseats at the valve setting and allows oil above the piston to bleed down to the tank port. The pressure at which the poppet valve cracks is determined by spring tension and can be varied from outside of the unit. As with most hydraulic components, this valve is adaptable to different applications. If the vent port is opened to the atmosphere the pilot circuit becomes inoperative and main-line pressure is regulated at 20 psi (a pressure determined by the tension of the piston spring). The vent line can be connected to a source of pressurized oil, in which case the valve operates remotely by opening a second valve.

The double flare on the bottom of the piston skirt is an example of the way valve elements are shaped ballistically, with reference to the oil stream. In this case, flow through the tank port strikes the top

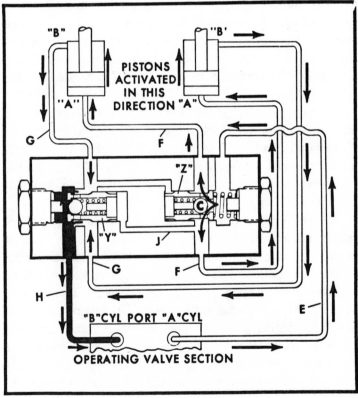

Fig. 2-20. Tilt control valve. (Courtesy Sperry Rand Corp.)

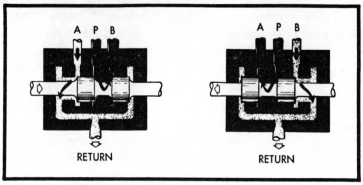

Fig. 2-21. Four-way valve operation. A and B are actuator ports; P is the pump or pressure port. (Courtesy Mobile Oil Corp.)

of the skirt and closes the valve more quickly then would be possible with a spring giving a 20 psi differential.

Tilt Control Valve. Figure 2-20 illustrates a rather complex tilt control valve sometimes found on the more carefully designed machines. The purpose is to give positive control of the tilt cylinders regardless of the load. As shown, pressurized oil enters through passage E and passes over the check valve C to extend the cylinders. Oil behind the pistons passes through G and out the return line H. So long as there is positive pressure in F and J the return flow is unrestricted. However should the load run away, the pressure on the inboard (A) face of the cylinder pistons drops. Valve Y closes, restricting return flow and slowing the cylinders. Operation is the same for retracting the cylinders, but the flow is reversed and valve Z provides control.

Directional Control Valves. In the broad sense a check valve is a directional control valve. But industry practice is to limit this designation to the reversing four-way valve. These valves have at least two positions (and in mobile applications have an infinite range between these positions) and four active ports. There must be a pump port (P), two actuator ports (A and B), and a return port. In the left drawing in Fig. 2-21, the pressure enters through the P port and exits through the B actuator port. In the right drawing the situation is reversed: pressure enters through P but leaves via A. In both cases the unpressurized side of the piston unloads through the return port into the reservoir.

If the valve has a center or neutral position it is defined by springs or detents. Neutral may deny pump output to all ports, in which case the valve is known as a closed center type; or it may unload pump output to the reservoir through the return port. The latter configuration is almost universal in lift trucks since a closed center valve must depend upon a relief valve to protect the pump when the valve is in neutral.

Another characteristic of this valve family is the use of sliding spools or lands acting in conjunction with ported bores to control the flow. The spools are hardened and usually chrome-plated while the valve body is of cast iron. Tolerances are critical. Some valves can be overhauled in the field by carefully matching bore diameter with available production spools, but most are individually fitted at the factory, and no overhaul is possible. Lapping can give tolerances on the order of 0.00004 inch and limit the working-pressure leak rate to two to four drops per minute.

Actuation is usually by means of a manually operated lever, although solenoids are sometimes used. Ease of operation and control-force balance (equal lever pressure in either direction should give equal response) require careful design. The ports must be angled so there is no side thrust on the spool and the inevitable

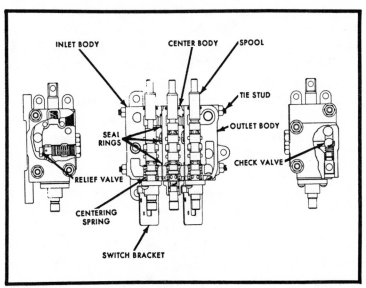

Fig. 2-22. Directional control valve nomenclature. (Courtesy Sperry Rand Corp.)

leakage must be apportioned equally around all sides of the spool. One way of doing this is to mill shallow grooves radially around the spool face channels for leakage. Hopefully, the spool will remain centered in the bore.

Valve Operation

Early valves were mounted in individual valve bodies. The contemporary approach is to combine spool and body assemblies into valve banks or clusters. The valve bodies are indexed by through bolts or tie studs and secured with through-bolts (see Fig. 2-22). Interconnecting passageways are sealed against leakage with o-rings. The inlet body is fitted with a check valve to regulate pressure at the valve bank. Each valve section contains a reversing spool and two cylinder ports in the valve body.

The internal plumbing consists of a pressure passage, a tank passage, and a bypass passage (Fig. 2-23). The pressure passage is connected to the pump at the inlet section and is regulated by the integral relief valve. It flows into a chamber surrounding the metering portions of the spool in each valve section and, according to valve position, can discharge into either of the two cylinder actuating ports. The bypass diverts pressure to the outlet (reservoir) port when the spools are centered. How much pump output is diverted in this way depends upon the position of the spools. When all are in neutral, all output is returned to the reservoir; the only pressure in the system is that generated by the restrictions in the plumbing and in the valve itself. As a spool is moved off center, the bypass progressively closes and an increasing pressure and flow goes to the cylinder in question. The tank passage also dumps into the reservoir, but it handles exhaust flow from double-acting cylinders. Each cylinder spool is fitted with a check valve to prevent backflow from the cylinder to the bypass when the valve is cracked.

This particular valve is a Vickers CM11, widely used on mobile equipment. As drawn it is fitted with two double-acting spools, B and D, and a single-acting T spool. Spools D and T are intended to operate cylinders. Typically, D controls the tilt and T the lift cylinders. Spool B is superficially similar to D, except that it is used to control a reversible hydraulic motor. Cylinder spools block the cylinder ports in neutral. The cylinders are locked suddenly on a

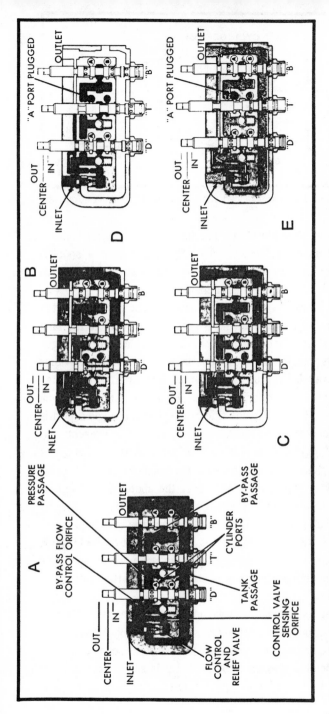

Fig. 2-23. The Vickers CM11 valve incorporated two double-acting spools (known as the B and D spools) and a single-acting (T) spool. In neutral all spools are centered on their detents (view A); with the D spool shifted inward, the cylinder fills through the B port and discharges through A port (view B); with the D spool shifted outward, pressure goes to cylinder port A and port B exhausts (view C); with the single-acting T spool in, the bypass is blocked and pressure goes to the cylinder through the B port (view D); with the T spool out, the cylinder discharges through B port (view E). (Courtesy Sperry Rand Corp.)

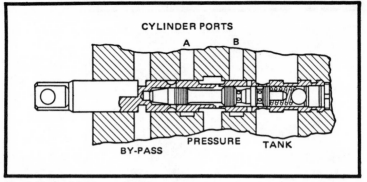

Fig. 2-24. A Vickers counterbalanced spool, used on tilt controls. (Courtesy Sperry Rand Corp.)

column of incompressible oil. A hydraulic motor is more fragile than a cylinder and must be decelerated gently. The motor or spool B allows leakage in neutral. Braking is handled by an additional valve mounted remotely from the directional bank.

In view B the D spool is shifted inward. The pressure port is connected to the B port and the A port is connected to the tank return. Thus the cylinder fills on the B port side and discharges through the A port. In view C the spool is shifted outward to its other extreme of travel. Pressure goes to port A and port B exhausts.

The T spool is used to control a single-acting cylinder. Since oil enters the cylinder on only one side of the piston, a single B port is used. For reasons of interchangeability, A port is present, but plugged. Shifting the T spool inland blocks the bypass and subjects port B to pressure (view D). In view E the cylinder is being lowered; reverse flow through port B goes over the spool and to the tank passage. In the case of lift cylinders, return flow is entirely a matter of gravity. Pump pressure is relieved through the bypass passage.

The operation of the B spool is similar to that of the D spool, with the exception noted already. It is an open-center spool and discharges its actuator ports in neutral to protect the motor from shock damage.

These spool combinations are not the only ones available from Vickers and from other manufacturers. Cylinder spools may incorporate restrictor passages to control the rate of descent or may be counterbalanced. An example of the latter is shown in Fig. 2-24. Usually found on tilt-cylinder applications, the counterbalance feature prevents the forks from tilting forward faster than the pump can deliver oil to the rod end (the working end) of the cylinder.

So long as there is inlet pressure, the cylinder is under control and the valve allows restricted bleed down from port A (the rod-end port). But should inlet pressure drop, the spring moves the internal spool to block all return from the cylinder until conditions stabilize.

Electric trucks with separate pump and traction motors often feature a switch at the pump. This switch opens in neutral and denies current to the pump motor, thus extending battery charge. The extension is small, since a free-wheeling pump consumes little energy, but significant enough to justify the additional circuitry.

Motors

In the strict sense a hydraulic motor is a device used to convert fluid energy into rotary motion. In the context of Fig. 2-6 the term is construed loosely to mean any sort of mechanism that converts fluid pressure into motion. In this broad sense a brake wheel cylinder is a kind of motor, as indeed are all hydraulic cylinders.

Cylinders

Hydraulic cylinders are a standard part of all lift trucks. Simple machines have a single lift cylinder to raise the mast; others have a pair of cylinders to tilt the mast; while others may have additional cylinders to move the forks fore and aft or to extend the carriage out from the mast. And except for the smallest machines, most have power steering operating through single or double cylinders.

Cylinders are described in terms of their construction and their actuation. Figure 2-25A shows a ram-type cylinder, distinguished from the others by the absence of a piston. The end of the rod itself serves as the piston. Because of their inherent strength, ram-type cylinders are customarily used to raise the mast. Extension masts employ telescoping cylinders (Fig. 2-25B). The ram extends, encounters stops, and pulls the next section out with it. In lift truck applications, telescoping cylinders are generally limited to two elements—a primary and a secondary cylinder. Dump truck bed cylinders may have five or more elements.

The cylinders shown in Figs. 2-25A and B are single acting. That is, oil enters from below and moves the ram upward. Return is

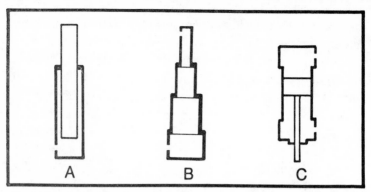

Fig. 2-25. Cylinder types. Rams do not have a piston as such: the end of the rod is the reaction member (A); telescopic rams are used where compactness is important (B); piston-type cylinders may be single or, as in the example shown, double-acting (C). (Courtesy Parker-Hannefin Corp.)

by means of gravity. (The second line that you will notice running to the top of the lift cylinder is a fluid return line that routes spillover past the seals back to the reservoir.)

Tilt and sterring cylinders are piston construction, double-acting designs. Hydraulic energy is exerted against the face of a piston mounted on a relatively small-diameter piston rod. Pressurized oil can enter (and leave) from either end of the cylinder as shown by the two oil ports in Fig. 2-25C. A characteristic of these cylinders is that forces generated by the two faces of the piston are not equal. On the extension stroke the full area of the piston is exposed to oil pressure; during retraction, effective piston area is partially masked by the connecting rod (Fig. 2-26). It follows, then, that for the same pressure the piston exerts more force on extension than on retraction. And it retracts more quickly than it extends since the piston rod displaces some of the oil.

Table 2-1 is a tabulation of pressure-force relationships. For double-acting cylinders the cross-sectional area of the piston rod must be subtracted to calculate the force present during retraction.

This table represents force at the cylinder and not the weight the machine will lift. Tilt cylinders act through what engineers call a first class lever; lift cylinders employ the differential lift principle. A pair of chains connect the ram with the carriage (Fig. 2-27). For each inch the ram moves, the carriage moves two inches. The drawing helps clarify this: the chain on the left side of the pulley must extend as far as the ram and, at the same time, the chain on the right must move an equal distance. Thus the carriage moves twice the distance of ram travel. The gain in movement is paid for by a reduction in force; the carriage has half the lifting force of the ram alone.

Unlike those favored for stationary and extremely rugged mobile service, lift truck cylinders are capped and welded at one end; the open end is threaded and sealed. This is the least imposing type of cylinder construction and has little to recommend it except low cost and compactness unobtainable with the traditional tie rods (Fig. 2-28). Installation of the piston and rod, always a ticklish procedure, becomes more so when the mechanic is working blind. Remachining—even if the thickness of the cylinder walls would allow it—is out of the question.

Cylinders are made of steel and microfinished. Normal production tolerances hold diameters to within 0.001 inch. Rods are

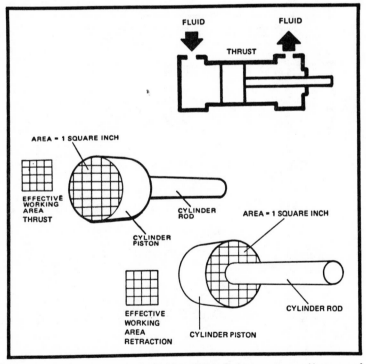

Fig. 2-26. The working areas in double-acting cylinders are unequal because of the displacement of the cylinder rod. (Courtesy Parker Hannefin Corp.)

Table 2-1. Cylinder Forces Under Various Oil Pressures. (Courtesy Parker Hannefin Corp.)

Cyl. Bore or Piston Rod. Dia. (in.)	Cyl. Bore Size (φ mm)	Area (sq. in.)	CYLINDER PUSH STROKE FORCE IN POUNDS AT VARIOUS PRESSURES (PSI)										Displacement per inch of Stroke (gallons)
			50	80	100	500	750	1000	1500	2000	2500	3000	
5/8	15.9	.307	15	25	31	154	230	307	461	614	768	921	.0013
1	25.4	.785	39	65	79	392	588	785	1,177	1,570	1,962	2,355	.0034
1-3/8	34.9	1.490	75	119	149	745	1,118	1,490	2,235	2,980	3,725	4,470	.0065
1-1/2	38.1	1.767	88	142	177	885	1,325	1,770	2,651	3,540	4,425	5,310	.00765
1-3/4	44.5	2.410	121	193	241	1,205	1,808	2,410	3,615	4,820	6,025	7,230	.0104
2	50.8	3.140	157	251	314	1,570	2,357	3,140	4,713	6,280	7,850	9,420	.0136
2-1/2	63.5	4.910	245	393	491	2,455	3,682	4,910	7,364	9,820	12,275	14,730	.0213
3	76.2	7.070	354	566	707	3,535	3,502	7,070	10,604	14,140	17,675	21,210	.0306
3-1/4	82.6	8.300	415	664	830	4,150	6,225	8,300	12,450	16,600	20,750	24,900	.0359
3-1/2	88.9	9.620	481	770	962	4,810	7,215	9,620	14,430	19,240	24,050	28,860	.0416
4	101.6	12.570	628	1,006	1,257	6,285	9,428	12,570	18,856	25,140	31,425	37,710	.0544
5	127.0	19.640	982	1,571	1,964	9,820	14,730	19,640	29,460	39,280	49,100	58,920	.0850
5-1/2	139.7	23.760	1,188	1,901	2,376	11,880	17,820	23,760	35,640	47,520	59,400	71,280	.1028
6	152.4	28.270	1,414	2,262	2,827	14,135	21,203	28,270	42,406	56,540	70,675	84,810	.1224
7	177.8	38.490	1,924	3,079	3,849	19,245	28,868	38,490	57,736	76,980	96,225	115,470	.1666
8	203.2	50.270	2,513	4,022	5,027	25,135	37,703	50,270	75,406	100,540	125,675	150,810	.2176
8-1/2	215.9	56.750	2,838	4,540	5,675	28,375	42,563	56,750	85,125	113,500	142,875	170,250	.2455
10	254.0	78.540	3,927	6,283	7,854	39,270	58,905	78,540	117,810	157,080	196,350	235,620	.3400
12	304.8	113.100	5,655	9,048	11,310	56,550	84,825	113,100	169,650	226,200	282,750	339,300	.4896

NOTE: Deduct Force of Piston Rod Size from Bore Size for Pull Applications.

finished to the same tolerances, hardened, and chrome plated. Piston material varies, but it is usually cast iron turned to the same tolerance as the bore. Some pistons are phosphor coated to extend working life, although this is rare.

Current piston-seal practice calls for synthetic rather than the cast-iron rings that were once almost universal. Cast-iron has two strikes against it; the rate of leakage is always high and cast-iron, while compatible with steel, accelerates bore wear. Its advantage is that cast-iron rings do not fail suddenly. Wear is slow, and the operator will have ample warning as the carriage slowly sinks in neutral. Other seals can blow, dropping the load without warning. But new technologies have made this very unlikely.

Filtering Systems

Dirt is the No. 1 enemy of hydraulic systems and is responsible for more than half of the downtime. In a carefully tabulated study of 48 aircraft and ground-support systems, the U.S. Navy found that

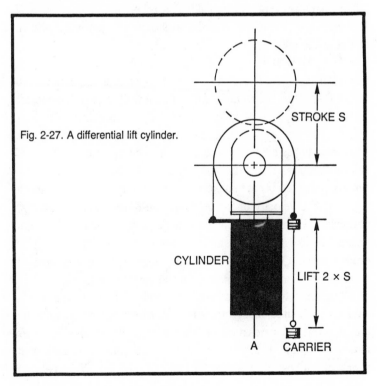

Fig. 2-27. A differential lift cylinder.

STROKE S

CYLINDER

LIFT 2 × S

A CARRIER

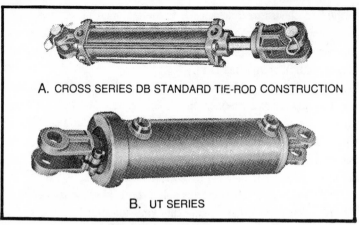

A. CROSS SERIES DB STANDARD TIE-ROD CONSTRUCTION

B. UT SERIES

Fig. 2-28. Cross series DB cylinder with conventional tie-rod construction (A) has advantages over the welded cap UT series (B).

dirt was responsible for the loss of four pilots, nine airplanes, and $33 million in maintenance and replacement costs. The Bertea Corporation found that dirt added some $50 million a year to the maintenance bill on a battery of numerically controlled machines. General Dynamics lost 10% of the cost of one machine-tool per year because of dirt in the oil.

Dirt (the term is a generic one for all solids) enters the system from many sources. During assembly, the reservoir is a natural trap for weld splatter, paint chips, and dust. New fittings, valve bodies, and pumps may have partially stripped threads that throw shavings when tightened. Most hydraulic components are sand cast and it is impossible to assure that the parts are absolutely clean. Particles of sand and metal shavings that have remained in place during manufacturing and assembly are shaken loose by hydraulic stress and shock impacts. The velocity of the oil is enough to erode internal parts, particularly if there is an angle change in the passage. It is not unusual to find 90-degree fittings that have seen lots of service eroded away. On new trucks every moving part is a source of contamination, and remains so until the parts wear in.

In addition to its vulnerability to assembly litter, the reservoir is a continuing source of contamination. Air freely circulates above the fluid, and this air carries moisture that rusts steel parts. Nor is the air filter always kept at top efficiency. Filters that are combined with filler pipes almost always develop leaks at the joint. When refilling the reservoir, few mechanics concern themselves with the possibility of dirt entering the system.

Leaks, particularly on the suction side of the pump, are another source of contamination. No seal is completely leakproof, and each cubic centimeter of air carries a burden of dust particles.

Effects of Dirt. Dirt has three significant effects on the system. In order of priority they are:

- Small orifices are plugged, particularly those associated with valve components. The result is erratic operation or complete failure.
- Working clearances silt over. Silting occurs when a heavily contaminated system remains idle for long periods. Particles drop out of the oil and block small passages, either radially as shown in Fig. 2-29A or axially as shown in B. Should the particles be the same diameter as the working

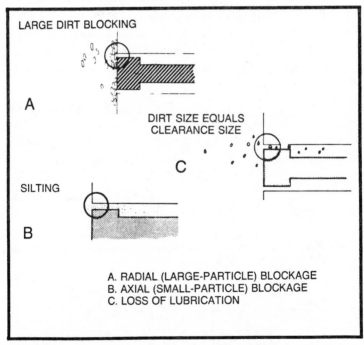

LARGE DIRT BLOCKING

A

DIRT SIZE EQUALS
CLEARANCE SIZE

C

SILTING

B

A. RADIAL (LARGE-PARTICLE) BLOCKAGE
B. AXIAL (SMALL-PARTICLE) BLOCKAGE
C. LOSS OF LUBRICATION

Fig. 2-29. The effects of dirt. Large particles can rapidly close working passages (A); smaller particles do their damage by slow accretation (B); particles that are the same size as the working clearances accelerate wear (C). (Courtesy Rosean Filter Div., Parker Hannefin Corp.)

clearance, the protective oil film is broken and rapid wear results. This condition is shown in Fig. 2-29C.

- Heat builds up. Dirt particles hold heat developed in the operation of the system, and also generate their own heat because of friction. Oil temperature increases causing increased maintenance, and, in extreme cases, sludge forms as the oil undergoes chemical change.

Particle-Size Standards. Particle diameters are measured in microns (micrometers). One micron is equal to 0.000039 of an inch. A grain of table salt averages about 100 microns in diameter, human hair about 70 microns, and talcum powder 10 microns. Since the lower limit of visibility is 40 microns, oil can be unacceptably dirty and still appear clear.

The Society of Automotive Engineers has developed a contaminant classification scale reproduced in Table 2-2. It ranges from Class 0, the cleanest oil practically attainable, to Class 6. The latter corresponds to hydraulic oil as received from the refinery. In spite of the great effort expended to keep hydraulic oil clean, a freshly tapped barrel will contain some 10 grams of dirt.

Class 6 contamination is tolerable for lift trucks. Of course, filters must be changed periodically to keep the oil at this standard. As pressure and reliability requirements go up, greater demands are put on the oil. For example, the Navy has learned from bitter experience to specify Class 5 for aircraft and ground-support systems. The Kearney & Trecker Corporation specifies Class 4 for servo systems, and Cincinnati Milacron has developed a standard for servos that approximates SAE Class 3. Classes 1 and 0 are specified for aerospace and certain national defense applications.

Table 2-2. SAE Contaminant Size Classification. (Courtesy Rosean Filter Division, Parker Hannefin Corp.)

SIZE RANGE	CLASS (Contamination standards per 100 ml)						
	0	1	2	3	4	5	6
5-10 um	2,700	4,600	9,700	24,000	32,000	87,000	128,000
10-25 um	670	1,340	2,680	5,360	10,700	21,400	42,000
25-50 um	93	210	380	780	1,510	3,130	6,500
50-100 um	16	28	56	110	225	430	1,000
>-100 um	1	3	5	11	21	41	92

Filter Design. One convenient way of classifying filters is in terms of the medium or the material used to trap dirt particles. *Depth filter* media may be made of paper, fiber, sintered metal, or layers of wire mesh. The media are usually formed into a cylindrical element for maximum space utilization and ease of replacement. Filtration is both on the surface of the element and through its cross section (Fig. 2-30).

Dirt is trapped in the interstices, or pores, between the fibers. Since the arrangement of fibers is usually random, the size of the pores (and the size of dirt particles that the pores trap) is distributed in the form of a bell curve (Fig. 2-31). Each filter medium has a mean pore size. That is, half of the flow is through smaller pores and half through larger ones. In the illustration shown, the mean pore size is 50 microns. Many manufacturers would give this medium a rating of 50 microns in their sales literature. However, this is misleading. In the first place, 50 microns refers to the mean pore size and not to the size of dirt particles trapped. And a few particles of 100-micron size will pass while others smaller than the mean size will be blocked. Note, however, that the bell curve is skewed to the left which means that the pore size is not entirely random. It is biased against the larger particles, although some of these will, nevertheless, pass.

Other manufacturers would describe this filter as having a nominal rating of 20 microns and more conservative manufacturers

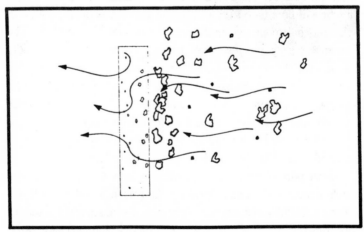

Fig. 2-30. Depth-type filter element traps particles throughout its cross section. (Courtesy Parker Hannefin Corp).

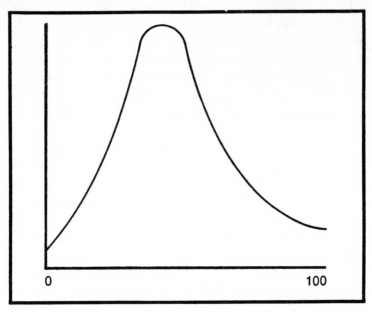

Fig. 2-31. Typical pore size distribution in a depth-type filter medium. The bell curve represents the holes of a given size per unit area. (Courtesy Rosean Filter Div., Parker Hannefin Corp.)

would say 80. The point is that you should realize that depth filter media ratings are statistical, not absolute.

Surface media provide a direct flow path for the fluid stream; dirt particles are trapped on the surface of the element that faces the direction of flow (see Fig. 2-32). The medium is made of wire or nylon monofilament woven in standard or Dutch wire cloth. The former is constructed of wires of the same diameter to give the cloth the general appearance of window screen. Dutch wire cloth has heavier warp wires (those running parallel to the long axis of the material) than shute (or crosswise) wires. The shute wires are pressed tightly against the warp to form triangular passageways. Dutch wire cloth has up to eight times the mechanical strength of standard wire cloth for the same particle retention.

Since pore size is controlled with precision, surface media have absolute ratings. For example, 200 × 200 mesh (standard) cloth has 200 vertical and horizontal wires per inch. Using standard-diameter wire, this results in square pores, with the distribution characteristics shown in Fig. 2-33.

Choosing a Filter. Depth-type medium filters have these advantages:

- Low cost (one of the most popular lift truck filters is identical to those used on Ford V-8 engines)
- High dirt-holding capacity
- High efficiency on a one-time fluid-pass base

The disadvantages are:

- Impractical to clean
- High pressure drop across the element
- Limited shelf life (paper) and low resistance to heat (paper and synthetic)

Surface-type medium filters have:

- Cleanability (74 microns and above)
- Repairability
- Control of pore size
- Low pressure drop (rising, of course, as the filter remains in service)

The disadvantages of surface-medium filters are:

- High initial cost
- Low efficiency on a one-time fluid-pass basis
- Limited dirt-holding capacity

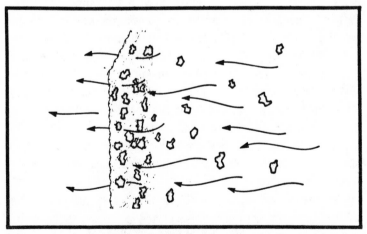

Fig. 2-32. A surface-type filter element has only one line of defense—the surface facing the direction of oil flow. (Courtesy Parker Hannefin Corp).

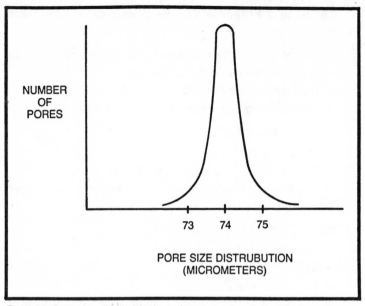

Fig. 2-33. Pore size distribution in surface-type wire cloth. (Courtesy Rosean Filter Div., Parker Hannefin Corp.)

How much filtration is enough? Ultimately, the answer to this question is a matter of machine downtime versus filter replacement costs. Machine downtime in this context is a function of its toleration for dirt, and it varies with the type and working clearances of components and most particularly with hydraulic pressure. Parker Hannefin recommends 40-micron filtration for circuits developing less than 2000 psi and 25-micron filtration for higher pressures. These are rule of thumb recommendations and do not take into account adverse working environments (such as foundries) or severely worn components. For example, the Basic Fluid Power Research Laboratory at Oklahoma State University found that a hydraulic cylinder with 100 hours of use fouls oil 100 times as rapidly as it did when new. The implication is that as the machine ages, more filtration (within acceptable pressure drop limits) and more frequent servicing is required.

Filter Installation. Lift truck filters are traditionally the full-flow type. That is, the filter is inserted in series with the circuit so that all flow passes through it. A bypass is opened by the pressure drop if the element clogs.

Proportional flow filters are rare as original equipment, but are sometimes installed in the field when oil contamination has been a problem. The disadvantage is that the fluid must be cycled more than once to get full filtration. No single component is positively protected.

Full-flow filters can be mounted in any of three locations: on the suction side of the pump, on the pressure side, or across the return line.

Filters mounted on the suction side of the pump require a bit of engineering to be properly mounted. The pump will tolerate very little restriction on the suction side without going into cavitation. Cessna Aircraft pumps (used on many trucks) have a suction specification of 7 in. Hg (inches of mercury). Pumping losses due to friction in the inlet line and the lift loss (if the pump is mounted above the reservoir) must be subtracted from the suction specification to obtain the allowable pressure drop of the filter. Typically you will find that the filter can impose no more than 3 or 4 in. Hg on the system. This means that a mesh filter must be used.

The major advantage is the direct and positive protection afforded the pump, particularly from catastrophic failure due to a single particle. In addition, the nature of suction filtration, low flow rates and low pressure drops, adds a bonus in the form of "cake" formation on the element. Dirt particles stratify on the upstream surface of the element and become themselves a kind of filter medium, stopping even smaller particles as the cake builds up.

The disadvantage is pressure sensitivity. As the filter cakes, pressure drop increases until the pump cavitates. Relatively coarse filtration is all that is possible (with decent filter life) and maintenance schedules must be religiously observed.

Pressure-line filters have two big advantages. Filtration can be in the 1 micron range, giving unsurpassed protection to individual components. The disadvantage is the added sophistication of a pressure filter. The housing must withstand several times the relief-valve pressure settings because of surges in the system. The medium must function without the benefit of caking and must be strong enough to withstand high pressure drops and pressure surges.

Most lift truck systems rely on a single return-line filter connected across the return line from the open-center control valve. In this way the reservoir is protected, and other components receive indirect protection. The filter housing is subject only to the pressure drop across the element and so can be designed quite inexpensively. However, the size of the filter must be generous to allow for return flow from the lift cylinder. Surging inhibits cake formation but makes the element less efficient than it would be in other locations. Excessive back pressure affects the operation of the control valves and cylinders, and in a poorly maintained system will be the first indication that the element needs to be replaced.

Magnets

Lift-truck designers often include a magnet in the base of the oil reservoir. The magnet holds small ferrous particles that enter the system during manufacture and during the course of normal operation. Since some of these particles are exceedingly small, removal by filtration is impractical.

While not all trucks have this feature, it is imperative that a magnet be installed if the system uses fire-resistant fluid. These fluids tend to keep particles in circulation.

Accumulators

Available as original equipment on some trucks, and as an after-market accessory, an accumulator functions as a shock absorber. It protects system components from the effects of sudden shock loads by introducing a degree of controlled compressibility into the oil stream.

Basically an accumulator is a cylinder with an upper chamber charged with gas (air or nitrogen) and the lower chamber with oil. In lift truck applications it is necessary to have some separation between the two, since system oil pressure is not always present. Without a separating element, gas pressure would dissipate.

Some machines have pistons between the two pressure zones. A mechanically simpler solution is as shown in Fig. 2-34. This accumulator can be charged with compressed air because there is no danger that air will enter the oil supply. The diaphragm is shaped like a pear and expands in accordance to Barlow's Formula for hoop stress. In paraphrase, the formula says that a hoop-shaped object will be stressed first on its long axis. If the diaphragm has a uniform wall thickness, it will expand lengthwise first and then downwards and out, pushing the oil ahead of it. At full expansion the diaphragm fills the cylinder almost completely. Some space is reserved for cushion oil.

Seals

Seals are intended to prevent or control external and internal leakage. Internal leakage is the more sanitary of the two, since the oil remains inside the circuit. It can offer benefits by way of lubrication, but severe internal leakage results in the loss of efficiency and in oil heating. External leakage is immediately obvious as oil accumulates on the machine and the floor. It becomes even more obvious when the reservoir has to be replenished. One drop every ten seconds will waste almost 3/4 of a 55 gallon barrel of oil in one year. One drop per second will spill 7 1/2 barrels during the same time period. If the reservoir holds 20 gallons, the same drop-per-second leak will require 2100% makeup. Seals are important.

In terms of function there are two basic types. *Static* seals are intended to hold pressure between two unmoving parts and gener-

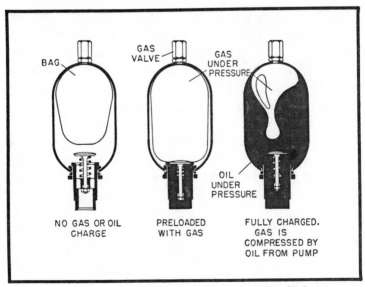

Fig. 2-34. A diaphragm-type accumulator. (Courtesy Mobile Oil Corp.)

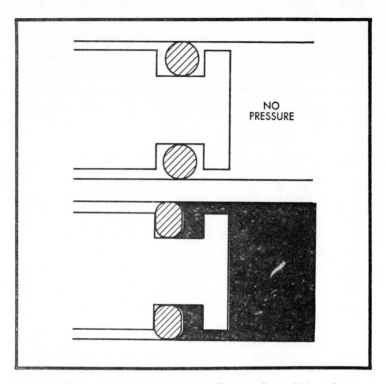

Fig. 2-35. O-rings deform under pressure. (Courtesy Sperry Vickers Corp.)

ally work by simple compression. A gasket is the classic example. *Dynamic* seals must function in the presence of movement between the parts and can, in some applications, be very complex. The simplest of seals, the ordinary O-ring, is the most versatile. These seals have replaced almost all gaskets in static applications and are popular on low-pressure reciprocating assemblies, such as valve spools. They are also finding increasing acceptance in hydraulic cylinders. Figure 2-35 illustrates the principle of the o-ring. It is assembled under slight compression—just enough to exert force by the seal on the groove. When subject to oil pressure, the seal distorts and forms a positive barrier. Within limits, the greater the pressure the more firmly the seal bites. Beyond these limits, the seal becomes increasingly liquid and its unpressurized edge balloons back. This can be circumvented by installing a backup ring behind the seal. Usually made of the same, but more rigid, variety of the material used in the seal, the backup ring gives additional support

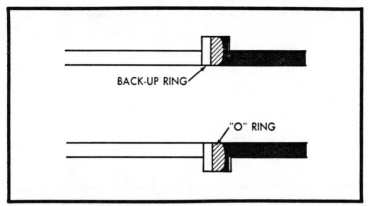

Fig. 2-36. Backup rings give better support. (Courtesy Sperry Vickers Corp.)

and is compatible with the moving part. This construction is shown in Fig. 2-36 and is the one used on Cross and other lift truck cylinders.

Most o-rings are round in cross-section. Lathe-cut rings are squared off and—as the name indicates—are face cut on a high-speed lathe (Fig. 2-37). In some applications it is possible to interchange lathe-cut and molded seals without a penalty.

T-ring Seals. T-rings are close cousins to o-rings (Fig. 2-38). The difference is in the shape of the seal and in the requirement for backup rings on both flanks. These seals are used on double-acting pistons where pressure can come from either side.

Cup Seals. Cup seals were a prerequisite for hydraulic brakes and are still favored wherever there are high-pressure and high-reliability demands. A typical double-acting cylinder application is shown in Fig. 2-39. In this case the cups are installed in pairs with their faces open to oil. As pressure builds, the cup cantilevers up and its feather edge generates tremendous unit force against the cylinder walls. These seals are classified as *positive*—that is, only enough oil to wet the seal gets past the lip.

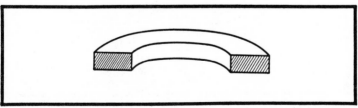

Fig. 2-37. A lathe-cut o-ring in cross-section. (Courtesy Sperry Vickers Corp.)

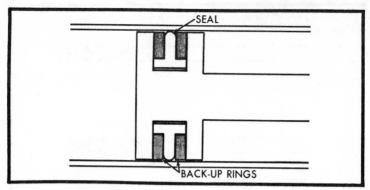

Fig. 2-38. T-ring seals are often used on double-acting cylinders. (Courtesy Sperry Vickers Corp.)

Lip Seals. You will find these seals (Fig. 2-40) doing sentry duty on pumps, motors, and engine shafts. Indeed, lip seals are used almost everywhere a wetted rotating shaft extends out of a fixed housing. At its simplest, the seal consists of three parts. The case is normally made of steel and is dimensioned for an interference fit with the stationary housing. The seal element is initially held against the shaft by means of a small garter spring. Actual sealing depends upon oil pressure acting behind the seal to force the tips against the shaft. The principle is the same as used with cup seals, although pressure tolerances are considerably lower. In most applications these seals are protected by a pressure barrier in the form of an antichamber with bleed-down ports.

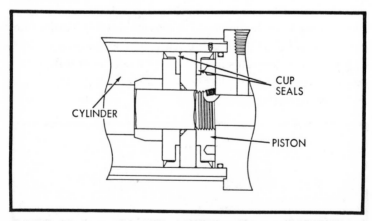

Fig. 2-39. Cup seals are installed with their faces toward the pressure side. (Courtesy Sperry Vickers Corp.)

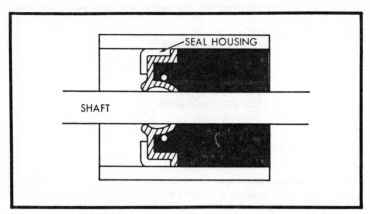

Fig. 2-40. A typical lip seal. (Courtesy Sperry Vickers Corp.)

Only one side of the seal responds to pressure—a fact some mechanics have learned through experience. In most applications, pressure is on the inboard side of the seal and a single element is adequate. Reversing pumps and motors require a pair of lip seals facing away from each other, since pressure relationships change with the direction of shaft rotation.

Piston Rings. While they do not have the positive action of lip or cup seals, metallic piston rings operate on the same general principle (Fig. 2-41). Pressure above the ring seeps past the upper edge and applies a force behind the ring to expand it and force it against the cylinder wall. The greater the pressure above the ring, the more pronounced the sealing action.

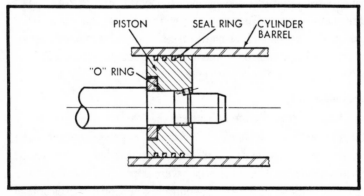

Fig. 2-41. Piston rings have the advantage of a controlled and predictable rate of failure. (Courtesy Sperry Rand.)

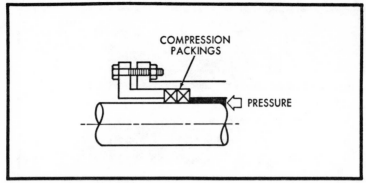

Fig. 2-42. Packing is obsolete, although it was once used extensively on tilt cylinders. (Courtesy Sperry Rand).

Piston-ring technology has not kept pace with the developments in pliable seals. Metallic rings were once quite common and had the advantages of low friction, durability, and predictable (and progressive) wear. Today rings are relegated to the engine itself, the transmission, and to very-high-pressure cylinders.

Packing. In the narrow sense, *packing* means a purely compressive seal between moving parts. A packing is a kind of gasket held in place by an adjustable flange or gland nut (Fig. 2-42). This type of seal requires frequent adjustment to compensate for wear.

Molded Seal Rings. Molded seal rings reflect the industry's commitment to *materials intensity* rather than to *labor intensity*. These seals are more expensive than packing, and require careful installation if they are to perform properly. But little or no maintenance is required (depending upon the type). Figure 2-43 shows three popular types. The one shown installed in a cylinder seals by oil pressure acting on its L-shaped cross-section. Chevron and rectangular seals function in the same manner, although they benefit from some initial compression during assembly.

Seal Materials

Early hydraulic systems, such as the 1907 example used to lay the guns on the battleship *U.S.S. Virginia*, depended entirely upon organic seals. These "natural" materials included leather, cork, cotton, and paper. Complex shapes were impossible to manufacture and none of these materials were entirely compatible with oil or high temperatures.

Since the Second World War, synthetic rubber (an elastomer) and plastic have displaced organic materials in most applications. Paper is still used for gaskets, impregnated cotton is present as an internal hose wrapping, and leather cup seals are still available. Leather is the most promising of these organic materials; it resists abrasion better than any synthetic. However, oil temperature must not be allowed to exceed 170°F. At 200° F leather literally cooks.

Buna-N or nitrile rubber has become the standard elastomer. This is the seal material that made the automatic transmission practical. Buna-N can be molded easily and inexpensively, and is happy at temperatures ranging from −65° to 250° F. Recommended for all petroleum and ethylene glycol-based fluids, it is generally agreed to be more stable than other materials at moderate temperatures.

Silicone has a wider temperature range than Buna-N—it tolerates a 5° lower temperature and lives at a sizzling 400° F. But

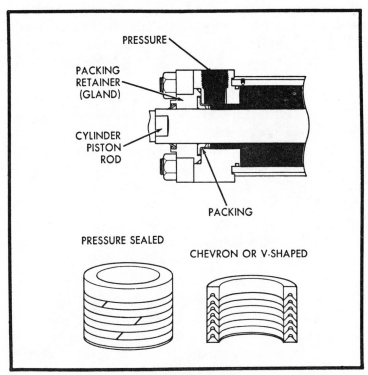

Fig. 2-43. Three types of molded seal rings. (Courtesy Sperry Vickers Corp.)

silicone is fragile. It elongates, tears, and abrades so easily that it cannot be used in cylinders or on reciprocating parts. Silicone is specified as a shaft seal for certain high-temperature pumps and motors, although great care must be taken to control the mechanical loads applied to the seal.

In contrast, neoprene is almost as tough as leather, but has a very limited temperature range. Applications have been curtailed as pumps become more compact and oil temperatures increase. Neoprene can tolerate 150°F well, but vulcanizes at higher temperatures.

Teflon and nylon are plastics rather than elastomers. Both have low coefficients of friction, and Teflon can tolerate frying-pan heats—temperatures well beyond those of present-day hydraulic fluids. But Teflon and, to a less marked degree, nylon are expensive.

Design Factors. Real progress has been made in the design of equipment to reduce the opportunities for leaks. For example, back-mounted valves are sealed by o-rings rather than by weepy gaskets. Piping and tubing is routed with an eye to stability and resistance to vibration. Further security of connections has come about by the use of straight threads backed with o-rings, rather than interference-fit tapered threads. Pipes are sealed with a thin layer of Teflon tape, applied at the factory or in the field. Another strategy has been to reduce the number of leak points by combining individual circuits into common manifolds.

Internal leakage has been minimized by closer tolerances, better inspection and post-assembly cleaning methods, coupled with more stringent filtration standards.

HYDRAULIC OIL

One manufacturer made an extended survey of the malfunctions in hydraulic systems. The results are enlightening:

- 10% were the result of ignorance on the part of repair personnel. Problems were misdiagnosed or repairs were made without reference to the ultimate cause of failure. For example, instead of replacing a scored piston rod, the mechanics merely replaced the seal. Naturally, the cylinder continued to leak.

- 10% were mechanical failures; some because of poor design, others because of inadequate maintenance or careless operation.
- 5% were due to operating the machines beyond their rated capabilities.
- 5% were unclassified, miscellaneous failures.
- 70% were traced to the hydraulic oil.

It is difficult to overemphasize the importance of the correct selection and care of hydraulic oil. No other single part of the system has so much bearing on its durability and operating costs.

Choosing the right oil is not difficult, particularly if your machine operates under average conditions. The lift truck manufacturer can recommend a number of oils available from major refiners and, in some instances, stocks these oils by part number.

Functions

The primary function of the oil is to transmit force applied at one point in the oil column to another point. The oil should reproduce the direction and intensity of the applied force with minimum hesitation. This means that hydraulic oil must flow easily while remaining relatively incompressible.

The oil must maintain enough film strength to deny metal-to-metal contact between moving parts, and must have enough body to seal against internal and external leaks. It should inhibit rust and foam, and allow solids to drop out harmlessly in the reservoir. And the oil must be easily obtainable in all parts of the world.

These requirements are most easily met by petroleum-based oils. Synthetic and silicon-based oils work, but are expensive and narrowly distributed. Water is an obvious choice. It has a higher specific gravity than oil, making it attractive for torque converters, and is the most plentiful liquid on this planet. Unfortunately, water is corrosive and its lubricating qualities are nil. And water severely limits the operating temperatures of the system, since there seems to be no practical way to lower its freezing point or raise its boiling point. Water or water-based fluids are used where there is extreme fire hazard and cycling rates are slow. Elevators and hot-forge presses are examples. Water-based fluids can be used in lift trucks operating in hazardous enviornments, but seals and filters must be

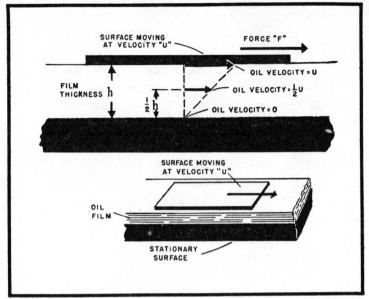

Fig. 2-44. Viscosity is the energy required to shear a film of oil sandwiched between a moving and a stationary surface. (Courtesy Mobile Oil Co.)

replaced with compatible components. Pump and valve-spool wear is accelerated.

Viscosity

Viscosity is a measure of an oil's resistance to flow. An engineer would say it is a measure of an oil's resistance to shear. The concept can be understood with reference to Fig. 2-44. The thin plate is supported over the thick plate by a film of oil. As the thin plate is moved oil adheres to its lower surface and to the stationary upper surface of the thick plate. Oil in contact with the moving surface moves at the same velocity; that in contact with the stationary surface remains motionless. In between the oil can be visualized as a series of very thin layers. Each layer is dragged by the layer above it at a speed proportional to its distance from the stationary layer. The force needed to move the thin plate is the force needed to shear the oil layers and is the same as the internal friction of the oil.

There are various ways to express viscosity. In metric terms the unit is a *poise*. When the moving surface has an area of 1 square centimeter (cm^2), the film thickness (h) is 1 cm, the velocity (U) is 1 cm per sec, and force (F) is 1 dyne, the viscosity of the liquid is 1 poise. These units are shown on the drawing.

A more convenient way to express viscosity and the one used by many oil companies in their literature is Saybolt Universal Seconds, abbreviated SUS or SSU. Oil samples are heated to 100° F, and the time required in seconds for 60 cubic centimeters to flow through an orifice of specified diameter is the Saybolt viscosity. This may be expressed as 100/100 SUS or simply as 100 SUS, without reference to the test temperature. Hydraulic oils have been traditionally tested at 100°F and, for the older blends, the temperature indication is superfluous. But new demands on hydraulic oil in lift trucks and other applications have made a second test at 210°F, meaningful, and Saybolt viscosity is now expressed in terms of both test temperatures.

The Society of Automotive Engineers, the American Petroleum Institute, and other professional organizations have urged refiners to discontinue expressing viscosities in terms of Saybolt Universal Seconds. The preferred test gives an answer in centistokes and can be used in scientific calculation. (Saybolt viscosities are purely empirical.) The test procedure is not unlike the traditional one. A particular oil is heated and the time required for a given amount to pass through an orifice of known size is determined. But centistokes (cSt) have no simple relation to SUS. A rule of thumb (courtesy of Mr. T.T. Ordiway of the Kendall Refining Co.) is to multiply the cSt value by 5.5 when cSt is less than 20, and by 4.6 when it is greater than 20. It is assumed that the fluid density of the oil is 0.9 grams per cc.

By whatever standard expressed, viscosity at operating temperature is the most important single variable in selecting a hydraulic oil. It represents the best compromise between the demands of the machine and the demands put on the system by working conditions.

The following points are prime factors in the selection of hydraulic oil.

- Lubrication. Because of internal friction, oil can be readily drawn into small pump and valve clearances and coats the parts with a protective film. This function is critical since the hydraulic oil is the only lubrication available for most components.

- Heat losses. By the very fact of high internal friction, oils with high viscosity resist movement and generate heat in service. Heat represents a loss of pump efficiency since no useful work is done. Indeed, oil and component life are shortened.
- Pressure losses. This is another factor to weigh when considering the use of high viscosity oils. Pressure drops are a function of oil velocity and oil body. The faster it moves and the thinner it is, the less energy is wasted in the plumbing.
- Cavitation. Sluggish oil, the bane of pumps, is not fluid enough to follow the convolutions of the pump and the stream separates. A vacuum is put on the oil and dissolved air is released in the form of bubbles that heat to very high temperatures and explode violently against the impellor. In the most carefully designed systems with broad gauge suction lines and the pump mounted under the reservoir, oil with a startup (cold) viscosity of more than about 4000 SUS will go into cavitation.
- Leakage. Pumps, motors, and spool valves generally do not have provision for internal packing. Liquids flow from a high-pressure to a low-pressure area, and the resistance to this flow depends upon viscosity or internal friction. External leakage on cylindrical parts—lift and tilt cylinders, transmission pistons, and the like—follows the *cube law*. As the clearance is doubled, leakage increases eight times. Triple the clearance and leakage increases thirty-six times. For this reason critical valve parts are lapped to 0.00004 of an inch per linear inch, and the standard of interchangeability in hydraulics is usually 0.0004 of an inch.

In summary, oils with high viscosity are needed to assure adequate lubrication and to control leakage losses. At the same time, low viscosity is required to minimize heat and pressure losses and to extend the threshold of cavitation.

Viscosity Index

All fluids tend to thin at high temperatures and to thicken as temperatures drop. The viscosity index (VI) is a measure of the rate of viscosity change as determined by test at 100°F and at 210° F. VI units are somewhat arbitrary since they are based on no standard other than on oils available at the turn of the century. A VI of 0 was assigned to a certain naphthenic oil showing marked viscosity changes due to temperature; a VI of 100 was given to a paraffinic oil that remained relatively stable. At the time it was believed that these oils represented the boundaries of the index. It is now possible to blend oils with a VI of less than 0 or with a VI well beyond 100, although the low VI of naphthenic oils and the high VI of paraffinic oil is characteristic of the stock, and is subject only to slight modification by additives and refinery techniques.

Artificially extended viscosity indexes are the hallmark of aircraft hydraulic oils. While ordinary hydraulic oil rarely has a VI of more than 100, aircraft oils are commonly in the 105–110 range, thanks to solvent refining and to a group of additives known as polymers or long-chain hydrocarbons. First-generation polymers become unstable—literally break—under high-shear velocities, but this problem is being solved. Should pump capacity and pressure outputs continue to increase as they have during the last decade, it is expected that these additives will find their way into ordinary hydraulic oils. Already one lift truck manufacturer specifies that a single grade of oil operate between 18 and 148° F.

But viscosity numbers have only a minute relationship with operating temperatures. In absoute terms, choosing an oil with a higher viscosity makes only a small dent in the temperature envelope. Figure 2-45 is informative: it compares two oils, one with a VI of 90 and the other with a VI of 50. Both have the same Saybolt viscosity at 100° F and the 40-point VI spread should do wonders for low-temperature operation. But this is not so. If we accept that no pump should be asked to move an oil thicker than 4000 SUS, then an oil with a VI of 50 can function down to 17° F, and an oil with a VI of 90 reaches the same viscosity at 12° F. In other words the 40-point VI spread is equivalent to only 5 degrees of temperature.

Some compensation can be had in the fact that an increase in pressure (accompanied, one can assume, by an increase in the temperature spread from startup to stable working temperature) increases the VI of any given oil. For example, a test batch of paraffinic oil with a VI of 94 was pressurized to 10,000 psi. The VI

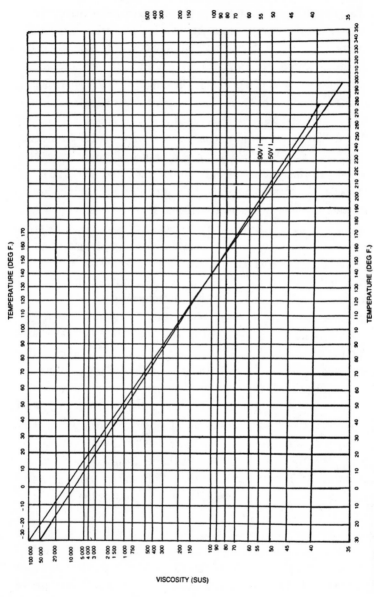

Fig. 2-45. Temperature vs Viscosity Index.

94

jumped 400% while another batch of low VI naphthenic oil underwent a sixfold increase in viscosity at the same elevated pressure.

Pour Point

The pour point is of more concern to the refinery than to the ultimate user. The term means the lowest temperature at which the oil will flow when chilled under controlled conditions. It is not an indication of the oil's "pumpability," since oils with identical pour points may pump readily or not at all. Nor does it have a standing relationship to viscosity for different oils. As a rule of thumb, the pour point should be 20 − 30°F lower than the lowest temperature the oil is expected to be exposed to.

Flash Point

The *flash point* is another characteristic of interest to refiners but not to users (although under certain hazardous storage and operating conditions, the fire marshall may have something to say about it. The flash point is the temperature at which the oil blend begins to distill and give off inflammable vapors. For hydraulic oils the flash point is some two and a half times maximum allowable operating temperature.

Specific Gravity and API Gravity

These two specifications say essentially the same thing. The specific gravity (sg) is the ratio of the weight of any volume of a substance to a like volume of water. Water has an sg of 1,000. Years ago it was thought that sg had bearing on an oil's ultimate performance, particularly since oils of demonstratively different characteristics had different sg's. Gravity API is another way of expressing specific gravity, except that the scale is reversed. As the sg of an oil increases, the American Petroleum Institute gravity drops. For example, an oil with an sg of 1.000 has an API gravity of 10; oil with an sg of 0.6852 has an API gravity of 75. Neither of these weight ratings is of more than academic interest, although both continue to be published in oil specification sheets.

Oxidation Stability

At atmospheric pressure, a typical oil sample contains 10% dissolved air by volume. At 200 psi the amount of air in the sample can be increased by a factor of 20. Air contains oxygen, a very active gas that combines with hydrocarbons to produce a range of acids, alcohols, aldehydes, ketones, and other oil-soluble compounds. An immediate effect of this mix is to increase the viscosity of the oil and, consequently, its temperature. The acids formed erode metallic and synthetic parts and release a stream of solids into the oil.

In relatively cool reservoir and elsewhere after shutdown, some soluble compounds precipitate to form sludge and varnishes. The latter floats in the oil stream and coats the system internals with a dark goo. The process is accelerated if the parts are heated and results in sticking valves, clogged passageways, sticking pump vanes, restricted oil clearances—the whole spectrum of malfunctions that result in sluggish machine action and erratic timing. Sludge collects in the reservoir and other low-velocity spots. In extreme form, it blocks the inlet screen and silts over control passageways. As harmful as ordinary sludge is, another variant—built around kernels of core sand, metal filings, and the like—has earned the name "super-sludge."

Some oxidation takes place as soon as the barrel of oil is opened. But room-temperature reactions are insignificant, since most of the hydrocarbon molecules that make up the oil remain inert until heated. With each 15° F increase in oil temperature, the rate of oxidation doubles. An oil temperature of 140° F at any point in the circuit is considered critical. Many petroleum chemists believe that certain forms of dirt hasten oxidation by acting as catalysts in the complex chain of reactions. Others reserve judgment on this point, but it has been well established that some metals, particularly copper, encourage oxidation. Copper is present in most hydraulic systems and its activities increase as these parts wear and pulverize.

Unfortunately, no single test or battery of tests for oxidation is absolute. The reactions involved are, for the most part, environmentally triggered and are influenced by the type of machine and the conditions under which it works. And most of the tests, including the one discussed here, were devised for crankcase oils and are made at higher temperatures than hydraulic oils are normally exposed to. The most accepted test is known as the ASTM (American Society for Testing Materials) D 943-54.

Sixty cc of water are added to 300 cc of the oil to be tested and the mixture is heated to 205°F in the presence of a copper-iron catalyst. Oxygen is bubbled through the oil-water mixture and test results are interpreted as the time required for the neutralization number (a measure of the acidity and an indirect measure of oxidation) to reach 2.0. But the results are not conclusive. A "2000-hour ASTM Oxidation Test oil" is probably superior to a "1000-hour oil," but not necessarily superior to a "1500-hour oil" for any specific application.

Resistance to oxidation can be controlled by careful refining (to weed out the more reactive hydrocarbons) and by the use of additives. Several hundred compounds are available to inhibit oxidation either by interrupting the reaction at some point in its progress or by neutralizing the catalytic effect of metals.

In the field, oxidation initially becomes evident as a color change and by an increase in the oil's viscosity and acidity. Eventually, enough sludge and varnish form to affect machine performance. Unfortunately, there is no simple and easy field test to determine the condition of lightly oxidized oil. The test most often used, the neutralization-number test is at best a rough guide. The neutralization number indicates the acidity of the oil and not the relative concentration of more and less corrosive acids. Under certain conditions, oil with a neutralization number of 2.0 may be more benign than oil that tests out at 3.0. As limited as it is, the neutralization number is more meaningful than attempting to measure small changes in viscosity or color.

Rust and Corrosion

Although the term is often used inclusively, in the context of hydraulics oil corrosion refers to the loss of metal because of acid attack. Acid literally dissolves the metal. Rust occurs in the presence of water and oxygen. Rust deposits are oxides and represent a reversion of the metal to its ore. So long as its rust adheres, a rusted part weighs more than it did in its refined state.

Corrosion is hardly desirable, particularly when one considers the tolerances of hydraulic machines. But it is relatively easy to control since the trigger mechanism is the collection of acids formed when oil oxidizes. Rust is a more serious problem. Not only does it attract metals directly, it flakes and causes secondary damage. Rust particles score valve and pump parts and clog filters.

It is impossible to prevent water entry into the system. Some water will condense in the reservoir and some water-laden air gets past seals on the suction side of the pump. Oxygen, the other precondition for rust, is present to one degree or another in the oil.

The problem then becomes one of discouraging rust formation by the use of additives. While the chemistry of rust inhibitors is still disputed, the most accepted theory is that they separate from the oil and adhere to metal parts, plating them and inhibiting rust. The plating process is not well understood, but is believed to be a molecular bond, some two or three molecules thick.

Inhibitors are evaluated by the ASTM Rusting Test. Highly polished steel rods are suspended in a mixture of oil and real or synthetic sea water. The mixture is agitated and heated to 140° F for 24 hours. The inhibitor is said to fail if any visible rust is present on the rods.

Unlike some tests used by the industry, the ASTM Rusting Test is quite reliable and has an almost direct correlation with field data. If an inhibitor passes, it can be expected to prevent rust in service, regardless of the level of humidity, temperature changes, or other working variables. And once a part has been submerged in oil containing an inhibitor, it retains its protection from rust, even though oil may be no longer present.

Straight mineral oil cannot be added to oil with an inhibitor. A small (less than 1%) but constant volume of inhibitor must be present to maintain the plating action. This is important since it contradicts the traditional view that cheap, untreated replenishing oil is acceptable.

Water-Separating Ability

Water entering the system through leaks or condensation in the reservoir should settle to a low point and remain there. Unfortunately, this is not always the case. Strong currents in the reservoir can sweep some water along in a kind of low-grade emulsion. As this mix enters the pump it is churned into the consistency of mayonnaise and circulated throughout the system. At this point the emulsion is described as "persistent" since it is stable. The water bubbles remain entrapped in the oil, regardless of how long the emulsion is idle or how often it is pumped through a filter. Besides encouraging rust, a water/oil emulsion has no lubricating qualities.

The best defense is to use an oil with a high resistance to oxidation and to see that every effort is made to keep the system clean and dry.

And, while many pump manufacturers recommend heavy-duty (SE) grade multiviscosity motor oils for their antiwear properties, these oils must be watched carefully. They are not noted for their water-separating ability. If system parameters are such that motor oil must be used, drain it often, particularly in humid climates.

Foaming

Some air, about 10% by volume, is dissolved in commercial grade oils. Under pressure, a great deal more can be absorbed. So long as the air remains dissolved, it offers no immediate problem and a well-designed system can handle it. But should the air escape, it will form into bubbles that ultimately produce foam.

Surplus air enters the system through leaks on the suction-side plumbing and through partially filled return lines such as those that service relief valves and lift-cylinder overflow circuits. Extreme aeration occurs when the reservoir empties and the pump pulls on the atmosphere.

Even in the presence of pump cavitation, air normally dissolves on the pressure side of the pump. It finds release in low-pressure zones, and this phenomenon helps to explain the erratic action lift cylinders sometimes have when operated under no load. A much more critical situation occurs when the oil is so saturated that bubbles appear on the pressure side of the pump. The pump protests noisily, control becomes erratic, and cylinders respond in fits and jerks. Quantities of foam collect in the reservoir and may overflow out the breather.

Air generates heat under compression. This is the ignition principle of the diesel engine, and gives minimum ignition temperatures of 750° F. The exact temperature of air bubbles in a stream of hydraulic oil has not been determined, but it is believed to approach 2000° F at 3000 psi. While the heating effect is local and confined to oil in the vicinity of the bubbles, it promotes disaster in the form of oxidation.

Straight mineral oils are prone to foaming, although the tendency is mitigated by the source of the crude and the refining processes used. Certain chemical additives inhibit foaming and have made these other considerations superfluous. The action of these additives is intriguingly indirect: the obvious solutions would have been to proof the oil against air entry or to prevent air escape. Instead, the approach is to encourage the formation of large and fragile bubbles, so that air can break out more easily. Air can still enter and foam is still formed, but the foam doesn't last long.

Wear Protection

Wear is concentrated at the pump and increases disproportionally high with pressure. Low-pressure trucks operated satisfactorily on straight mineral oil, although premium hydraulic oils are a better choice insofar as pump life was concerned. Today's high-pressure, small-diameter pumps virtually demand oil with superior wear protection. Known in the trade as "antiwear hydraulic oil,", this oil or heavy-duty motor oil is recommended by most pump (and indirectly, lift truck) manufacturers. Some oil refiners are leery of using motor oil in hydraulic applications, arguing that it does not have the rust and oxidation inhibition of the better hydraulic oils. In terms of wear protection, both seem equal.

Hydraulics Repair

Hydraulic components have an almost naive simplicity about them. Pumps contain three or four wearing elements, cylinders amount to hardly more than a collection of seals, and control valves are an assemblage of single-function parts.

This simplicity makes things easier for the mechanic. Most failures are obvious—as obvious as a puddle of oil on the floor—and there is little difficulty in searching out the site of failure. Disassembly and assembly procedures are, for the most part, self-evident.

But the Mickey Mouse simplicity of most hydraulic components should not lead to complacency. There is more to successful hydraulics repairs than merely replacing worn or ruptured parts.

The component parts of any vehicle system—fuel, ignition, charging and starting, cooling—are interrelated to a degree. A battery that refuses to hold a charge will increase the rate of wear on the alternator and starter motor. A dirty fuel tank pollutes the whole system with sand and rust; faulty ignition cables lead to spark-plug fouling. Good mechanics take these interrelationships into account and are not content merely to replace the failed part.

This attitude, the willingness to search out and to correct the ultimate cause of failure, is essential to hydraulic system repair. Hydraulic components are tied together by a column of pressurized oil. The failure of any component can be the result of failure elsewhere in the circuit, and can itself be the cause of other failures. For example, a loosely fitting breather on the reservoir allows dirt to contaminate the oil supply. Dirt, even the few specks of dirt that find their way around the breather, can destroy the pump and every other component. As each of these components disintegrates, it releases a stream of metallic and synthetic particles that intensify and accelerate the damage.

For example, the most critical of all components is the relief valve. Should it be maladjusted or slow to crack, the whole system suffers a kind of hypertension. Replacing failed parts and not correcting the ultimate problem is futile and wasteful.

Hydraulic systems have a very strict performance envelope. These systems are intended to repeat the same stress/relaxation cycle millions of times before something fails. Since the operation is so predictable, great care has been lavished upon the details of construction.

Hydraulic systems work in a very predictable environment. Peak pressures and forces can be calculated mathematically and the design engineer can rest easy knowing that these forces will not be exceeded in millions of cycles of operation. It is relatively simple to design the system to match its performance requirements, using parts that are just strong enough and no stronger. While this kind of economy reduces costs, it puts a burden on the mechanic. Designing for the best cost effectiveness means that any irregularity in working conditions or in assembly puts intolerable stresses on the system and leads to early failure.

A hydraulics mechanic has a few simple chores to attend to. But these chores must be performed correctly and with the greatest emphasis upon inspection and cleanliness.

Figure 3-1 illustrates the standard fork-lift truck system. Individual circuitry may vary somewhat, but the basic configuration is the same. A constant-volume (gear or vane) pump delivers oil to the selector (or directional-control) valve block. The valve block contains check valves and a pressure relief valve. With the valves in neutral, all pump output is shunted to the reservoir. No pressure (other than that required to overcome line friction) is developed. When activated, the lift-control valve diverts oil to the underside of the single-acting lift cylinder. The overflow hose, shown at the upper

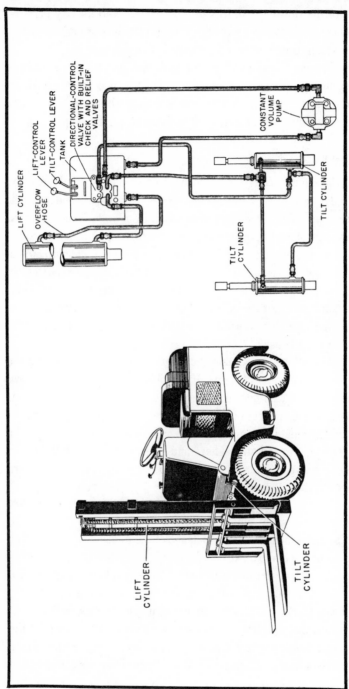

Fig. 3-1. The basic hydraulic system. (Courtesy Mobile Oil Corp.)

left of the drawing, returns oil that has worked its way past the cylinder seals to the reservoir. The tilt cylinders are double-acting and accept pressure on either side of their pistons.

The next drawing, Fig. 3-2, is a diagram of a more complex system with power steering, shift cylinder, and provision for an additional accessory cylinder. As is usually the case, the power steering pump is a separate entity, distinct from the system pump.

PUMPS

The pump converts mechanical energy to hydraulic energy. Standing as it does on the frontier between mechanical and hydraulic forces, the pump is subject to stresses from both. Hydraulic loads vary from almost nothing when the selector valves are in neutral to full system pressure. At full pressure, the pump may absorb 50% of engine power. A careless operator or a poorly designed circuit can send shock loads reverberating through the oil column. While all components suffer the effects of shock loading, the pump seems to get the worst of it. Fractured pump housings, split like an orange, are the usual result.

The pump is vulnerable to cavitation damage. Air can enter the system at a number of points. If the oil level in the reservoir is low, the oil forms a whirlpool, or vortex, as it is drawn into the pump. This condition is more serious when a great deal of oil is displaced (as when extending the mast). The vortex opens the center of the suction pipe to the atmosphere and air is drawn in with the oil. In addition, air can enter at the suction pipe, pump seals, and (where present) the head gasket.

Air bubbles seem innocuous enough. But when compressed and broken by the pump, these bubbles collapse with implosive force. Some measure of the violence of their collapse can be had by the sound the pump makes during cavitation. When back pressure is present—when the pump is loaded—the result is a high-pitched shriek. With the controls in neutral, the pump sounds as if it were pumping marbles. You can actually hear the marbles rattle.

Because the pump operates continuously—all of the time the engine is running—degradation of the oil affects the pump more than other components. Engineers at Commercial Shearing estimate that fully 85% of all pump failures are the result of oil contamination.

The effects of contamination are cumulative. Initial contamination increases the rate of pump wear. As the parts erode, they release a stream of solids into the oil stream. These solids further accelerate wear and the effect is to open the working clearances between the pump parts. More and more oil slips back past the pump. This slippage heats the oil and causes it to undergo chemical changes that make it less of a lubricant and more of an abrasive.

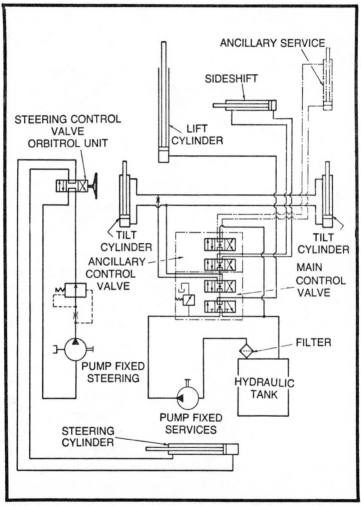

Fig. 3-2. The arrangement currently used in the Bonser RT 2500K and RT 3500K series. Power steering, sideshift, and the provision for an additional double-acting cylinder add complexity to the circuit.

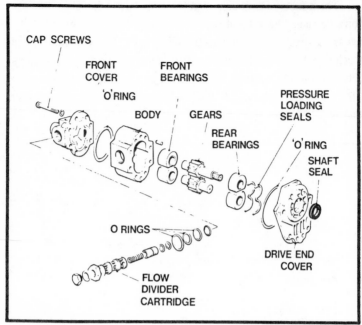

Fig. 3-3. This gear-type pump features sliding bearing blocks and supplies oil to the power steering pump as well as to the main hydraulics. (Courtesy Lansing Bagnall Ltd.)

Pump Types

Lift trucks use gear- or vane-type pumps in single and tandem configurations. Drive is by direct coupling, gears, or belts. Power steering cylinders may be fed from the main pump through a diverter that gives the steering function priority, or may be powered by a pump of their own. In the latter case, the pump is a belt-driven, vane-type that is similar to those found on automobiles.

Most modern pumps are self-adjusting over a narrow range. Wear on the gear and rotor sides and some small degree of housing distortion is compensated for by means of sliding bearing blocks or pressure plates. This type of construction was pioneered by Commercial Shearing in the U.S. and by Plessey, Hydromeca, S.I.G.M.A. and other firms in Europe. Not coincidentally, it came about as manufacturers demanded greater pump outputs from smaller packages.

Figure 3-3 illustrates a typical sliding block gear-type pump. The bearing blocks—the figure 8 castings that support the shaft bearings—are free to move fore and aft in the pump housing. Oil pressure, acting on carefully contoured impact surfaces on the outboard sides of the bearing blocks, overcomes the separating forces inside the pump. The blocks move together, sandwiching the gears between them. In a correctly designed pump the end clearance between the gears and the bearing blocks is just large enough to accommodate the oil film needed for lubrication.

Sliding bearing blocks are, of course, not the only way to arrange for pressure compensation. The Cross pump shown in cutaway in Fig. 3-4 uses loading plates on both sides of the gears; the Cessna pump in Fig. 3-5 uses a diaphragm.

Pump Overhaul

Most pumps can be overhauled in the field with parts supplied by their makers. This procedure is economic if the housing and other major castings have not been damaged. Otherwise, parts cost and availability are such that it is better to purchase a factory rebuilt or new pump.

New and repaired pumps should be run-in on a test stand. If a stand is not available, back off the relief valve and allow the pump to idle for a minute or so. Then slowly increase the pressures.

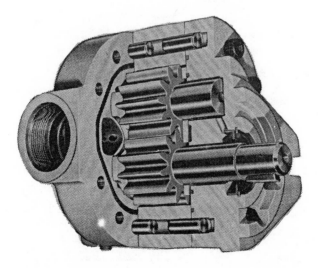

Fig. 3-4. Cross pumps use loading plates (shown on each side of the gears) rather than sliding bearing blocks.

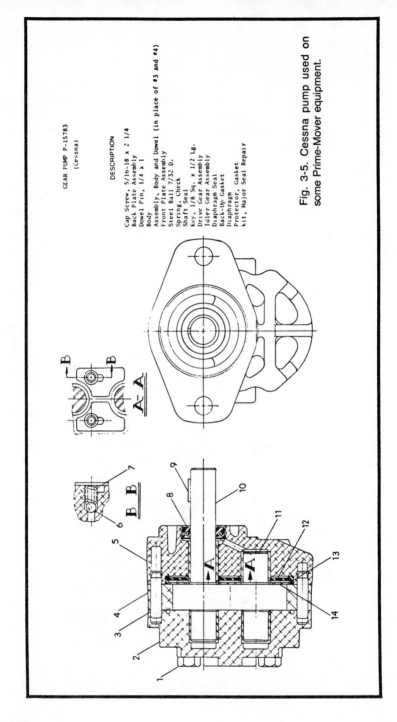

GEAR PUMP P-15783
(Cessna)

DESCRIPTION

Cap Screw, 5/16-18 x 2 1/4
Back Plate Assembly
Dowel Pin, 1/4 x 1
Body
Assembly, Body and Dowel (in place of #3 and #4)
Front Plate Assembly
Steel Ball 7/32 D.
Spring, Check
Shaft Seal
Key, 1/8 Sq. x 1/2 Lg.
Drive Gear Assembly
Idler Gear Assembly
Diaphragm Seal
Back-Up Gasket
Diaphragm
Protector, Gasket
Kit, Major Seal Repair

Fig. 3-5. Cessna pump used on some Prime-Mover equipment.

Gear-Type Pump. Figure 3-3 is our reference drawing. With the exception of the flow diverter cartridge (used to supply oil to the power steering cylinder), this pump is typical of the breed.

1. Drain the oil from the system.
2. Carefully clean the outer surfaces of the pump and fittings.
3. Remove the flow divider cartridge. Remove the snap ring and allow the piston to slide out. The relief valve should not be disturbed unless it has failed and must be renewed.
4. Remove the hex-head screws securing the end covers. Note the length of the screws for correct assembly.
5. Lift off the drive end cover and drive end bearing block.
6. Lightly tap the front cover to disengage the dowel pins that hold it to the front cover.
7. Remove and discard the o-rings and seals from the end covers.
8. Pry the oil seal out of the drive end cover and discard it. Wash the parts in hydraulic oil and blow dry.

To assemble:

1. Insert the piston and spring into the flow divider port. Secure the assembly with the snap ring. Press and release the piston a few times to check its response.
2. Clean any traces of hydraulic oil off the drive side seal bore with lacquer thinner or some other volatile solvent. The bore must be completely dry.
3. Lightly coat the inside of the bore with gasket sealant.
4. Install a new shaft seal with the help of a driver bar cut off square and turned down slightly less than the outside diameter of the seal.
5. Install a new o-ring on the drive end cover.
6. Install new pressure-loading seals on the drive end cover.
7. Press the body on the drive end cover, positioning it as it was found originally.
8. Mount the drive end bearing block after determining that the pressure-loading seals are in place.
9. Install the drive gear and shaft, being careful not to damage the seal during the operation.
10. Align the front bearing block with the shaft ends and slide it home into the pump housing.

11. Place a new o-ring and pressure loading seals on the front cover.
12. Fit the cover to the pump body.

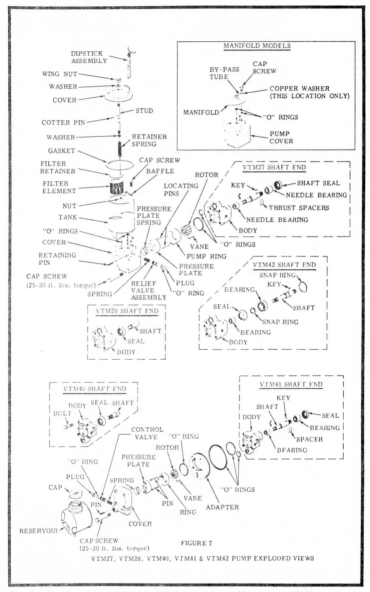

FIGURE 7

VTM27, VTM28, VTM40, VTM41 & VTM42 PUMP EXPLODED VIEWS

Fig. 3-6. Sperry Vickers VTM27, VTM28, VTM40, VTM41, and VTM42 pumps in exploded view.

13. Torque the cap screws evenly and in several increments to 29 ft-lb.
14. Place new o-rings into the threaded bore on the front cover and over the grooves on the flow divider valve assembly.
15. Install and tighten the flow divider valve assembly on the front cover.
16. Mount the pump on the engine and install the lines.
17. Fill the reservoir.

Vane-Type Pumps. Sperry Vickers VTM series pumps are intended for power steering applications, but are functionally similar to those used for the main hydraulic system. Five pumps in this series are in current production: VTM27, VTM28, VTM40, VTM41, and VTM42. Model differences involve drive arrangements, bearing types, reservoir styles, and capacity (Fig. 3-6). With these differences aside, all pumps are mechanically similar. The principal parts consist of the reservoir, body, cover, ring, rotor, vanes, pressure plate, relief valve, and drive shaft. The combined flow control and relief valve is complex and requires some explanation.

FLOW CONTROL AND RELIEF VALVE

Figure 3-7 illustrates the valve in operation. In view A, the total pump delivery goes to the steering cylinder. This condition is rare and comes about when the pump is idling. View B depicts normal operation. The pump delivers more oil than the orifice can pass. Consequently, pressure on the pump side of the orifice (above it in the drawing) is greater than pressure on the cylinder side (or under the orifice). The spring-loaded relief valve is free to slide in its bore. When the difference in pressure sensed on the two sides of the valve is great enough to overcome spring tension, the valve opens as shown. Some of the pump output is throttled back to the reservoir. In view C the system is subject to excess pressure (as when a wheel is chocked against a curb). The pilot poppet is forced off its seat and all pump delivery is shunted to the reservoir.

Disassembly

Remove the pump from the vehicle and clean its external surfaces. Drain the reservoir.

Reservoir: VTM40 and VTM41. These two pumps are distinguished by an integral reservoir. To remove, follow these steps:

1. Remove the discharge fitting together with the backup washer and o-ring.
2. Pull the reservoir free from the pump assembly.

Reservoir: VTM27, VTM28, and VTM42. These pumps have the reservoir mounted over the pump body. To remove, follow these steps:

1. Clamp the pump-mounting flange in a vise. Protect the flange with copper or lead sheeting over the jaws.
2. Remove the wing nut, washer, cover, and gasket.
3. Extract the cotter pin from the reservoir nut.
4. Lift out the flat washer, spring, filter, retainer plate, and filter element.
5. Loosen the reservoir stud nut and unthread the stud from the pump cover.
6. Remove the two capscrews, lockwashers, and baffle.
7. Lift the reservoir free.
8. Remove the o-rings from their grooves in the pump cover.

Manifold: VTM27, VTM28, VTM42. This part is shown in the upper right-hand inset in Fig. 3-6. Remove the capscrews, copper washer, manifold, and o-rings from the pump cover.

Cover and Cartridge: All Models. While pump covers and cartridges (rotor, pump rings, pressure plate, and other working parts) are not always identical, the disassembly procedures are the same.

1. Clamp the pump-mounting flange in a vise with its jaws sheathed to protect the machined surfaces.
2. Remove the cover mounting capscrews.
3. Separate the cover from the body.
4. Remove the pressure-plate spring and pressure plate.
5. Remove the adapter plate and o-rings (VTM40 and VTM41 only).
6. Note the position of the pump ring relative to the locating pins. Remove it together with the locating pins, rotor, and vanes, and the two O-rings.

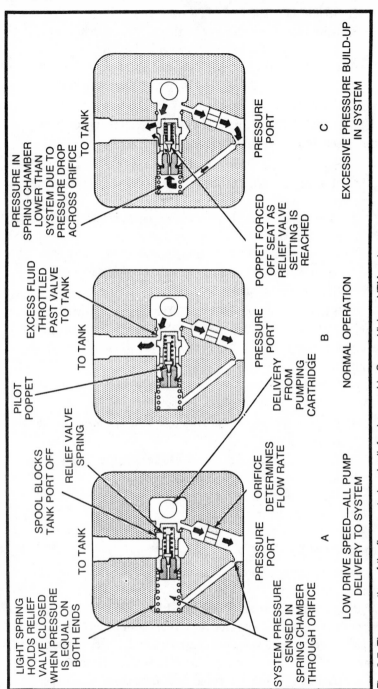

LIGHT SPRING HOLDS RELIEF VALVE CLOSED WHEN PRESSURE IS EQUAL ON BOTH ENDS

SPOOL BLOCKS TANK PORT OFF

RELIEF VALVE SPRING

TO TANK

PRESSURE PORT

ORIFICE DETERMINES FLOW RATE

SYSTEM PRESSURE SENSED IN SPRING CHAMBER THROUGH ORIFICE

A

LOW DRIVE SPEED—ALL PUMP DELIVERY TO SYSTEM

PILOT POPPET

EXCESS FLUID THROTTLED PAST VALVE TO TANK

TO TANK

PRESSURE PORT

DELIVERY FROM PUMPING CARTRIDGE

B

NORMAL OPERATION

PRESSURE IN SPRING CHAMBER LOWER THAN SYSTEM DUE TO PRESSURE DROP ACROSS ORIFICE

TO TANK

POPPET FORCED OFF SEAT AS RELIEF VALVE SETTING IS REACHED

PRESSURE PORT

C

EXCESSIVE PRESSURE BUILD-UP IN SYSTEM

Fig. 3-7. The operation of the flow control and relief valve used in Sperry Vickers VTM series pumps.

7. Secure the pump cover in a vise.

8. Drive out the retaining pin with a suitable punch. Do not allow the relief valve to fall out of its bore.

9. Carefully work the relief valve and spring free. You can reach the valve through the large chamfered hole inside of the cover.

Shaft End: VTM27 and VTM41: The shaft is supported on caged needle bearings. To disassemble:

1. Supporting the shaft end of the pump body in a 2 inch straight pipe coupling, press the shaft assembly out of the pump cover.

2. Remove the shaft thrust spacers, outer needle bearing, and shaft seal.

3. Drive the inner needle bearing from the body with a hammer and punch. Of course, once the bearing is removed in this manner, it cannot be reused.

Shaft End: VTM28 and VTM40. The shaft is supported on a bushing on these models. Withdraw the shaft and remove the seal. The bushing is integral with the pump body and cannot be serviced separately.

Shaft End: VTM42. The shaft is supported on a large ball bearing on the drive end. To disassemble:

1. Remove the large snap ring that retains the outer ball bearing in the body.

2. Press the shaft and the outer ball bearing from the body.

3. Remove the inner snap ring and ball bearing.

4. Use a punch and hammer to drive the needle bearing and seal from the pump body.

Inspection and Repair

Wash all metallic parts in mineral oil. Replace all seals and o-rings at assembly.

Ring, Rotor, Vanes, Pressure Plate, and Body. Light scoring can be removed with crocus cloth, India stone, or by lapping the parts together with valve grinding compound. Check the edges of the vanes for burring, chipping, and wear. Replace the whole set if any are damaged. Check the rotor slots for excessive side play (since the manufacturer has not supplied wear limit specifications, all that you can do is to compare the rotor with a new one) and for burrs. When the parts are dry, the vanes should fall into the rotor slots by their own weight.

Relief Valve. Examine the valves and bore for wear or scoring. Do not attempt to polish out these imperfections—replace the cover instead. The valve should move freely in the bore without the slightest bind or hesitation.

Bearings. Roller and ball bearings must be replaced if they have been removed. The shaft bushing cannot be serviced on VTM28 and VTM40 pumps. If it is worn, replace the pump body.

Body and Cover. Go over the mating surfaces with medium India stone to remove burrs and sharp edges. Wash the parts afterwards.

Assembly

Immerse the parts in clean hydraulic oil and keep Fig. 3-6 before you as a guide.

Shaft End: VTM27 and VTM41. These pumps use needle bearings at both ends of the shaft.

1. Install the needle bearing into the pump body with an arbor press.
2. Assemble the split-ring thrust spacer on the shouldered portion of the shaft.
3. Install the shaft in the pump body.
4. Press the outer needle bearing onto the shaft. The edge of the bearing must be 1/64 inch below the shaft seal shoulder when assembled. This provides 0.010—0.015 inch shaft endplay.
5. Press the seal into the body. Seal drivers are available commercially, or you can machine one from a length of steel tubing. The business end of the driver should be slightly smaller than the seal case dimensions. Square off the ends so that pressure is applied evenly.

Shaft End: VTM28 and VTM40. Carefully install the shaft through the seal. Use plenty of hydraulic oil for lubrication and work slowly to prevent damage to the shaft bushing and oil seal lips.

Shaft End: VTM42. This pump features a ball bearing on the drive side, and a caged needle bearing on the pump or blind side.

1. Press the blind side bearing into the body with an arbor press.
2. Install the shaft seal with the aid of a driver. See step No. 5 given for VTM27 and VTM41.
3. Press the ball bearing on the shaft and secure it with the small snap ring.
4. Place the shaft assembly in the body.
5. Insert the large snap ring to retain the bearing.

Cover and Cartridge: All Models. Follow these steps in the sequence given:

1. Insert the locating pins in the pump body.
2. Install the ring over the pins as found originally. The position of the ring determines whether the pump is for left- or right-hand rotation. A mistake can be expensive.
3. Install the rotor with the chamfered edge of the splined hole toward the pump body.
4. Install the vanes with their curved edges toward the inner ring contour
5. VTM28 and VTM40: Install the adapter plate and o-rings.
6. Oil the cartridge with clean hydraulic oil.
7. Install the pressure plate.
8. Place the o-rings in their grooves.
9. Install the pressure plate spring and cover. Torque the cover screws 25–30 ft-lb.
10. Install the pressure-compensating spring in the relief-valve bore.
11. Insert the valve assembly with the hex head toward the spring.
12. Insert the plug and o-ring into the bore. Hold it while driving in a *new* retaining pin.

Reservoir VTM27, VTM28, and VTM 42. Installation of the reservoir completes assembly of these pumps. Follow these steps:

1. Install o-rings on the pump cover.
2. Position the reservoir on the cover, being careful not to unseat the o-rings.

116

3. Install the capscrews, washers, reservoir stud, and locknut.

4. Install the filter element. It must be located over the reservoir return-tube orifice.

5. Install the filter retainer spring, flat washer, and cotter pin.

6. Install the reservoir cover, gasket, washer, and thumb screw.

7. Replace the dipstick assembly.

8. Rotate the pump shaft by hand to detect possible binds. If the shaft is reluctant to turn, disassemble the pump to determine why.

Manifold: VTM27, VTM28, and VTM42. Install new o-rings in the pump cover and secure the manifold to the pump body with screws. The copper washer is used on the screw whose tapped hole leads to an oil passage.

Reservoir: VTM40 and VTM41. Integral reservoirs are installed as follows:

1. VTM40: thread the two pump mounting bolts in the body flange.

2. Install a new o-ring on the adapter plate.

3. Mount the reservoir so the hole is aligned with the cover discharge port.

4. Place an o-ring on the discharge fitting and install the fitting. The reservoir is now secure.

5. Check pump operation by hand. Do not hesitate to disassemble the pump if the shaft binds.

DIRECTIONAL CONTROL VALVES

The most basic arrangement consists of two spring-loaded *open-center* (sometimes called tandem-center) valve spools (Fig. 3-8). In the neutral position, pump output is shunted to the reservoir and no pressure is developed in the system.

The lift cylinder is controlled by a *three-way* (single-acting) spool (No. 125 in the drawing). This valve has three functional ports: a *pump* or *inlet* port, a *tank* or *return* port, and a *work* or *cylinder* port. The pump port supplies oil to the valve; the tank port completes the circuit to the reservoir when the spool is in neutral; and the work port supplies the lift cylinder.

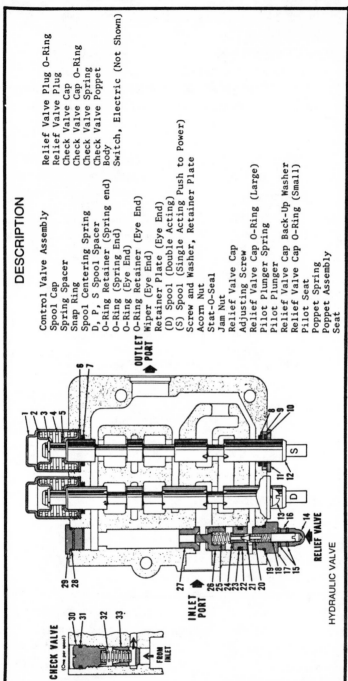

DESCRIPTION

Control Valve Assembly
Spool Cap
Spring Spacer
Snap Ring
Spool Centering Spring
D, P, S Spool Spacer
O-Ring Retainer (Spring end)
O-Ring (Spring End)
O-Ring (Eye End)
O-Ring Retainer (Eye End)
Wiper (Eye End)
Retainer Plate (Eye End)
(D) Spool (Double Acting)
(S) Spool (Single Acting Push to Power)
Screw and Washer, Retainer Plate
Acorn Nut
Stat-O-Seal
Jam Nut
Relief Valve Cap
Adjusting Screw
Relief Valve Cap O-Ring (Large)
Pilot Plunger Spring
Pilot Plunger
Relief Valve Cap Back-Up Washer
Relief Valve Cap O-Ring (Small)
Pilot Seat
Poppet Spring
Poppet Assembly
Seat

Relief Valve Plug O-Ring
Relief Valve Plug
Check Valve Cap
Check Valve Cap O-Ring
Check Valve Spring
Check Valve Poppet
Body
Switch, Electric (Not Shown)

Fig. 3-8. A Vickers two-spool valve used in Prime Mover equipment.

118

The tilt cylinder is controlled by a *four-way* (double-acting) spool No. 12D. This valve has pump port, a tank port, and two work ports. One work port opens to the front of the cylinder and the other to the rear.

In addition to the spools, the valve body contains at least three other valves. The relief valve limits system pressure to protect the pump and other components (this valve is named in the drawing). Each spool is fed through a check valve across its inlet port (Nos. 30–33 in the reference drawing). If hollow spools are used the check value is mounted at the spool ends. The load or lift check prevents backflow to the pump when the valve spool is shifted. It remains closed until pump pressure exceeds the load requirement. Failure of the valve to seat would allow the load to drop a few inches until pump output caught up with demand. Failure would not affect the load-holding ability of the circuit in neutral.

Some valve bodies feature *prefill check valves* (Fig. 3-9). Imagine a situation where the tilt cylinder falls rapidly due to gravity or an excess load. Both sides of the cylinder are filled with oil. As the oil under the piston escapes from the cylinder, the oil above the piston also drops and reduces the pressure above the piston. If the pressure above the pistons drops below atmospheric pressure, air can enter the cylinder. And since air is compressible, it can cause problems. The prefill check valve prevents this situation by sensing low cylinder pressure and opening the tank port to the cylinder. Oil in the tank or reservoir is then permitted to flow through the valve to fill the cylinder. Hence, no air can enter.

A *cylinder port relief valve* can be incorporated in the prefill check-valve assembly. Such a dual-function valve is shown in the upper left of Fig. 3-9. The port relief valve guards against excessive pressures in the cylinder when the valve spool is in the neutral position. (The system relief valve, discussed earlier, protects the system only when a spool is shifted.) It is possible to overload the cylinders while in neutral through collision or by adding weight to the forks. In either event, the port relief valve opens and bleeds the excess pressure back to the tank. With the valve open the cylinder falls, but in a more controlled fashion than it would if a seal or hose failed.

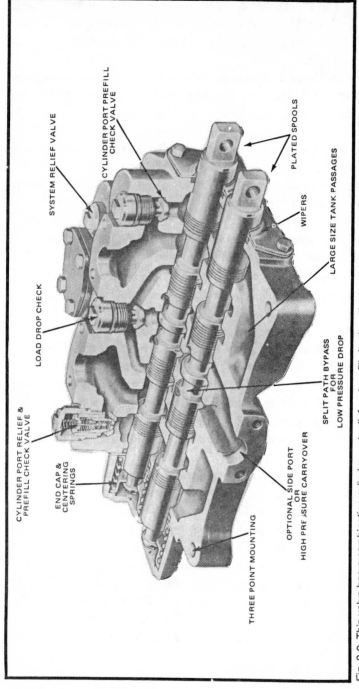

SYSTEM RELIEF VALVE

CYLINDER PORT PREFILL CHECK VALVE

PLATED SPOOLS

WIPERS

LOAD DROP CHECK

LARGE SIZE TANK PASSAGES

CYLINDER PORT RELIEF & PREFILL CHECK VALVE

END CAP & CENTERING SPRINGS

SPLIT PATH BYPASS FOR LOW PRESSURE DROP

OPTIONAL SIDE PORT OR HIGH PRESSURE CARRYOVER

THREE POINT MOUNTING

Fig. 3-9. This valve has a combination cylinder-port relief and prefill check and a load-drop check. (Courtesy Sperry Rand Corp.)

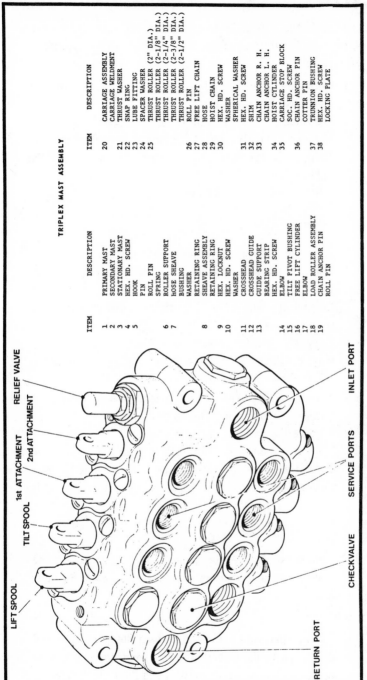

TRIPLEX MAST ASSEMBLY

ITEM	DESCRIPTION
1	PRIMARY MAST
2	SECONDARY MAST
3	STATIONARY MAST
4	HEX. HD. SCREW
5	HOOK
	PIN
	ROLL PIN
6	SPRING
7	ROLLER SUPPORT
	HOSE SHEAVE
	BUSHING
	WASHER
8	RETAINING RING
	SHEAVE ASSEMBLY
	RETAINING RING
9	HEX. LOCKNUT
10	HEX. HD. SCREW
	WASHER
11	CROSSHEAD
12	CROSSHEAD GUIDE
13	GUIDE SUPPORT
	BEARING STRIP
	HEX. HD. SCREW
14	ELBOW
15	TILT PIVOT BUSHING
16	FREE LIFT CYLINDER
17	ELBOW
18	LOAD ROLLER ASSEMBLY
19	CHAIN ANCHOR PIN
	ROLL PIN

ITEM	DESCRIPTION
20	CARRIAGE ASSEMBLY
	CARRIAGE WELDMENT
21	THRUST WASHER
22	SNAP RING
23	LUBE FITTING
24	SPACER WASHER
25	THRUST ROLLER (2" DIA.)
	THRUST ROLLER (2-1/8" DIA.)
	THRUST ROLLER (2-1/4" DIA.)
	THRUST ROLLER (2-3/8" DIA.)
	THRUST ROLLER (2-1/2" DIA.)
26	ROLL PIN
27	FREE LIFT CHAIN
28	HOSE
29	HOIST CHAIN
30	HEX. HD. SCREW
	WASHER
	SPHERICAL WASHER
31	HEX. HD. SCREW
32	SHIM
33	CHAIN ANCHOR R. H.
	CHAIN ANCHOR L. H.
34	HOIST CYLINDER
35	CARRIAGE STOP BLOCK
	SOC. HD. SCREW
36	CHAIN ANCHOR PIN
	COTTER PIN
37	TRUNNION BUSHING
38	HEX. HD. SCREW
	LOCKING PLATE

RELIEF VALVE

1st ATTACHMENT
2nd ATTACHMENT

INLET PORT

TILT SPOOL

SERVICE PORTS

LIFT SPOOL

RETURN PORT

CHECKVALVE

Fig. 3-10. Dowty Husco valve body. (Courtesy Lansing Bagnall Ltd.)

Overhaul

Although it is impossible to describe every valve and its variants, the type illustrated in Figs. 3-10 through 3-12 is typical.

Removal:

1. With the engine stopped, move the valve levers both ways to release line pressure.
2. Disconnect and plug hydraulic lines to the valve.
3. Remove the cotter and clevis pins at the valve spools.
4. Remove the fasteners securing the valve assembly to the vehicle frame.
5. Lift the valve assembly free.

Disassembly:

1. Wash the external valve surfaces in solvent.
2. Unthread the screws holding the seal plates to the valve housing. Remove the seal plates.
3. Remove the cap screws securing the end caps (plunger spring covers).
4. Tag each spool for correct assembly.
5. Run a bar through the clevis-pin holes of adjacent spools to prevent the spools from turning.
6. Press inward on the centering springs and release the springs by unthreading the cap screws.
7. Remove the springs, spring seats, and seal plates.
8. Work the spool back and forth to free the o-rings and backing washers. A locally made tool, such as the one shown at the left of Fig. 3-11, can be used to pry the seals out of their grooves.
9. Slide the spools out of the valve housing from the control end.
10. Remove the check-valve plugs and o-ring seals. Lift the valve poppets from their bores, tagging each for later assembly.

Inspection:

1. Clean the parts in solvent and dry with filtered compressed air. Pay particular attention to removing any accumulated dirt from the seal recess grooves in the valve housing.

2. Examine the spools and valve housing bores for signs of scoring. No servicing or repair attempts are allowed since it is impossible to reproduce factory fits in the field. If these parts are scored, replace the whole assembly.

3. Inspect the remaining parts for evidence of serious wear or damage.

Assembly:

1. Clean the parts one more time in fresh solvent.

2. Dry with filtered compressed air.

3. Lubricate replacement o-rings and backing rings with light grease.

4. Install the o-ring seals and backing washers over the spool lands. The stepped side of the backing washers is out. Be very careful not to damage these parts on the sharp edges of the spool lands.

5. Lightly oil the spools and insert them into their bores until the edge of the land carrying the seals has passed through the seal recess.

6. Press the o-rings and backing washers into their recesses using the locally made tool (Fig. 3-11).

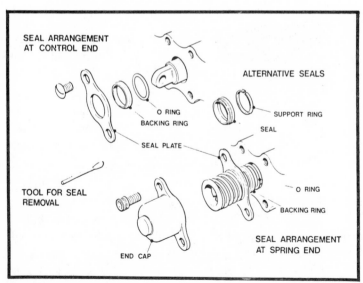

Fig. 3-11. Each side of the spools is fitted with a seal and backing ring. (Courtesy Lansing Bagnall Ltd.)

7. Position the seal plates.
8. Assemble the springs between the spring seats and slide the assemblies over the spool ends.
9. Pin the spools with a rod through adjacent clevis-pin holes and tighten the cap screws to secure the springs.
10. Secure the caps and seal plates with their screws.
11. Fit o-rings and backing washers to the recesses at the control end of the spools. Stepped sides of the backing washers are out.
12. Mount the control end seal plates.

Installation:

Installation is the reverse of removal.

MASTS

Masts are available in partial (sometimes called nominal) free lift and full free lift versions. The forks of a full free lift mast can be elevated to the full lowered height of the mast without increasing the overall height of the vehicle. This construction is convenient for trucks that work under low roofs. Partial free lift allows a foot or so of fork elevation before the mast is engaged.

Mast Types

Most masts are built on the pattern shown in Fig. 3-13. The outer frame pivots on impulse from the tilt cylinders, but has no vertical movement. The inner frame extends by means of the lift cylinder and chains. The Triplex mast illustrated in Fig. 3-14 features an additional set of uprights. The primary set (No. 1) is extended by the free lift cylinder (No. 16) and the secondary set (No. 2) is extended by the hoist cylinder (No. 34). The outer or stationary set (No. 3) pivots but does not move up or down.

The movable masts and carriage are supported on guide rollers that, on heavy duty trucks, bear against replaceable rubbing strips. Lift chains attach to the fork carriage and run over pulleys located on both sides of the cylinder body. The ends of the chains are anchored to the bottom of the lift cylinder. On triple lift masts, a second pair of chains runs from the outer set of uprights to anchor on the inner set. Forks attach to the carriage by means of a key and notch arrangement, or by means of an eyelet and cross pin. The whole assembly—uprights, lift cylinder, carriage, and forks—is secured to the vehicle chassis by means of pivot pins.

Maintenance

The lift chains are the major concern. Should these chains fail, the carriage and load has nothing to support it. Some manufacturers insist that the lift chains be replaced after 200 hours of operation,

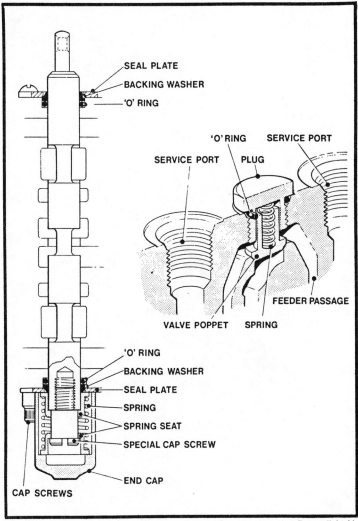

Fig. 3-12. Spool and check valve arrangement. (Courtesy Lansing Bagnall Ltd.)

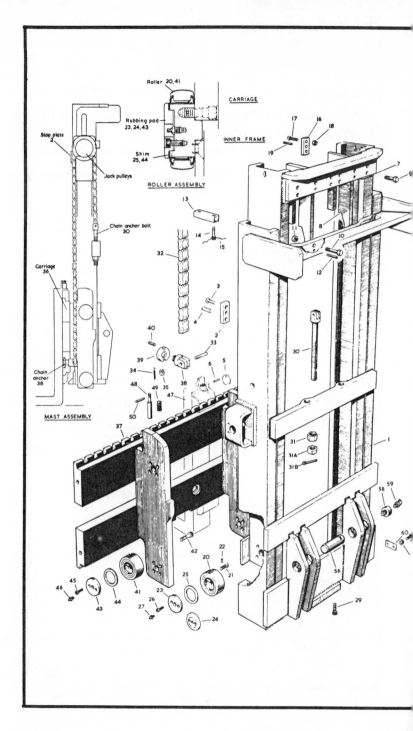

Roller 20,41

CARRIAGE

Rubbing pad
23,24,43

INNER FRAME

Stop plate
2

Shim
25,44

Jack pulleys

ROLLER ASSEMBLY

Chain anchor bolt
30

Carriage
36

Chain
anchor
38

MAST ASSEMBLY

Description

Mast – nominal free lift assembly
  for truck with single drive wheels
  for truck with twin-drive wheels

    each comprising items 1 - 50 as applicable

Outer frame assembly c/w items 2-6

    Stop plate
    Screw, csk skt hd, $\frac{3}{8}$" UNF x 1$\frac{1}{2}$"
    Pin, $\frac{3}{8}$" x 1$\frac{1}{2}$", "Spirol" 375-1500 HBK
    Cover plate
    Pin, $\frac{1}{16}$" x $\frac{3}{8}$", "Mills" GS.1A

Inner frame assembly c/w items 8-27

    Pulley guide bracket
    Screw, hex. hd, $\frac{1}{2}$" UNF x 1$\frac{1}{2}$", "Wedglok"
    Bolt, hex. hd, $\frac{1}{2}$" UNF x 2$\frac{1}{2}$"
    Nut, hex. $\frac{1}{2}$" UNF, "Cleveloc" type P
    Pin, $\frac{5}{16}$" x 1$\frac{1}{2}$", "Spirol" 312-1500 HBK
    Retainer, jack pulley
    Capscrew, drilled skt hd, $\frac{5}{16}$" UNF x 1$\frac{1}{4}$"
    Locking wire
    Stop plate
    Screw, csk skt hd, $\frac{3}{8}$" UNC x 2$\frac{3}{4}$"
    Nut, hex. $\frac{3}{8}$" UNC, "Cleveloc" type P
    Pin, $\frac{3}{8}$" x 2", "Spirol", heavy duty 375-2000 HBK
    Needle roller
    Screw, csk skt hd, $\frac{1}{2}$" UNF x 1", drilled for item 22
    Nylon insert
    Rubbing pad, bottom roller
    Rubbing pad, top roller
    Shim
    Capscrew, skt hd, $\frac{1}{2}$" UNF x $\frac{5}{8}$" "Wedglok"
    Nipple, grease, "Tecalemit" NA.5704

    Lift jack. See E—Lift jack—Nominal free lift
    Capscrew, skt hd, $\frac{5}{16}$" UNF x $\frac{3}{8}$" "Wedglok"
    Chain anchor bolt
    Nut, spherical
    Locknut, hex. $\frac{7}{8}$" UNF
    Split pin, 1$\frac{1}{8}$" x 1$\frac{1}{2}$"
    Lift chain

    Chain pin, each c/w split pin and washers
    included with item 32

  Carriage assembly
    for truck with single drive wheels
    for truck with twin-drive wheels
      each comprising items 37-46 as applicable

  Carriage weldment
    for truck with single drive wheels
    for truck with twin-drive wheels
    Chain anchor
    Locking ring
    Setscrew, skt hd, 2 BA x $\frac{3}{4}$"
    Needle roller assembly
    Capscrew, skt hd, $\frac{1}{2}$" UNF x 1$\frac{1}{2}$", "Wedglok"
    Rubbing plate
    Shim
    Capscrew, skt hd, $\frac{1}{2}$" UNF x $\frac{5}{8}$", "Wedglok"
    Nipple, grease, "Tecalemit" NA.5704

  Fork s.a. 6" x 2" section type (supplied in pairs)
    each c/w items 48-50
    Peg, locating
    Spring, compression
    Pin, $\frac{1}{4}$" x 1$\frac{3}{4}$", "Mills" GP8

Fig. 3-13. Mast used on the Conveyancer TC4SS series.

TRIPLEX MAST ASSEMBLY

ITEM	DESCRIPTION
1	PRIMARY MAST
2	SECONDARY MAST
3	STATIONARY MAST
4	HEX. HD. SCREW
5	HOOK
	PIN
	ROLL PIN
	SPRING
6	ROLLER SUPPORT
7	HOSE SHEAVE
	BUSHING
	WASHER
	RETAINING RING
8	SHEAVE ASSEMBLY
	RETAINING RING
9	HEX. LOCKNUT
10	HEX. HD. SCREW
	WASHER
11	CROSSHEAD
12	CROSSHEAD GUIDE
13	GUIDE SUPPORT
	BEARING STRIP
	HEX. HD. SCREW
14	ELBOW
15	TILT PIVOT BUSHING
16	FREE LIFT CYLINDER
17	ELBOW
18	LOAD ROLLER ASSEMBLY
19	CHAIN ANCHOR PIN
	ROLL PIN
20	CARRIAGE ASSEMBLY
	CARRIAGE WELDMENT
21	THRUST WASHER
22	SNAP RING
23	LUBE FITTING
24	SPACER WASHER
25	THRUST ROLLER (2" DIA.)
	THRUST ROLLER (2-1/8" DIA.)
	THRUST ROLLER (2-1/4" DIA.)
	THRUST ROLLER (2-3/8" DIA.)
	THRUST ROLLER (2-1/2" DIA.)
26	ROLL PIN
27	FREE LIFT CHAIN
28	HOSE
29	HOIST CHAIN
30	HEX. HD. SCREW
	WASHER
	SPHERICAL WASHER
31	HEX. HD. SCREW
32	SHIM
33	CHAIN ANCHOR R. H.
	CHAIN ANCHOR L. H.
34	HOIST CYLINDER
35	CARRIAGE STOP BLOCK
	SOC. HD. SCREW
36	CHAIN ANCHOR PIN
	COTTER PIN
37	TRUNNION BUSHING
38	HEX. HD. SCREW
	LOCKING PLATE

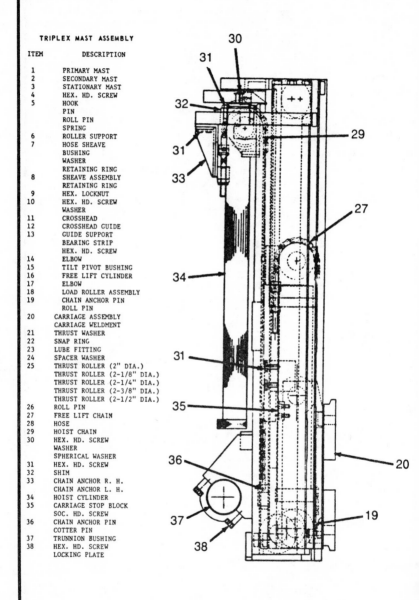

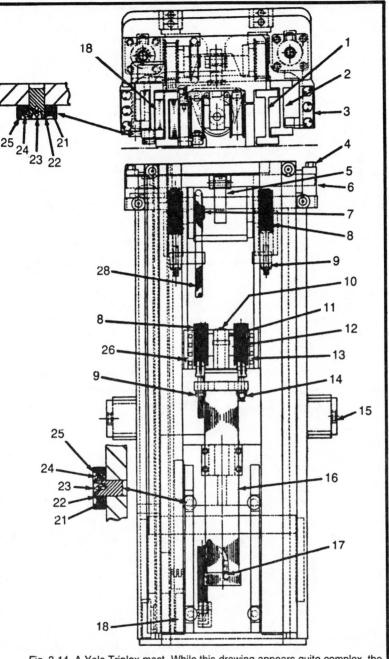

Fig. 3-14. A Yale Triplex mast. While this drawing appears quite complex, the hardware is less imposing.

Fig. 3-15. A chain wear gauge is almost a necessity when servicing lift trucks. (Courtesy Eaton Corp., Industrial Truck Division.)

regardless of apparent condition. Others are more liberal and suggest that all chains be replaced if a cracked, stiff, or excessively worn link is found in the lot. No attempt should be made to repair chains in the field. Wear or chain "stretch" is most severe at the portion of the chain that lies over the pulleys when the carriage is in the normal traveling position. Gauge this portion of the chain with the tool shown in Fig. 3-15.

To remove the chains, follow this procedure (double masts):

1. Raise the carriage about a foot and support it on blocks.
2. Lower the cylinder until it is completely collapsed.
3. Remove the carriage-side chain anchors. I cannot be specific about this, since anchor design varies. But in all cases it is possible to remove the chains without disturbing their adjustment.
4. Remove the cylinder side anchors.

Correct chain adjustment is important, since excessive slack can allow the chain to bounce off its pulleys and too much tension prevents full cylinder extension. Manufacturers tend to specify adjustment in terms of a carriage cross brace or some other machine feature. No generalizations can be given here except to say that there should be almost zero slack with the fork heels just touching the ground, and no clearance between the inner and outer frame stop plates with the lift cylinder in full extension. The masts must remain parallel.

Chains and other wearing surfaces require periodic lubrication. You will find grease fittings on the mast rollers, carriage rollers, mast pivots, tilt-cylinder pivots, and on the lift-chain pulley assembly (or crosshead, as it is generally known). Mast rails should not be lubricated—grease encourages the rollers to skid rather than turn.

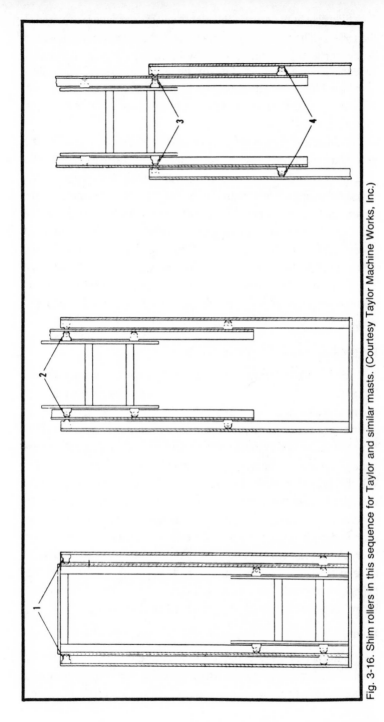

Fig. 3-16. Shim rollers in this sequence for Taylor and similar masts. (Courtesy Taylor Machine Works, Inc.)

Side play between mast elements and the carriage is adjusted at the rollers. The usual arrangement is for the rollers to be mounted on eccentric shafts and secured by locknuts. Large construction-type machines sometimes employ shims at the rollers. The rollers should just touch the channels over the full length of the run. Several tries are needed to minimize side play without hampering free movement.

Things get critical with triple masts. Figure 3-16 shows the procedure used with Taylor Y-8 through Y-30 Yardsters. With the carriage lowered, shim the outer mast until all slack is removed (No. 1 in the drawing). Then, with the top carriage rollers in line with the outer mast rollers, shim the top carriage rollers (No. 2). Raise the carriage to align the bottom carriage rollers with the outer mast rollers and shim (No. 3). Without moving the carriage, shim the inner mast (bottom) rollers. Lower the carriage. If the carriage binds, remove shims from the inner mast. Do not reshim the carriage. If the carriage is loose, add shims to the inner mast rollers to snug them against the outer mast (No. 4).

CYLINDERS

Figure 3-17 illustrates a typical, single-stage lift cylinder with an integral flow control valve. The valve limits the rate of fall by restricting oil flow out of the cylinder. The next drawing (Fig. 3-18) illustrates a double-acting tilt cylinder, similar in basic construction to power steering and shift cylinders. Cylinder repair procedures are quite obvious and little needs to be said here about them. However, you should be alert to the fact that the mast must be supported when the cylinders are not in place. Check the cylinder mounts and pivots for cracking and the piston shafts for distortion. Light scores can be removed with emery cloth. Lubricate the seals with grease or hydraulic oil prior to assembly. Lift cylinders are generally fitted with a bleed screw (shown in Fig. 3-17). After installation, extend the cylinder and crack the screw until clear oil runs out. Tighten the screw with pressure still on it and refill the reservoir.

HOSES

Different hoses are required for different applications on lift trucks. Care must be taken when selecting and routing hoses to assure that the hoses (and their fittings) will withstand the pressures

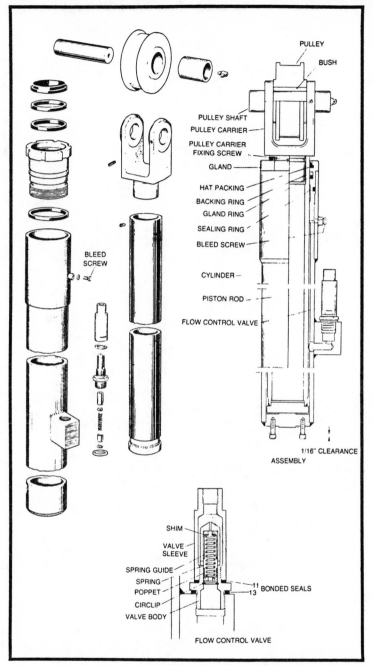

Fig. 3-17. Lift cylinder with integral flow control valve. (Courtesy Rubery Owen Conveyancer Ltd.)

133

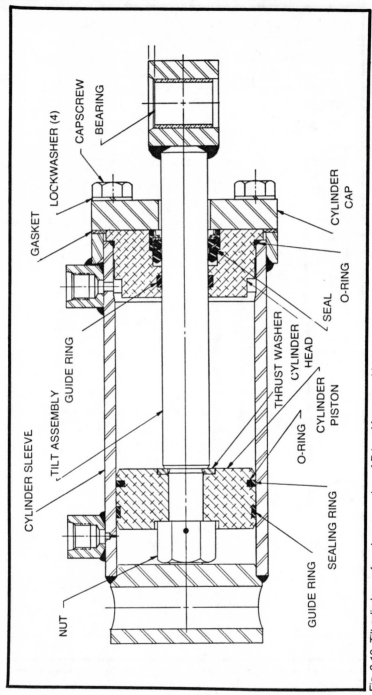

LOCKWASHER

CAPSCREW

BEARING

GASKET

CYLINDER CAP

O-RING

SEAL

TILT ASSEMBLY

GUIDE RING

THRUST WASHER

CYLINDER HEAD

CYLINDER SLEEVE

CYLINDER PISTON

O-RING

NUT

GUIDE RING

SEALING RING

Fig. 3-18. Tilt cylinder as found on a number of Prime-Mover machines.

applied to them, will be properly tensioned, will have accessible connections, and will be subjected to a minimum of abrasion.

Synthetic Rubber Hoses

Four types of hoses are used, according to the pressure requirements.

- Suction hose (SAE Specification 100RH). Used for suction and return lines, this hose is usually made of cotton-braided synthetic rubber and may have spiral wire reinforcement to prevent collapse under pump suction. Secured by hose clamps.
- Low-pressure hose (SAE Specification 100R3). Sometimes used for bleed lines, low-pressure hose is made of synthetic rubber with internal cotton reinforcement and a rubber or cotton cover (Fig. 3-19). The hose is secured by pushon fittings or clamps.
- Medium-pressure hose (SAE Specification 100R5). This type of hose is good for 3000 psi and is standard on most lift trucks. The hose is reinforced with a single layer of carbon steel wire braid and has a cotton inner braid between the wire and the synthetic rubber inner tube (Fig. 3-20). Crimped-on or threaded-on fittings are used.

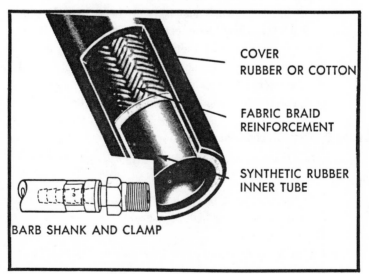

Fig. 3-19. Aeroquip low pressure hose and typical fitting.

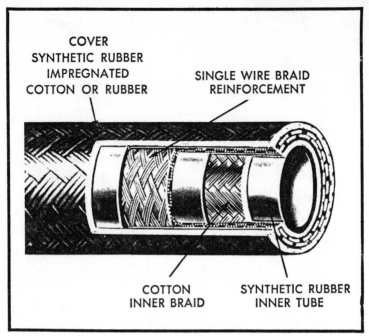

COVER
SYNTHETIC RUBBER
IMPREGNATED
COTTON OR RUBBER

SINGLE WIRE BRAID
REINFORCEMENT

COTTON
INNER BRAID

SYNTHETIC RUBBER
INNER TUBE

Fig. 3-20. Aeroquip medium pressure hose has a single wire braid reinforcement.

- High-pressure hose (SAE Specification 100R2, 10, 11, 12). Capable of withstanding 5000 psi, high-pressure hose is favored by some truck manufacturers because of the protection it gives from the effects of pressure surges. High-pressure hose has a synthetic rubber cover, heavy cotton braid, synthetic rubber innertube and two piles of braided steel reinforcement (Fig. 3-21). Special high-pressure crimped-on or threaded-on fittings are required.

Fitting Synthetic Rubber Hoses

Observe these precautions when fitting synthetic rubber hoses:

- Use the correct type of hose (suction, low pressure, medium pressure, or high pressure).
- Do not shorten.
- Do not twist. Aeroquip hoses have a linear strip to act as a guide.

136

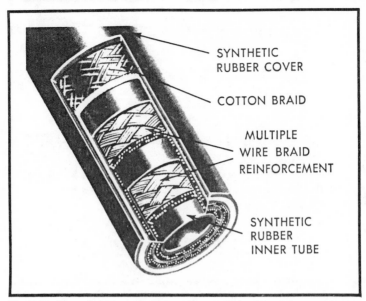

Fig. 3-21. Aeroquip high pressure hose has multiple wire reinforcement.

- Avoid sharp bends.
- Do not allow the hose to foul against other hoses or moving parts.

Suction Hoses. Secure with a hose clamp. If the hose includes an internal coil spring for reinforcement, shorten the spring to leave 1 inch of plain tubing at each end.

Low-Pressure Hoses. These hoses are secured by barbed end fittings (Fig. 3-22). To dismantle, slit the hose lengthwise and twist. To fit, follow these steps:

1. Cut to length with a sharp knife.
2. Apply heavy oil (transmission oil is ideal) to the inside of the hose and over the barbed end of the nipple.

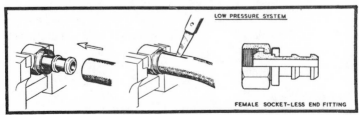

Fig. 3-22. Low-pressure system. (Courtesy Rubery Owen Conveyancer Ltd.)

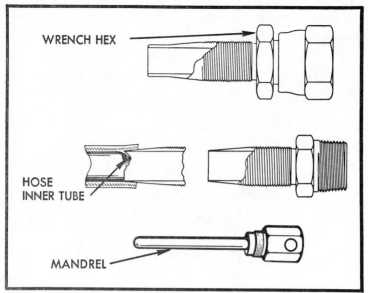

Fig. 3-23. Aeroquip hexed nipples are intended to be installed without special tools; hexless types require a mandrel.

3. Secure the nipple in a vise and bottom the hose against the protective cap.

Medium-Pressure Hoses. Two nipple styles are available. Those with rounded ends are recognized by the wrench hex on the nipple and are installed without the help of a special tool (Fig. 3-23). Hexless nipples have sharp edges and require that the hose be spread with a mandrel. To fit, follow these steps:

1. Cut the hose square to the correct length.
2. Grip the socket in a vise and turn counterclockwise until it bottoms (Fig. 3-24). Turn back 1/4 turn.
3. Apply heavy oil to the nipple threads.
4. Force the mandrel into the hose.
5. Female fitting: Tighten the nipple and coupling on the assembly tool. Screw the assembly clockwise into the socket and hose. Allow 1/16 inch between the nut and socket so the coupling nut can swivel when the assembly tool is removed.
6. Insert the assembly tool into the nipple. Turn the nipple clockwise into the socket and tighten.

High-Pressure Hose. High-pressure fittings look almost identical to medium-pressure types, but are stamped HP. *Do not confuse the two*.

1. Cut the hose to the required length.
2. Make a cut around the outer cover using the notches on the HP fitting as a guide. See Fig. 3-25.
3. Slit the cover from the mark to the end.
4. Remove the cover with pliers.
5. Remove any rubber adhering to the wire braid with a wheel, but be careful not to fray the braid in the process.
6. Apply heavy oil to the nipple threads and the inside of the hose.
7. Female fitting: Tighten the nipple and coupling nut on a mandrel. Screw the nipple clockwise into the socket, turning it with a wrench. Allow 1/32 of an inch or so of clearance between the nut and socket so the coupling nut can swivel.
8. Male fitting: Insert assembly tool into the nipple as a guide. Screw the nipple clockwise into the socket and tighten, turning with a wrench.

Hose (Elastomer)

Plastic hose, meeting SAE specification 100R7, is becoming increasingly popular on trucks. It weighs about a third as much as the

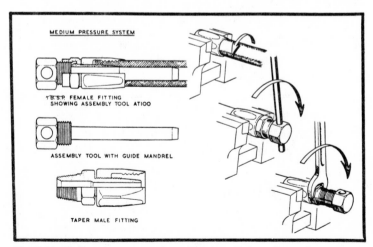

Fig. 3-24. Medium-pressure system. (Courtesy Rubery Owen Conveyancer Ltd.)

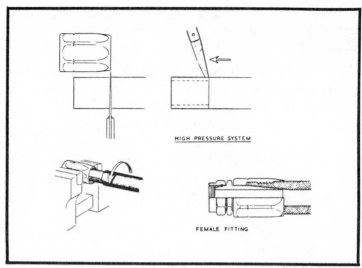

Fig. 3-25. High-pressure system. (Courtesy Rubery Owen Conveyancer Ltd.)

equivalent synthetic rubber hose, is extremely flexible, and has excellent chemical resistance. The polyurethane cover resists abrasion and makes this hose ideal for use with counterweights and sheaves. The latter application, using Synflex hose, is discussed here.

Fitting Elastomer Hoses

To fit a Synflex (elastomer) hose, use the following steps:

1. Assemble the appropriate coupling to a substantial length of hose and attach it to the port closest to the sheave (port A in Fig. 3-26).
2. Run the hose over the sheave to port B. Pull the hose taut and mark it at the seat of port B.
3. Reduce the length obtained in Step 2 by 4%, then subtract the cutoff length of the hose coupling for port B.

    Example:

Distance from A to B	100 inches
Cutoff of coupling	1.5 inches
100 in. less 4%	96 inches
96 less 1.5 inches	94.5 inches

    Therefore, 94.5 inches is the correct hose length.

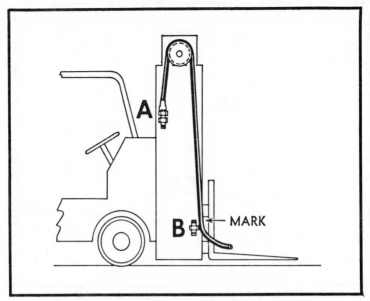

Fig. 3-26. Synflex hose is wonderful stuff, but it expands when heated. Care must be taken to prestress the hose for oversheave applications. First measure the overall length of the hose between the couplings.

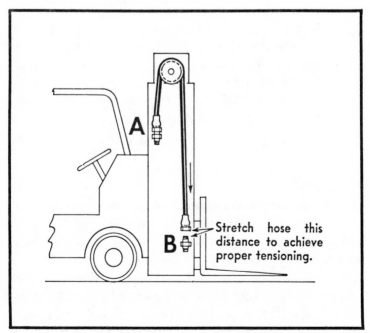

Fig. 3-27. When cut properly for this application, Synflex hose is some 4% short.

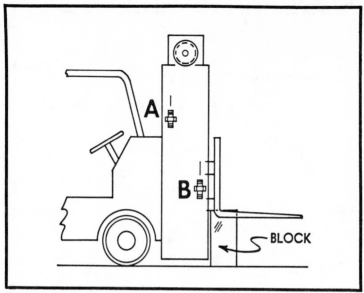

Fig. 3-28. Synflex hose can be connected by main force or the sheave can be lowered to accommodate.

4. Attach the trimmed hose to port A and route it over the sheave.

5. Connect to port B by stretching the hose as in Fig. 3-28. (This requires a 20–50 pound pull or by lowering the mast on blocks (Fig. 3-28).

6. Use bulkhead fittings to shield the hose couplings from tension (Fig. 3-29). Do not use clamps since the hose will eventually slip through them.

Elastomer hose can be fitted with reuseable or crimped couplings.

Routing Hoses

Since replacement hoses are normally purchased in bulk and cut to length, the mechanic has some discretion in routing. He should use his best judgment particularly if the hose in question frequently ruptures or gives other signs of distress.

Connections must be accessible to hand tools without the need to dismantle the assembly. The upper drawing in Fig. 3-30 illustrates a poor example of hose routing since the union nut is almost impossible to reach. In this case the 90° adapter should be replaced by a straight adapter and an elbow nipple as shown in the lower drawing. This sort of problem is frequently encountered when accessories—barrel forks, "squeeze boxes," and the like—are mounted in the field. It pays to reengineer the connections before the accessories are installed.

Another consideration is hose abrasion. Abrasion is caused by contact with moving parts, the improper use of clamps, and crisscrossing the hose (Fig. 3-31). The problem can be avoided or minimized by relocating the clamps or by using elbow adapters. If at all possible, clamps should be mounted equidistant from the hose ends.

High working or surge pressure increases the diameter of hose while at the same time reducing its length. Flexible hoses can shrink as much as 6% under pressure. Unless slack is allowed, the hose puts intolerable strain on its fittings (Fig. 3-32).

Flexible hoses should be bent in generous arcs. The severity of the bend (the bend radius) is the distance from the center of the bend to an imaginary center point. Take the measurement 1 in. out from each fitting. (Fig. 3-33). The allowable radius depends upon hose construction (particularly the reinforcement), diameter, and anticipated working pressures. Table 3-1 gives the minimum suggested bend radii for three popular Aeroquip hoses operating at full rated

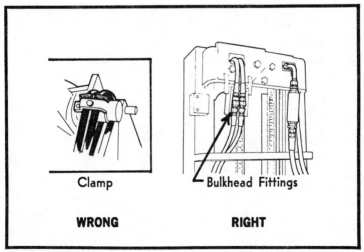

Fig. 3-29. Synflex must be secured with bulkhead fittings. Clamps slip on the polyurethane surface.

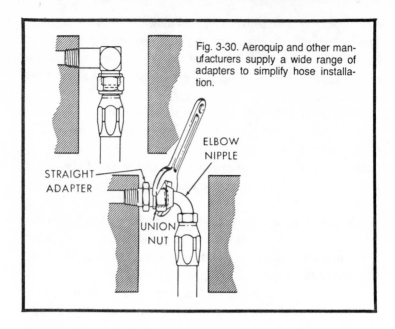

Fig. 3-30. Aeroquip and other manufacturers supply a wide range of adapters to simplify hose installation.

ELBOW NIPPLE

STRAIGHT ADAPTER

UNION NUT

pressure in nonflexing applications. If you are in doubt about the correct bend radius, err on the side of generosity. In tight quarters it may be necessary to use spring guards (Fig. 3-34).

Flexing applications—when one end of the hose must move— require special consideration. Hose abrasion and bend radius are especially critical, and sufficient hose must be provided to allow for movement. Figure 3-35 illustrates the right and wrong ways to connect a pivoting cylinder.

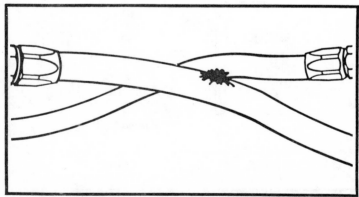

Fig. 3-31. Abrasion can be avoided by the proper use of clamps and adapters. (Courtesy Aeroquip Corp., a subsidiary of Libby-Owens-Ford Co.)

SYSTEM TROUBLESHOOTING

While there are times when troubleshooting can benefit from use of vacuum, pressure, and flow gauges, oscilloscopes, and surface pyrometers, most problems can be pinpointed by a combination of observation and common sense. Some common problems, their causes, and their remedies follow:

No or Low System Pressure

Possible Causes	*Remedies*
Low reservoir oil level— especially critical when the cylinders are extended or if the machine is operated at an angle.	Add recommended oil.
Suction-side filter clogged.	Clean or replace filter.
Air leak in suction line—often accompanied by pump noise and erratic cylinder operation.	Repair leak.
Slipping pump drive.	Adjust or replace.
Failed pump.	Repair or replace.
Failed relief valve	Repair or replace.
Leaking control valves or cylinders.	Progressively block off system to determine which components are at fault. Repair or replace.

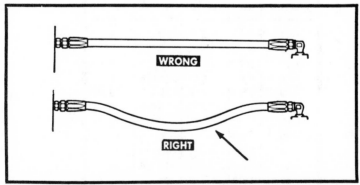

Fig. 3-32. Allow slack in straight runs. If the hose needs support, install a single clamp in the middle. (Courtesy Aeroquip Corp., a subsidiary of Libby-Owens-Ford Co.)

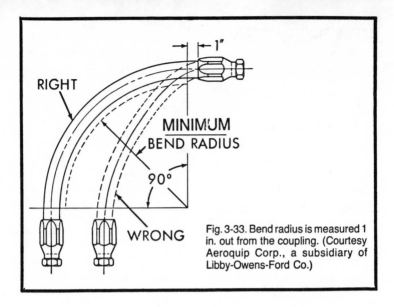

Fig. 3-33. Bend radius is measured 1 in. out from the coupling. (Courtesy Aeroquip Corp., a subsidiary of Libby-Owens-Ford Co.)

Sluggish Operation—Indicated by Slow Cylinder Filling

Possible Causes

Low oil level.

Remedies

Refill reservoir and cycle the selector valves a few times to purge air from the system.

Table 3-1. Minimum Bend Radii For Three Popular Aeroquip Hose Types.

DASH SIZE	I.D.	1525 LOW PRESSURE	1503 MEDIUM PRESSURE	1509 HIGH PRESSURE
— 4	1/4	3	3	4
— 5	5/16	—	3 3/8	—
— 6	3/8	3	4	5
— 8	1/2	5	4 5/8	7
—10	5/8	6	5 1/2	8
—12	3/4	7	6 1/2	9 1/2
—16	1	—	7 3/8	12
—20	1 1/4	—	9	16 1/2
—24	1 1/2	—	10 1/2	20
—32	2	—	13 1/4	25
—40	2 1/2	—	24	—

All dimensions in inches.

146

Possible Causes	Remedies
Wrong oil viscosity—system operation is close to normal when oil is cold or hot	Drain and refill system.
Internal leak in cylinder.	Check by observing flow out of cylinder.
Internal leak in selector valve.	Repair or replace.
Worn pump.	Repair or replace.

Excessive Oil Temperature

Possible Causes	Remedies
Relief valve set at higher pressure than necessary. The surplus pressure is dissipated through slippage, heating the oil in the process.	Reset valve to factory specs.
Internal leakage at the relief valve.	Repair or replace.
Internal leakage at the pump.	Repair or replace.

Noise

Possible Causes	Remedies
Low oil level in reservoir.	Add recommended oil.

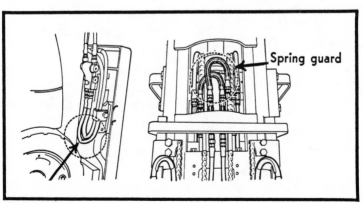

Fig. 3-34. Hose kinks (view A) can be eliminated with spring guards (view B). (Courtesy Samuel Moore and Co.)

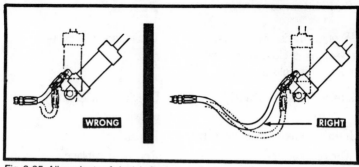

Fig. 3-35. Allow plenty of slack in flexing applications. (Courtesy Aeroquip Corp., a subsidiary of Libby-Owens-Ford Co.)

Possible Causes	*Remedies*
Restricted suction line.	Clean the strainer and verify that the suction line is clear.
Air leak at suction line joints.	Test by pouring oil over joints. Listen for changes in operation. Tighten and regasket joints as required.
Air leak at pump seal.	Test by pouring oil over the pump shaft. Listen for changes in operation. Replace seal as required.
Coupling misalignment.	Realign and replace oil seal and bearings if damaged by misalignment.
Stuck vanes (vane-type pumps).	Dismantle the pump, free the vanes, and check for sticky oil or metal chips.
Worn or broken pump parts.	Replace.

Gasoline Fuel Systems

While real and anticipated fuel shortages have cut into the sales of gasoline-powered trucks, these vehicles still outnumber all others. A mechanic must learn gasoline fuel systems first, before going on to LPG and diesel.

The intake stroke occurs just after the exhaust valve closes. The piston moves down, away from the chamber. The previous stroke has fairly well emptied the cylinder of exhaust gases, and now the cylinder is at less than atmospheric pressure. It is under a vacuum that grows stronger as the piston opens the distance between itself and roof of the chamber. The intake valve opens. Air and fuel rush in to fill the void above the piston. Air and fuel are at atmospheric pressure and are literally pushed into the cylinder by the weight of the atmosphere. Nature, as they say, abhors a vacuum.

The vacuum generated by the engine is measured at some point below the throttle plate and is known as manifold vacuum. At idle, the throttle plate is nearly closed and manifold vacuum is very strong. A gauge would give us readings of 18—22 inches of mercury. As the throttle plate swings open, more fuel and air enter the engine. The engine speeds up—but the manifold vacuum valves drop. The partially-open throttle valve causes a loss of vacuum. At wide-open throttle, the only vacuum generated in the manifold is due to carburetor and intake track restrictions. The gauge will register these restrictions as a few inches of mercury. These are steady-state conditions. The situation changes when the throttle is moved suddenly.

When the throttle is opened quickly, manifold vacuum momentarily disappears. The restrictions are still there, but the engine is not turning fast enough to pull a vacuum. If the throttle valve stays open for more than a second or so, the engine will "catch up" and our gauge will show a slight vacuum. Under coastdown the reverse happens. The throttle valve suddenly snaps shut. The engine is turning relatively fast because of the inertia of the flywheel (or of the whole drive train if it happens to be in gear) and pistons pull against the closed throttle valve. Gauge readings peg near 29.92 inches of mercury—the perfect vacuum at sea level.

CARBURETORS

The carburetor responds to manifold vacuum. As you can appreciate from the last paragraph, manifold vacuum levels change with operating conditions. If the carburetor were operated by electricity, its battery would give 6 volts, then 3, and then maybe 15 as the throttle closed. The situation is further complicated by the engine's demands. It is a fussy eater. At idle the engine is happiest with air/fuel ratios on the order of 2 to 1 (by volume). At cruise, it will tolerate a lean diet of 21 parts of air to 1 part of gasoline.

In addition to regulating the strength of the mixture, the carburetor must prepare the fuel for combustion by breaking it into tiny droplets. This process is called atomization. Once ingested, the droplets are heated by the manifold and combustion chamber and boil into a highly explosive vapor. Gasoline vapor is more explosive on a per-pound basis than TNT.

The third function of the carburetor is to regulate the amount of mixture in order to throttle the engine.

Early engines, those built in the days of King Edward, were fitted with very simple carburetors. These carburetors were entirely adequate for the job because these engines operated over a narrow rpm range. Manifold vacuum levels were fairly consistent and mixture demands were uniform. Some engines did not even require a throttle. Speed was regulated by opening the intake valve or by retarding the spark. But as engines became more flexible, demands on the carburetor increased. Additional jets and feed circuits were added, principles gleaned from half a dozen branches of physics were applied, and the end result was that the carburetor became educated.

Modern carburetors have inherited this complexity and have added a few tricks of their own to cope with emissions regulations. And carburetors—even those relatively simple types used on lift trucks—vary quite a bit between manufacturers and countries of origin. Japanese and English carburetors have certain family resemblances, while American carburetors represent another tradition entirely. And within these broad traditions manufacturers solve problems their own unique ways.

But the principles are basically the same. Once you understand the principles you will have little difficulty with the hardware. And you have to know what you are about in order to troubleshoot carburetors. You should know what to expect when you take one apart for cleaning and overhaul.

Venturi

All carburetors operate because of the difference between atmospheric pressure and manifold pressure. At low speeds, this difference is considerable and the carburetor needs no additional help. But at wide throttle-plate angles, the only vacuum drop is that caused by the carburetor itself. There is not enough differential to guarantee fuel flow through the jets.

The venturi is a kind of vacuum generator. Basically, it is merely a restriction in the carburetor bore. Any kind of restriction will do, but in the interest of keeping pumping losses low, the venturi is streamlined as shown in Fig. 4-1.

The venturi principle was discovered some two hundred years ago by an Italian scientist who was investigating the behavior of moving fluids. When air or any other moving fluid encounters a restriction, a strange thing happens. The air speeds up and at the same time loses pressure.

This comes about because the same amount of air enters the pipe as leaves it. The obstruction lengthens the flow path and to keep the balance between input and output, the air in the vicinity of the

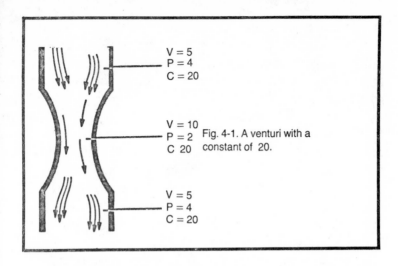

Fig. 4-1. A venturi with a constant of 20.

obstruction must speed up. At the same time we cannot get something (increased velocity) for nothing. The only currency moving air has is pressure. And so pressure is traded for velocity.

Venturis can best be described with a bit of very simple arithmetic. Every venturi has a pressure/velocity constant. In the one shown in the drawing the constant is 20. Initial and final velocity is 5 and pressure is 4. Multiplying these two together gives us 20. At the venturi, pressure drops to 2 and is accompanied by a rise in velocity to 10. The constant is still 20. Of course in the real world things are not quite so orderly. The constant is compromised by flow losses, but its basic outline is true.

Daniel Bernoulli must have been thinking about carburetors back in 1775 when he hit upon the venturi. At any rate it seems so. The discharge nozzle for the main jet empties at the apex of the venturi—in the region of lowest pressure and hurricane-like velocities. The low pressure at the end of the nozzle conspires with atmospheric pressure to force fuel through the main jet and through the nozzle. Also, the air velocity rips into tiny, easily digestible droplets.

The main venturi is often supplemented by one or two other venturi rings arranged in a cluster. The discharge nozzle empties into the center of the smallest one. Because of their small diameter, these venturis respond earlier than the main venturi and allow the main jet to flow long before it normally would.

Main Metering System

The main metering system includes the discharge nozzle that I've been talking about, the main jet, a passageway connecting the two, and an air bleed. The main jet is usually found in the bottom of the fuel bowl. On a few foreign designs, it is remote from the bowl and buried deep below the level of fuel.

The main jet is very critical since it determines the mixture strength at part throttle. On some designs it is dominant all the way to wide-open throttle, but on most the jet takes a back seat as the throttle opens past cruise. The amount of fuel that passes is a function of the area of the orifice and of the entry angles. Figure 4-2 shows three jets. If each had the same orifice diameter, the jet on the far right would flow best. Its entry angle is somewhat less restrictive than the one in the middle and considerably less than the one on the left. Butchered screw slots can also change flow characteristics.

Jets are identified by a code number stamped on the face. Most manufacturers merely stamp the orifice size in decimals of an inch or in tenths of a millimeter. Mikuni goes one better and codes the jets in terms of flow. The number represents the cubic centimeters of water that pass through the jet at given pressures and temperatures.

Raw gasoline leaves the jet. To guarantee atomization, it must first be premixed with air. Otherwise, the discharge nozzle would dribble and sputter. An air bleed introduces bubbles into the fuel. This process might take place at the nozzle or earlier at some point just aft of the jet. The main metering system used in Rochester single barrels is shown in Fig. 4-3. The system air bleed is located in a well just under the discharge nozzle. In this particular design, the bleed is part of the casting. Most foreign carburetors use a brass tube.

This picture is very instructive. You will notice the booster venturis above the main venturi and the calibration screw under the

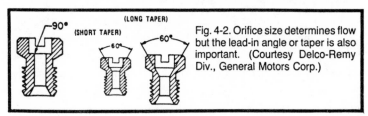

Fig. 4-2. Orifice size determines flow but the lead-in angle or taper is also important. (Courtesy Delco-Remy Div., General Motors Corp.)

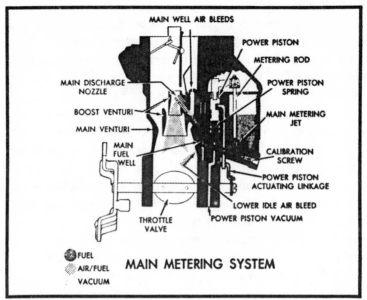

Fig. 4-3. The main metering system. Fuel flows from the main jet to the main discharge nozzle. Other parts shown include the booster venturi cluster and power system components. (Courtesy Rochester Products Div., General Motors Corp.)

main jet. The calibration screw is one of those expedients called for by tight emissions requirements. It gives the factory a final adjustment on the amount of fuel that passes through the jet. It is not supposed to be tampered with in the field. But there are carburetors around on some very old trucks that had adjustable main jets. The adjustment was by way of a tapered screw as shown here.

The next drawing (Fig. 4-4) shows the main metering system on the Holley 1920. Holley is famous for building clean, simple carburetors and the 1920 is no exception. Fuel leaves the main jet and is aerated by way of an integral bleed.

Power System. At this point the language gets a little sticky. Some people call a main jet the high-speed or power jet. Fine. It does work at high speed and does determine to a great degree the engine's power. But in most designs, the main jet is supplemented by the power system. (Some carburetors have another system yet— the high-speed pullover—but lift trucks have been spared that.)

The power system discharges through the main nozzle and consists of a valve and its trip mechanism. There are two kinds of power valves: those that use a metering rod in conjunction with the main jet and those that employ a second jet parallel to the main jet. The first type, with metering rod, is shown in Fig. 4-3. The tapered rod moves up and down in the main jet. As it retracts it amounts to progressively less of a restriction and more fuel flows. The second type is shown in Fig. 4-4. When open this jet adds to the delivery of the main jet.

The power valve is triggered by vacuum or more exactly, the near absence of vacuum. Both types are spring loaded in the closed position. A piston or diaphragm is linked to the valve and subject to manifold vacuum on one side. Manifold vacuum is, you'll remember, a creature of the throttle plate. At low speeds, the plate is almost closed and vacuum is high. At high speeds, there is little restriction in the bore and vacuum drops to something just under atmospheric pressure. The piston or diaphragm senses this loss of vacuum and opens the power valve. Thus, the mixture goes rich at high speed.

Incidentally, certain carburetors will go rich in response to a manifold vacuum leak. If the leak is at a cylinder flange, that particular cylinder will lean while the rest coke their spark plugs.

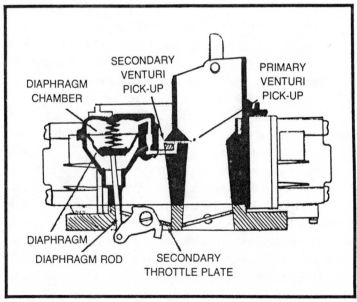

Fig. 4-4. A power system triggered by a valve. Compare this arrangement with the one shown in the previous drawing. (Courtesy Chrysler Corp.)

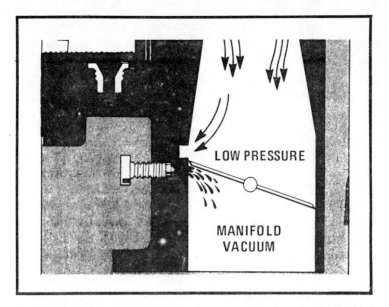

Fig. 4-5. The idle system. With the throttle cracked, fuel flows through the idle port and the off-idle port (shown directly above it) acts as an air bleed. As the throttle is opened wider the off-idle port passes fuel. The screw regulates the mixture strength at low speeds varying the amount of fuel through the idle port.

Idle System. The venturi, even a triple cluster of venturis, cannot create much of a vacuum when the throttle plate is nearly closed. The venturi is triggered by air velocity, and with the plate closed there is very little air movement in the bore. Consequently, an additional system is needed to assure smooth idle and to give the engine the rich mixture it needs to tick over.

The basic idle system is shown in Fig. 4-5. The edge of the throttle plate almost fills the bore and so becomes a venturi. Flow velocity over the plate increases and pressure drops. The idle port discharges into this miniature maelstrom.

Of course the idle system is a bit more elaborate than the drawing in Fig. 4-5. Figure 4-6 gives more details. A transfer slot is milled above the port. (In some, one or two additional round ports are used rather than a slot.) At idle, the slot is far enough above the throttle plate to be in an area of positive pressure. Air is forced into it and thus it becomes an air bleed for the idle jet. As the plate opens wider, the transfer slot comes into the low pressure zone and begins to deliver fuel. The idle aid bleed shown in Fig. 4-6 emulsifies the fuel. The purpose of the transfer slot is to smooth the transition between the idle and the main metering systems.

Manifold vacuum drops to almost zero during sudden acceleration. The throttle plate opens faster than the pistons can accelerate and the engine's ability to pull a vacuum is momentarily undone. The engine continues to run because of the charge already in the manifold. Upon recovery, air again moves through the carburetor bore. The booster venturi responds first, and then the main venturi. But the fuel lags, since gasoline is heavier than air and has more inertia.

The accelerator pump masks this momentary fuel shortage by discharging a stream of raw gasoline into the carburetor bore. This discharge is triggered by the throttle plate and occurs only at wide throttle angles by virtue of a slot and link arrangement. Pump output is governed by a spring working against the diaphragm or plunger. Output is independent of the pressure on the throttle plate for a smooth response, regardless of how vigorously the operator stands on the accelerator.

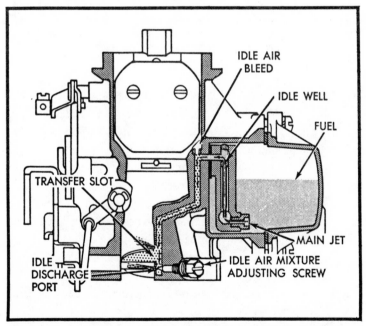

Fig. 4-6. The idle system as it functions on the Holley 1920. As in the case of almost all truck carburetors the idle system feeds from the main jet and is bled from some point inside of the air horn. (Courtesy Chrysler Corp.)

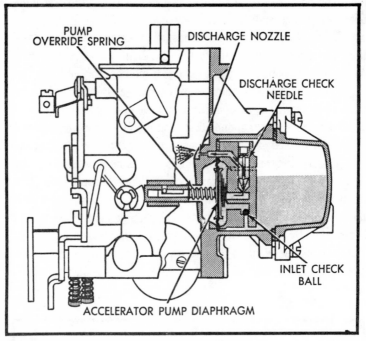

Fig. 4-7. An accelerator pump with a diaphragm element and needle-type discharge valve. Under positive pressure the needle unseats and allows fuel to pass to the discharge nozzle. (Courtesy Chrysler Corp.)

Figure 4-7 pictures the typical diaphragm pump. In this particular design, the inlet check valve uses a ball while the outlet side employs a needle. Other carburetors may employ a plunger and use ball check valves at both positions (Fig. 4-8).

Pump failures rarely involve the diaphragm or plunger, although these parts are replaced during carburetor overhaul. The usual culprit is a leaking discharge valve. As you can see from the drawings, the valve is under vacuum. Failure to seat results in a constant dribble of fuel into the carburetor bore.

Figure 4-9 shows an interesting variation. This plunger-type pump is actuated by two springs—the duration spring above the plunger and the return spring below it. The tug of forces between the two is claimed to give more consistent action than a single spring would allow. Another feature is the novel intake check valve. The pump plunger is free to move up and down on its shaft. When the plunger is moved upward, the flat on top of the cup unseats from the flat on the plunger head. Fuel moves through the inside of the cup and into the pump well. The valve also vents any vapors in the pump well so that a solid charge of fuel is always ready for injection.

Internal Fuel Level

Fuel enters the carburetor at a fitting on the top or (in the case of some foreign designs) on the side of the float chamber. The level of fuel in the chamber is critical since it determines how high the fuel stands in the jets. Too high a level causes rich mixtures, and too low a level results in fuel starvation and lean ratios. The level must be maintained regardless of fuel pump pressure or the head of fuel in the tank. While there are various ways of regulating the internal fuel level, lift truck carburetors all use a float and inlet valve. The float is pivoted against the valve and closes it when chamber level reaches its predetermined height (Fig. 4-10).

Most floats are made of crimped and soldered brass sheet stock. Brass is not an ideal material; it is subject to corrosion and

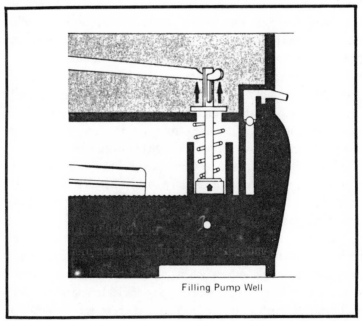

Filling Pump Well

Fig. 4-8. A simplified drawing of a piston-type accelerator pump with a ball-type discharge valve. In some cases the discharge valve is weighted or spring-loaded to keep it closed against carburetor vacuum.

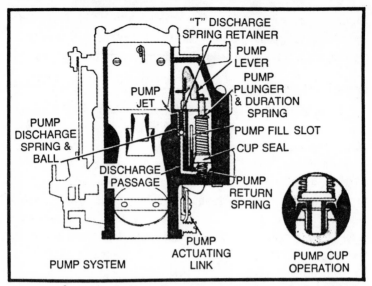

Fig. 4-9. A clever variation in check-valve design. This Rochester combines the pump cup with the inlet valve. Note the use of a spring over the discharge ball.

leaks. A single pinhole leak can sink the float and cause an engine fire. Some European carburetors use hollow thermoplastic bulbs that are not much more reliable than brass. The best approach is that pioneered by Rochester and other American carburetor builders—nitrated plastic foam. These floats appear solid, but are hardly more than a latticework of nitrogen-filled bubbles. There have only been two problems associated with them. Early production types could absorb gasoline because of some error in manufacture. These floats can be recognized by the brownish tinge left by the dye in the fuel. Another problem is caused by faulty adjustment procedures. It is important to support the brass tang so that bending pressure is isolated from the joint at the float. Otherwise, the tang will break free of the plastic.

The inlet valve, known in the trade as the needle-and-seat, comes in a variety of styles. Some are integral assemblies and cannot be opened in the field; others consist of a brass seat and a stainless-steel needle that may be cushioned by a spring and plunger or coated with synthetic rubber. It is important that these are designed to wear well; the needle and seat meet and part about 200 times a minute.

160

Cold Starting

When cold, the engine demands mixtures as rich as 2 to 1. The engine operates on gasoline vapor, and liquid fuel, even if the plugs could ignite it, gives off very little energy. While the tag ends of the

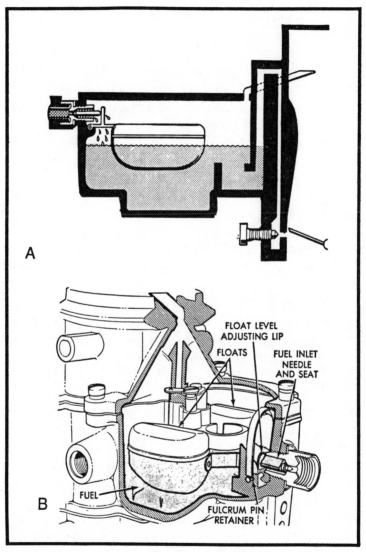

Fig. 4-10. The float system. View A shows the basic operation of any float and view B illustrates a pontoon float of the type used with the Carter BBD series carburetors. (Courtesy Chrysler Corp.)

gasoline blend evaporate at temperatures as low as −45°F, large amounts of fuel are needed to combat the effects of condensation. Fuel condenses (liquifies) on contact with the cold walls of the intake manifold and puddles under the carburetor. When atomized or vaporized fuel contacts these wetted surfaces it immediately condenses. The only way we can get any vapor into the engine is to pump about nine times more fuel than the engine needs for a warm start.

There are various types of cold enrichment devices. Weber and certain Japanese carburetors use a starting jet with an orifice a good sixteenth of an inch in diameter. SU and a number of European derivatives increase the effective size of the main jet for cold starts. But the most popular approach, and the one that is almost universal in lift trucks, is to fit a choke valve above the main venturi.

Closing the choke blocks air entry into the carburetor and increases manifold vacuum. The engine is, in effect, pulling on a blind pipe. All jets flow to deliver a very rich mixture.

Chokes on the older trucks were manually operated through a Bowden cable. These chokes need very little maintenance, but can quickly wear the piston rings out if the operator forgets to open the choke. The rich mixtures wash the oil from the upper cylinders. Late-model trucks use some form of automatic choke—a feature that complicates maintenance, but that increases engine life by varying the mixture strength with temperature. Automatic chokes are pretty well standardized, but the arrangement of the hardware varies.

One type is shown in Fig. 4-11. The choke plate is held closed by a temperature-sensitive coil spring. The coil is wound in two metals placed back to back. One, usually an aluminum alloy, has a high rate of thermal expansion. The other, iron, has a lower rate of expansion when heated. The hotter the environment the more the spring coils and the more pressure is exerted on the choke plate to hold it closed.

The thermostatic spring can be mounted on the carburetor proper, as shown here, or it can be buried in a well in the exhaust manifold. If it is on the carburetor, heated air from the exhaust manifold is piped to it.

Choke *pulloff* is more elaborate. Three distinct mechanisms are involved. The vacuum piston shown in the drawing senses manifold vacuum and opens the choke a few degrees when the engine starts. A cranking engine needs a richer mixture than one that is running. In addition the choke valve is mounted off-center in the bore. As the engine speeds up, air velocity nudges the valve open to allow more air to enter. These two mechanisms—the vacuum piston (or diaphragm) and the eccentric valve pivot—are inadequate to cope with large throttle angles. An additional mechanism—the choke pulloff—is needed. It consists of a linkage that ties the throttle to the choke valve. Opening the throttle past midway mechanically opens the choke.

A cold engine is reluctant to idle and would not, in any event, idle at the usual throttle angle. Some provision is needed to hold the throttle open further than normal until the engine warms. This is

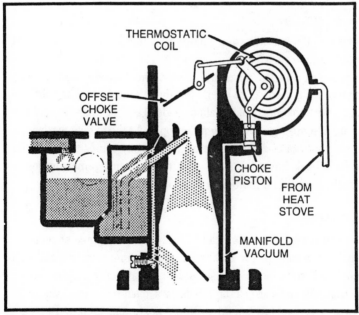

Fig. 4-11. A typical automatic choke. The thermostatic spring holds the choke closed against force generated by manifold vacuum on the head of the piston. The same vacuum line draws heated air from the manifold over the spring. While all automatic chokes operate in the same general way, some mount the thermostatic spring on the manifold. Others employ a diaphragm rather than a piston to counterbalance the spring. (Courtesy Rochester Products Div., General Motors Corp.)

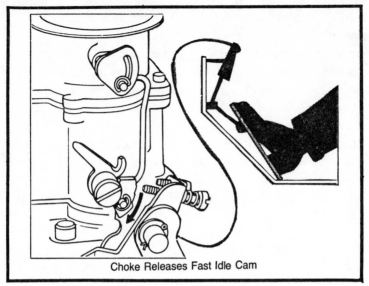

Choke Releases Fast Idle Cam

Fig. 4-12. The fast-idle cam is disengaged by the accelerator.

done with the fast-idle cam. Figure 4-12 shows a fast-idle cam that doubles as the curb (or warm) idle stop. The rounded part of the cam is the part that is normally against the fast-idle screw. The sawtooth-like steps each opens the throttle further. When the engine is very cold the choke is almost closed and the idle stop screw is on the first step (counting from the top). As the engine warms the stop screw works down on the cam and finally comes to rest on its rounded heel. Since the steps are steep, disengagement requires that the throttle be momentarily depressed.

Refinements

Lift truck carburetors can be fairly simple. Engine speeds are usually governed below 2500 rpm, engine compartments are well ventilated, and federal emissions controls are only a cloud on the horizon. All the carburetor needs is a main-metering system, a power valve, a low-speed system, float, and choke. But carburetors, such as the Holley 1920 or the Carter BBD, were developed for automobiles and entered lift truck service as part of the engine package. These devices have refinements absent in those that were built for industrial use from the first.

164

The hot-idle compensator opens when engine compartment temperatures get hot enough to boil gasoline in the carburetor. When this happens, fuel is forced through the jets by the pressure of its own vapor and the mixture goes rich. The compensator—a thermostatically controlled air bleed—opens to dilute the mixture with air.

It may be mounted as shown in Fig. 4-13 or it may empty into the idle circuit. As far as mechanics are concerned, the compensator is important because it must be removed before putting the carburetor in solvent and because it must be closed when making idle mixture adjustments.

The throttle-return dashpot is a delay mechanism used to hold the throttle open for a second or so after the accelerator is released. Some have appeared on lift trucks with Chrysler engines. In Fig. 4-14, the throttle pivots counterclockwise to close and must force the dashpot diaphragm full right. Before the diaphragm seats, the air in the right side of the chamber must be forced out through a small vent. The size of this vent restricts the air flow and the throttle remains open for a second or so to keep the transmission happy.

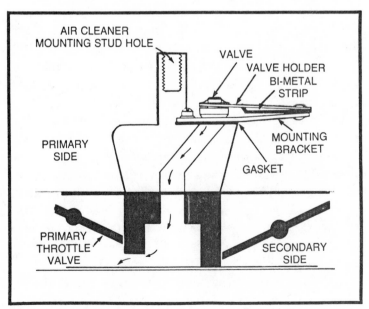

Fig. 4-13. The hot-idle compensator combats the effect of fuel percolation by leaning the mixture.

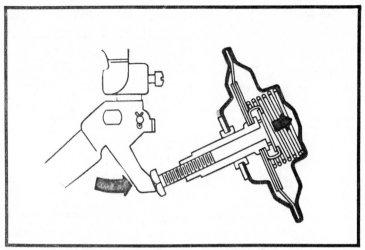

Fig. 4-14. Some truck carburetors are fitted with throttle-return dashpots. Throttle closing is delayed until air trapped on the right side of the diaphragm can escape through a tiny vent port.

Multibarrel Carburetors

Studies have shown that the best torque is produced when the airstream moves through the carburetor at approximately 300 ft-sec. The exact figure varies with different engine/carburetor combinations, but torque is always sensitive to air velocity. Velocities above or below the optimum cost torque (and fuel).

It is not difficult to size a carburetor for an engine that runs at a constant speed. But vehicle engines have a fairly wide rpm spectrum and the carburetor is necessarily a compromise.

One way around this is to use a carburetor with a variable venturi. The most famous of these types is built by SU in England. Mikuni and other Japanese manufacturers produce similar carburetors for motorcycle engines. However, to my knowledge, no variable venturi carburetor has been used on lift trucks. Another approach would be to use multiple carburetors timed to open progressively. The most impressive example of this was on prewar Buick Century series automobiles. Again, however, there has been no lift truck application.

Instead lift truck manufacturers favor two- and four-barrel carburetors. A two-barrel carburetor consists of a fairly small primary barrel (known in England as a choke) and a large secondary. The

166

primary is, in essence, a complete carburetor with choke valve, low and high-speed jets, and accelerator pump. The secondary is a vestigal affair without a cold-start provision, pump-discharge port, or (in most cases) low-speed circuit. Both primary and secondary throttle plates are tied together. The secondary comes on the line when its flap-like air valve is tripped. The mechanism may be a linkage from the primary throttle, a vacuum diaphragm, or a velocity-sensitive counterweight.

A four-barrel amounts to a pair of two-barrels sharing the same casting. In lift-truck (and most passenger car) applications, the secondaries are much larger than the primaries and are innocent of low-speed circuitry. There are exceptions, generally confined to racing. The secondary pair of barrels is controlled by the throttle plates or by air valves.

Two-barrel designs are hardly more difficult to service than single-barrels. But four-barrels can get hairy, with the 208-piece Quadrajet winning top honors. One must be careful to mark parts since it is possible to confuse seemingly identical parts between barrels. The Carter AFB, for example, can be assembled with the primary and secondary clusters confused. The mixture will be rich at lost speed and lean out dangerously as the throttle is opened.

Troubleshooting Carburetors

Carburetors are very reliable mechanisms. Most engine faults are caused by failures in other systems—notably the ignition. And the ignition system can mimic most carburetor maladies, including flat spots during acceleration, hesitation, and spitback. Check the ignition before you turn to the carburetor.

Flooding. Flooding is a general term and applies to the combustion chambers as well as to the carburetor itself. Mild flooding, characterized by wetted plugs and the odor of gasoline at the exhaust, accompanies prolonged cranking.

Flooding after 15 seconds or so of cranking is normal and inevitable, particularly if the carburetor is fitted with an automatic choke. Check the ignition system and then make a compression test.

Carburetor-induced flooding occurs early in the cranking cycle (or even after shutdown) and may continue after the engine has started. Check the choke first. Automatic chokes should be set to specification (summer operation is shown by an index mark on the housing) and should open slightly as the engine catches. The choke should open fully within 2 or 3 minutes, and the throttle should slowly close as the fast-idle cam disengages.

Binding is caused by dirt and gum accumulations on the choke linkage and pivots. Various patented "automatic choke cleaners" are available in aerosol cans. If the problem is external these cleaners will work, enough to get the machine back into service. A more complete fix involves soaking the carburetor in immersion-type cleaner and replacing the leaking gaskets. Slow pulloff usually does not result in obvious flooding, but the smell of the exhaust betrays a rich mixture. Check the choke linkage for freedom of movement and, if necessary, replace the thermostatic spring or the heated air plumbing associated with it.

Manual chokes operate by brute force and give little trouble, so long as the control cable is secure.

Carburetor flooding is always a serious matter. It means that the mixture is too rich, with the attendant loss of power, wasted fuel, high emissions, and accelerated bore wear. In severe cases, flooding can lead to an engine fire.

But flooding should not be confused with those darkish red or brown deposits on the outside of the carburetor body. All in-service carburetors leak a bit around the throttle shaft and at the gaskets. And deposits would still form even if the carburetor were fuel-tight. Pot metal—the zinc and aluminum alloy used for carburetor castings—is porous.

Flooding is quite obvious. The carburetor bore, underside of the choke, and ultimately the exterior of the casting will be wetted with raw fuel. In severe cases, gasoline can be seen bubbling from the main discharge nozzle even after the engine is stopped.

The first thing to check is the interior fuel level. In some carburetors this can be done while the engine is running. Many Holleys feature a transparent fuel bowl and most Hitachis have a sight glass. Certain foreign and obsolete American types were fitted with fuel-level plugs. The fuel level should come to the bottom of the threads. Others require minimum disassembly. For example, the fuel level of the 1920 series Holley can be checked by removing the power valve diaphragm on the top of the assembly. (Holley and engine builders who use these carburetors prefer to call the power valve an economizer—it's like saying extravagance promotes thrift.) Carburetors with horizontally split bowl covers can be opened relatively easily. Those with straddle-mounted bowls have to be checked by intuition (or with a length of clear neoprene hose).

The inlet valve is the most vulnerable part of the regulating mechanism. Horizontal valves, such as those found on the Stromberg, Holley 1908, and others, seem to be more sensitive to dirt than the vertical types. Usually a rap with a wrench is all that is required to dislodge the obstruction and get the carburetor back into service. However, it is always wise to clean or replace the filter element after such an episode.

Wear on the valve means that the needle and seat must be changed as an assembly. Steel needles are unfit for service if a ridge has formed at the contact surface. The ridge increases the area of contact and makes sealing problematic. Valves tipped with Viton or some other rubberoid substance wear as shown in Fig. 4-15. These valves require careful assembly. The traditional wrench blow that mechanics give steel valves to seat them will only deform the soft-tipped type.

The float may also be at fault. Hollow floats can develop leaks and the solid types have been known to absorb gasoline after long service. Unless it is absolutely necessary, do not attempt to repair floats. For even if all the fuel can be baked out, any kind of repair, whether by epoxy, solder, or varnish, adds weight to the float and upsets the fuel mixture.

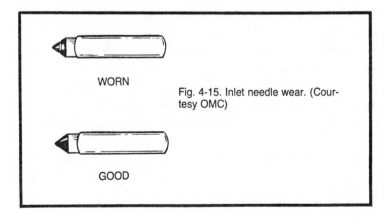

Fig. 4-15. Inlet needle wear. (Courtesy OMC)

Some carburetors have a float-drop adjustment. If this adjustment is not made to specification, the float can fall far enough to disengage the needle.

Mixture Too Rich. Overly rich mixtures leave carbon accumulations on the spark plugs. The carbon should be dry and, if the mixture is very rich, will have a fluffy texture. Oil-induced carbon is typically damp and greasy to the touch. These distinctions come into play only if the problem is extreme; slightly rich mixtures or moderate oil pumping merely give the firing tip a brown or dull black cast. Any sort of spark plug analysis assumes that the engine is running under normal loads, that the spark plug heat range is correct, and that the ignition system is completely reliable. The slightest misfire shows up as a rich mixture.

Check the choke first. The choke, whether automatic or manual, should open fully when the engine is warm. Next change the air filter element. Even though modern float bowls are vented to the carburetor bore, a clogged air filter will send the instrument rich. Early carburetors vent the float bowl to the atmosphere, and are extremely sensitive to pressure drops across the filter element. More modern designs have gained some immunity by venting the bowl internally, from the float bowl. But a clogged filter will still play havoc with the mixture strength.

Look carefully at the accelerator-pump discharge nozzle with the engine running. At a steady speed, the nozzle and the area immediately below it should be dry. If not, replace the outlet check valve.

Ball-type valves usually benefit from reforming the seat. With the help of a small punch, give a sharp rap to the ball. One well directed hammer blow is enough. Replace the ball with a new one. This technique does not work with needle-type valves since the old needle and seat deforms in use.

Check the fuel level as described previously. If the level drifts out of adjustment, replace the inlet needle and seat together with its gasket. Occasionally you may encounter a fuel pump that delivers too much pressure. Upper ratings are 5–6.5 psi at 2000 rpm. If you suspect that this is the case—two or three inlet valve failures in a row are a good indication—check the pressure with a gauge and tee-fitting.

Mixture Too Lean. Lean mixtures are characterized by loss of power, flat spots on acceleration, and by bleached white spark-plug tips. But before you accept plug color as gospel, check the heat range and ignition timing. If you really want to make a thorough job of it, check the compression. Carbon buildup can raise the compression ratio and skyrocket chamber temperatures.

Air leaks in the intake tract are the major culprit. Check the manifold and carburetor hold-down bolts. Gasket leaks can be detected by squirting oil on the joints. If the oil is sucked into the engine, you can be sure that the gasket has failed. (Some mechanics use gasoline and listen for a telltale increase in rpm, but squirting gasoline on a hot manifold is not the way to collect your Social Security.) Examine the hoses for vacuum leaks.

Once you are satisfied that the intake plumbing is sound, turn your attention to the fuel supply. Replace the fuel-filter element at the carburetor. Modern elements are made of pleated paper and usually have a failsafe feature. Should the element clog, the whole assembly retracts a fraction on an inch to allow some fuel to pass. The engine will run, but reluctantly. Earlier filters were made of sintered bronze or brass and, contrary to popular belief, cannot be effectively cleaned. These filters may be backstopped by a brass screen just forward of the inlet valve. See that the screen is open.

The next step is to check the fuel output volume. Disconnect the fuel line at the carburetor and catch the pump output in a container as the engine idles. (There should be enough fuel in the bowl for several minutes of operation.) A healthy system will deliver 1 pint of fuel every 30–45 seconds.

If delivery is much less than this, replace the filter between the pump and carburetor. Chrysler filters are threaded into the pump body; most other manufacturers use an in-line filter. Should the problem persist, check the connections on the suction side of the pump. Air leaks here can disable the pump entirely.

Gravity-feed systems should be opened at the tank as a check on the tank screen, and opened again at the carburetor. A head of fuel develops little pressure and it is possible for the line to clog.

Turning to the carburetor, check the internal fuel level as described under "Flooding." Open the float chamber and check the condition of the main jets. If they are silted over or there are

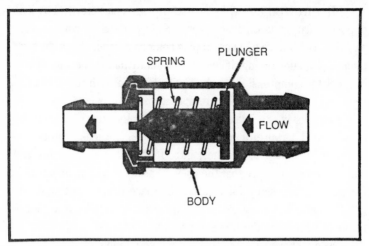

Fig. 4-16. PCV valve. These valves are fairly sophisticated and must work in three positions. The full-open position shown corresponds to large throttle-plate angles. At idle, the plunger is pulled to the right and restricts gas flow. In the event of backfire, the plunger moves to the left and seals the crankcase from flame.

accumulations of muck in the bottom of the float chamber, the carburetor needs cleaning and overhaul.

Refusal to Idle. This symptom includes two kinds of behavior: the engine may run at higher than idle rpm regardless of the position of the accelerator pedal, or it may die or run erratically when the pedal is released.

In the first case, check the linkage and the governor setting. A very remote possibility is that the throttle plate has become detached and is binding the throttle shaft. Worn linkage pivots can upset the leverages of the system enough to justify the use of a booster spring. These springs are available from auto-parts stores or you can use a Ford throttle spring. Ford springs last longer than the aftermarket variety, but they're bulky and can be a headache to install. The spring should be at 90° to the throttle-plate lever at idle, and should be mounted as close as possible to it.

The second case—the engine dies when the accelerator is released—can be caused by improper ignition timing or low-speed ignition failure. Don't overlook the positive crankcase ventilation (PCV) valve or its associated plumbing. These valves are fairly complex and are difficult to test other than by substitution (Fig. 4-16). Be sure the replacement carries the same part number.

A strobe light will detect either. If the search narrows to the carburetor, you can be almost certain that the problem is fuel scarcity. Turn the idle-mixture screw counterclockwise while releasing pressure on the throttle plate. Should this adjustment solve the problem, the machine can be returned to service with the note that the carburetor should be dismantled and cleaned during the next scheduled maintenance.

Failure to respond to adjustment means a serious stoppage somewhere in the low-speed circuit. Screw the adjustment needle all the way out. Inspect the tip. It is not impossible that a ham-fisted mechanic has tightened the adjustment screw until the tip snapped off in the jet. The broken tip can be dislodged by working from the bore side, and the adjustment screw can be replaced. In an ideal world the carburetor would be replaced, since the slightest deformation of the jet will cause a ragged idle.

Gum and varnish can be temporarily dislodged with a blast of high-pressure air directed at the adjustment screw boss. In severe cases it may be necessary to cover the idle and off-idle discharge ports.

Poor Acceleration. "Flat spots" in acceleration are usually the fault of the carburetor, although a weak spark or vacuum-advance troubles can give the same symptoms. The major carburetor problems are dirt in the main-metering circuit and accelerator-pump failure. The pump can be checked by stopping the engine, removing the air filter, and blipping the throttle. It should discharge a steady stream of gasoline into the carburetor bore. Failure to deliver any fuel can be traced to a leaking inlet or discharge valve, or to a torn pump diaphragm. Insufficient delivery is most often the fault of a stretched diaphragm or by a severely worn plunger.

Refusal to Run at Full Throttle. Connect a strobe light to No. 1 spark plug and operate the engine at idle to verify the initial timing. Some distributors require that the vacuum-advance line be disconnected and plugged. Now run the engine up to its best speed and observe the timing marks. They should advance in step with engine rpm (advance will be sudden if the vacuum mechanism is connected).

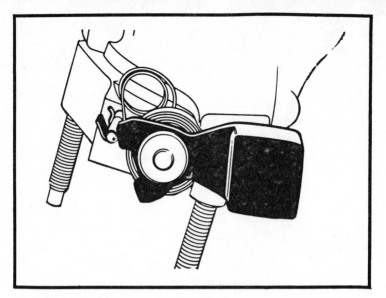

Fig. 4-17. A typical heat-riser valve. The thermostatic spring is counterbalanced by the weight. The second spring dampens rattles.

Some truck engines have a heat-riser valve mounted at the exhaust manifold collector. The purpose is to better vaporize the fuel while the engine is cold and to actuate the choke-pulloff mechanism early. The valve is closed by a thermostatic spring and opened by a weight (Fig. 4-17). It must move freely. Should it stick closed, back pressure in the system will reduce power at high speed and burn the exhaust valves in the process. Lubricants are available for these valves (ordinary oil is worse than useless), although the best fix is to disassemble it and wire-brush the shaft. In warm climates, mechanics have been known to tie these valves open.

If the carburetor itself is concerned, the problem is almost always associated with the main metering circuit. The jets must be open and the passageways they serve clean. Power-valve failure is rare in clean carburetors, although it can come about through vacuum leaks or tired diaphragms. Since there is no practical way to check power-valve action (unless one has access to an exhaust-gas analyzer), the best insurance is to replace the valve and those parts of the mechanism supplied in the rebuild kit.

Other possibilities are a governor malfunction or a binding accelerator linkage.

Carburetor Overhaul

In this context the terms *overhaul, rebuild,* and *tuneup* mean the same. The carburetor is almost completely disassembled, immersed in chemical cleaner, rinsed with solvent, and revamped with parts from a standard overhaul kit. Parts include gaskets, accelerator-pump elements and valves, and inlet-needle and seat assemblies. More complete parts assortments are known as major overhaul or rebuild kits and are generally available through dealer sources. These kits are complete with idle mixture screws, float shafts, linkage hardware, power valves, plus all the parts in the standard kit. Other parts can be purchased on an individual basis from the engine or carburetor manufacturer. But one part—usually a major casting—is held back to make it impossible to assemble a bootleg carburetor from inventory stock.

An overhaul is usually sufficient. Carburetors do not wear out in any real sense, or in any way that cannot be corrected with a kit or over-the-counter parts. About the only justification for purchasing a new or factory rebuilt carburetor is physical damage to the castings. But there are carburetor malfunctions that defy correction. However distasteful an admission of defeat may be, another carburetor is the only alternative.

Overhaul Procedure. Detach the carberetor from the engine, noting the lay of the lines and linkages. Figures 4-18 through 4-20 show three representative types. Working on a clean bench, disassemble the carburetor far enough to remove all soft parts. Plastic, synthetic rubber, and paper are attacked by the cleaning compound. Diaphragm chambers should be wiped off with a solvent-dampened rag. In some cases certain soft parts—usually made of nylon and associated with the hot idle compensator or power valve—are integral and cannot be removed. Nylon will tolerate 20 minutes or so in the cleaner and this is adequate. Normally jets and air-bleed tubes are left in place. If the carburetor is particularly dirty, remove them with a socket or, depending upon the type, with a screwdriver. *Grind the blade to fit the slot in the jet.* Damage to the slot will affect the flow characteristics.

It is important to make note of the sequence of parts and their relationships to each other.

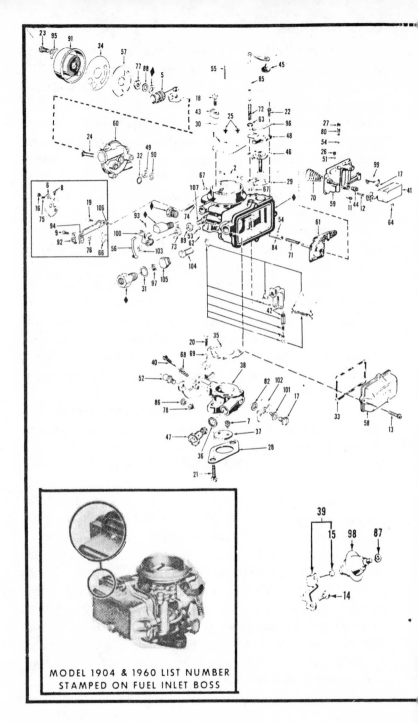

MODEL 1904 & 1960 LIST NUMBER
STAMPED ON FUEL INLET BOSS

ITEM NO.	DESCRIPTION	ITEM NO.	DESCRIPTION
1	Choke Plate Assy.	57	Choke Hsg. Plate
2	Choke Shaft or Shaft & Lever Assy.	58	Float Bowl
5	Choke Therm. Lev. Link & Piston Assy.	59	Main Well & Econ. Body & Plugs Assy.
6	Choke Lev. Assy.	60	Choke Hsg. & Plugs Assy.
7	Throt. Plate Scr. & L. W.	61	Pump Diaph. & Rod Assy.
8	Choke Lev. Swivel Scr.	62	Spark Check Ball Ret.
9	Choke Brkt. Clamp Scr.	63	Vent Rod Sprg. Ret.
11	Main Well & Econ. Body Scr. & L. W. (Short)	64	Float Ret.
12	Main Well & Econ. Body Scr. & L. W. (Long)	66	Choke Shaft Ret.
		67	Air Cleaner Bail Ret.
13	Float Bowl Clamp Scr. & L. W.	68	Idle Adj. Needle Sprg.
14	Dashpot Lev. Scr.	69	Throt. Stop Scr. Sprg.
15	Dashpot Lev. Adj. Scr.	70	Pump Return Sprg.
17	Baffle & Vent Scr. & L. W.	71	Pump Oper. Sprg.
18	Pump Discharge Nozzle Scr.	72	Vent Rod Sprg.
19	Choke Brkt. Scr. & L. W.	73	Pump Oper. Lev. Sprg.
20	Throt. Stop Scr.	74	Choke Lev. Sprg.
21	Throt. Body Scr. & L. W.	76	Choke Brkt. Clamp Nut
22	Econ. Body Scr. & L. W.	77	Choke Shaft Nut
23	Therm Hsg. Scr.	78	Throt. Lev. Ball Nut
24	Choke Hsg. Scr. & L. W.	80	Pump Discharge Valve Weight
25	Choke Plate Scr. & L. W.	82	Vent. Oper. Lev. Spacer
26	Pump Inlet Ball Ret.	84	Pump Push Rod Sleeve
27	Pump Discharge Ball Ret.	85	Vent Rod
28	Flange Gskt.	86	Throt. Lev. Ball L. W.
29	Econ. Body Gskt.	87	Dashpot L. W.
30	Pump Discharge Nozzle Gskt.	88	Choke Shaft Nut L. W.
31	Fuel Inlet Fitting Gskt.	89	Pump Oper. Lev. Sprg. Washer
32	Choke Hsg. Gskt.	90	Choke Shaft Seal Washer
33	Float Bowl Gskt.	91	Choke Therm. Hsg. Assy.
34	Choke Therm. Hsg. Gskt.	92	Choke Brkt. Clamp
35	Throt. Body Gskt.	93	Pump Oper. Link Cotter Pin
36	Spark Valve Gskt.	94	Choke Brkt.
37	Throt. Plate	95	Choke Therm. Hsg. Clamp
38	Throt. Body, Shaft & Lev. Assy.	96	Vent Rod Guide
39	Dashpot Lev. Assy.	97	Filter Screen
40	Idle Adj. Needle	98	Dashpot Assy.
41	Float & Lev. Assy.	99	Fuel Inlet Baffle
42	Fuel Inlet Valve & Seat Assy.	100	Pump Oper Lev.
43	Pump Discharge Nozzle	101	Vent Control Lev.
44	M.M.J. - 22R-40-(Size)	102	Vent Oper. Lev.
45	Vent Rod Valve	103	Pump Oper. Lev. Ret.
46	Econ. Stem Assy.	104	Fuel Inlet Seat Screw
47	Spark Valve Assy.	105	Fuel Inlet Plug
48	Econ. Body Cover Assy.	106	Choke Brkt. Scr. L. W.
49	Choke Shaft Seal	**	Fast Idle Adj. Scr.
51	Pump Inlet Ball	**	Fast Idle Adj. Scr. Nut
52	Throt. Lev. Ball	**	Fuel Bowl Vent Lev. Sprg.
53	Spark Check Ball	**	Fuel Bowl Vent. Lev.
54	Pump Discharge & Push Rod Sleeve Ball	**	Fuel Bowl Vent Valve
		**	Fuel Bowl Vent. Lev. Ret.
55	Distribution Pin	*	Air Horn Adapter Gskt.
56	Pump Oper. Link	*	Fuel Line Fitting Elbow
		*	Fuel Line Adapter Assy.
		*	Air Horn Adapter
		*	Gulp Valve Connector
		107	Pump Oper. Lever Stud

Fig. 4-18. Holley Model 1904 and 1960 carburetor in exploded view. This carburetor is used on Tow Motor trucks. Note the econ. stem assembly (No. 46), the spark-valve assembly (No. 47), and the side-mounted float bowl (No. 58). (Courtesy Colt Industries)

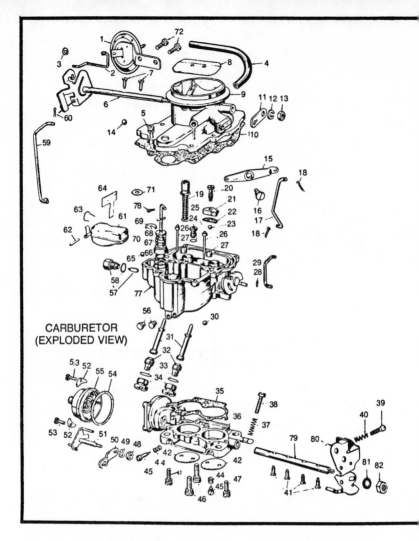

CARBURETOR
(EXPLODED VIEW)

It is not necessary or desirable to disturb the throttle and choke plates.

A notebook should be at hand, particularly when dealing with multibarrels. Clusters, bleeders, jets, check valves and other parts must not be confused between barrels. Factory manuals are not a reliable guide since production changes are rarely noted in these manuals. Make a sketch of the linkage routing, and scribe marks on the outboard surface of the upper end of each link as an assembly guide.

ITEM NO.	DESCRIPTION	ITEM NO.	DESCRIPTION
1.	DIAPHRAGM ASSEMBLY – Choke kick	40.	SPRING – Fast idle screen
2.	ROD – Choke kick	41.	SCREW – Throttle valve
3.	RETAINER – Choke kick rod	42.	VALVE – Throttle
4.	HOSE – Vacuum	44.	SPRING – Idle needle valve
5.	SCREW & LOCKWASHER – Air horn	45.	VALVE – Idle needle
6.	SHAFT & LEVER – Choke	46.	SCREW & LOCKWASHER – Throttle body
7.	SCREW – Choke valve	47.	SCREW & LOCKWASHER – Throttle body
8.	VALVE – Choke	48.	NUT – Thermostat lever
9.	AIR HORN ASSEMBLY	49.	WASHER – Spring lock
10.	GASKET – Air horn	50.	LEVER – Thermostat
11.	LEVER – Fast idle	51.	LEVER & SHAFT – Thermostat
12.	WASHER – Spring lock	52.	WASHER – Thermostat cover
13.	NUT – Lever	53.	SCREW – Thermostat cover
14.	PLUG – Lead ball	54.	GASKET – Thermostat cover
15.	LEVER – Pump	55.	COVER ASSEMBLY – Thermostat
16.	SCREW – Pump lever	56.	PLUG – Main body channel
17.	ROD – Pump	57.	VALVE & SEAT ASSEMBLY – Float
18.	PIN – Cotter	58.	GASKET – Float needle seat
19.	PISTON – Vacuum power	59.	ROD – Choke
20.	SCREW – Pump nozzle	60.	PIN – Cotter
21.	NOZZLE – Pump	61.	FLOAT & LEVER ASSEMBLY
22.	GASKET – Pump nozzle	62.	PIN – Float fulcrum
23.	BALL – Pump outlet check	63.	SPRING – Fulcrum pin
24.	JET – Pump by-pass	64.	BAFFLE – Float chamber
25.	GASKET – Power by-pass jet	65.	BALL – Pump inlet check
26.	TUBE – Idle	66.	SPRING – Pump bottom
27.	BLEEDER – High speed	67.	SPRING – Pump duration .
28.	RETAINER – Fast idle rod	68.	WASHER – Duration spring retainer
29.	ROD – Fast idle	69.	WASHER – Duration spring clip
30.	PLUG – Lead ball	70.	PISTON ASSEMBLY – Pump
31.	JET – Main discharge	71.	WASHER – Idle vent
32.	JET – Main metering	72.	SCREW – Diaphragm attaching
33.	GASKET – Metering jet plug	77.	BODY ASSEMBLY – Main
34.	PLUG – Main metering jet	78.	PIN – Cotter
35.	GASKET – Main body	79.	SHAFT – Throttle
36.	BODY ASSEMBLY – Throttle	80.	LEVER – Throttle
37.	SPRING – Slow idle screw	81.	WASHER – Throttle lever nut
38.	SCREW – Slow idle	82.	NUT – Throttle lever
39.	SCREW – Fast idle		

Fig. 4-19. A two-barrel carburetor with some very European features. Main jets are under removable plugs (No. 34) and can be serviced without disturbing the bowl. (Courtesy General Motors—Holden's Pty. Ltd.)

Immerse the metallic parts in cleaner and rinse with solvent. Blow out with compressed air. High-pressure air is best, but an OSHA-approved 30 psi source is better than nothing. (OSHA has limited shop air pressures to this figure because higher pressures can penetrate the skin and send bubbles into the blood stream.)

Assembly Procedure. Lay the parts out on the bench in the order of assembly. Read the instructions in the kit and become familiar with the exploded view. The carburetor illustrated by the kit manufacturer may not be like yours in all details, but the parts

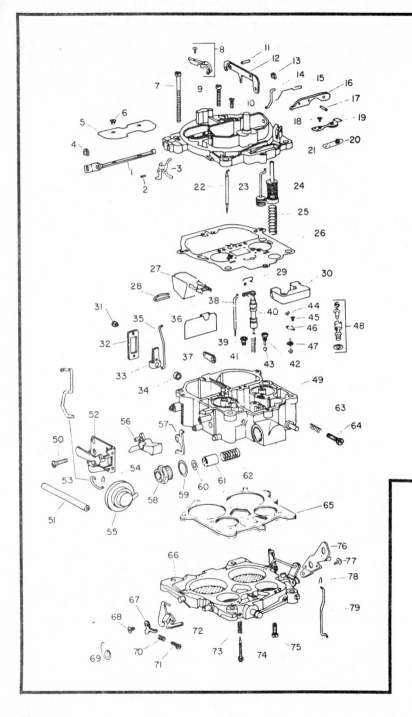

ITEM NO.	DESCRIPTION
1.	Choke shaft and lever assembly
2.	Roll pin — Air valve lockout lever.
3.	Lever — Air valve lockout.
4.	Clip — Choke rod (upper).
5.	Choke valve.
6.	Screw — choke valve (2).
7.	Screw — Air horn (long).
8.	Secondary metering rod holder and screw.
9.	Screw — air horn (short).
10.	Screw — air horn (countersund) (2).
11.	Roll pin — Dash pot lever
12.	Dash pot actuating.
13.	Clip — air valve rod.
14.	Rod — air valve
15.	Lever — Idle vent valve.
16.	Lever — Pump actuating.
17.	Roll pin — Pump lever.
18.	Screw — Idle vent valve.
19.	Idle vent valve.
20.	Idle vent valve (Thermostatic type).
21.	Air horn assembly.
22.	Metering rod — Secondary (2).
23.	Dashpot assembly (Early).
24.	Pump assembly.
25.	Spring — Pump return.
26.	Gasket — Air horn.
27.	Float assembly.
28.	Hinge pin — float assembly
29.	Spring — Primary Metering rod retainer.
30.	Insert — Float bowl.
31.	Screw — Idle Compensator cover (2)
32.	Cover — Idle Compensator.
33.	Idle Compensator assembly;
34.	Seal — Idle Compensator.
35.	Choke rod.
36.	Baffle — Secondary bores.
37.	Lever — Choke rod (lower end).
38.	Primary metering rod (2).
39.	Main metering jet — Primary (2).
40.	Power Piston assembly.
41.	Spring — Power piston.
42.	Retainer — Pump discharge ball.
43.	Ball — Pump discharge.
44.	Pull clip float needle (Early).
45.	Screw — Float needle diaphragm retainer (Early).
46.	Retainer — Float needle assembly (Early).
47.	Float needle and diaphragm assy. (Early).
48.	Needle and seat assembly (standard).
49.	Float bowl assembly.
50.	Screw — Vacuum break control.
51.	Hose — Vacuum control.
52.	Vacuum break control assembly.
53.	Rod — Vacuum break control.
54.	Clip — Vacuum break rod.
55.	Vacuum diaphragm assembly.
56.	Fast Idle cam.
57.	Lever — Secondary lockout.
58.	Filter nut — Fuel Inlet.
59.	Gasket — Filter Nut.
60.	Gasket — Fuel Filter.
61.	Filter — Fuel Inlet.
62.	Spring — Filter relief.
63.	Spring — Idle adjusting screw.
64.	Screw — Idle adjusting.
65.	Gasket — Throttle body to bowl.
66.	Throttle body assembly.
67.	Fast Idle lever.
68.	Screw — Cam and fast idle lever attaching.
69.	Spring — Cam and fast idle lever.
70.	Spring — Fast Idle screw.
71.	Screw — Fast Idle adjusting.
72.	Fast Idle cam follower lever.
73.	Spring — Idle mixture needle (2).
74.	Idle mixture needle (2).
75.	Screw — Throttle body to bowl attaching.
76.	Throttle lever — primary.
77.	Screw — Throttle lever attaching.
78.	Clip — Pump rod.
79.	Pump rod.

Fig. 4-20. The Quadrajet. This four-barrel carburetor is used on a number of V-8 truck engines manufactured by General Motors and others.

relationship will be the same. Select gaskets from the kit that match the originals. Every hole and slot should be duplicated.

Inspect each part with particular attention to the expansion plugs pressed into the main castings. These plugs are a manufacturing convenience and can mean trouble if they leak. Perhaps the worst are those under the float-bowl casting on the Quadrajet. These plugs can vibrate loose in service and spill raw gasoline down into the bore. Plug repair kits are available through dealers.

Throttle-body to float-bowl casting screws should be doped with Loctite and torqued down hard. Other fasteners (e.g., float cover screws) must be treated with more discretion and torqued in a crisscross pattern from the center of the casting out. Install a new needle-and-seat assembly.

Float-level adjustments are described in the overhaul kit. Most are set with reference to the tip of the float and the float-cover casting. The specification may include the thickness of a new cover gasket or may be taken from bare metal. The distinction is important.

Bend the float tang as needed with a pair of long-nosed pliers. A second pair of pliers can be used as a holdsteady to protect the needle and seat from bending forces. Work with the adjustment until you are completely satisfied with it.

Some mechanics fill the float bowl before mounting the carburetor on the engine. Replace the fuel filter as needed and connect the fuel line. Turn the line fitting at least two full revolutions by hand before you put a wrench to it. Connect the vacuum lines and control linkages.

Start the engine. Keep a weather eye cocked for fuel leaks.

Idle Adjustments

There are two curb-idle adjustments. The idle mixture adjustment screw is located on the throttle body near the throttle plate. The screw in question is shown in Fig. 4-18 as part No. 40. The two-barrel carburetor in the next drawing (Fig. 4-19) is typical of multibarrels in that it has two mixture screws (both under part No. 45). These screws control the strength of the mixture by regulating the amount of gasoline that passes through the idle jet. The idle rpm adjustment screw is threaded through the throttle shaft lever and bears against a stop on the side of the casting. A second screw to regulate fast-idle rpm may also be present. It is difficult to confuse these two screws because the fast-idle screw is associated with the fast-idle cam and indirectly with the choke.

The idle mixture has precedence over other adjustments and is made first. Bring the engine up to operating temperature and verify the ignition timing with a strobe light. Most carburetors are in adjustment when the screw is between 1 1/2 to 2 turns out from being lightly seated. This rule of thumb is *not* an industry standard and must be used with discretion. Carburetors are different. But an engine that responds only to extreme adjustments is trying to tell

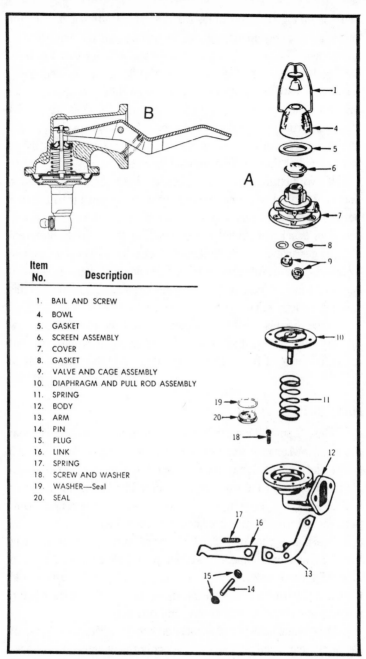

Item No.	Description
1.	BAIL AND SCREW
4.	BOWL
5.	GASKET
6.	SCREEN ASSEMBLY
7.	COVER
8.	GASKET
9.	VALVE AND CAGE ASSEMBLY
10.	DIAPHRAGM AND PULL ROD ASSEMBLY
11.	SPRING
12.	BODY
13.	ARM
14.	PIN
15.	PLUG
16.	LINK
17.	SPRING
18.	SCREW AND WASHER
19.	WASHER—Seal
20.	SEAL

Fig. 4-21. Fuel pumps. The pump shown in view A is supplied with Holden 6-cylinder engines and is fully repairable. View B is a cutaway of the Chrysler unit used on the Slant-Six engine family.

you something. For example, if the best adjustment is with the screw almost bottomed, you can be certain that the carburetor is going rich. The usual cause is a deformed idle jet that has been damaged by bottoming the adjustment needle. If, on the other hand, the engine responds best when the screw has been backed out so far that it wobbles, the problem is a lean mixture. Chances are the idle circuit is partially clogged. If the engine refuses to come into adjustment, check for air leaks at the throttle shaft, the carburetor flange gasket, and at the manifold to head flanges.

If two mixture screws are present, both should be moved in unison. The final adjustment should vary by no more than 1/2 turn between screws. Greater consistency than this is not possible.

The exact adjustment is best made with a reliable (infrared) exhaust gas analyzer. The next best approach is to adjust for highest manifold vacuum. Adjustment by ear should be discouraged since it can waste fuel and inevitably increases exhaust emissions. (In this context a happy engine is a dirty engine.)

Once the mixture is satisfactory, adjust the idle-speed screw for 500–600 rpm. Fast idle settings vary between carburetors, but are in the range of 1650–1700 rpm and taken at the second step of the fast idle cam.

FUEL PUMPS

The AC pump shown in Fig. 4-21 has all the traditional virtues: the glass bowl enables the mechanic to check pump performance at a glance and doubles as a water trap, and the pump can be disassembled for inspection and parts replacement. The Mopar pump shown in Fig. 4-21B is a more up-to-the-minute design; it is simple, compact, inexpensive to produce, and nonrepairable.

Fuel pumps should be checked for pressure (the rig is shown in Fig. 4-22) and for volume. A good pump will deliver at least a pint in 30 to 45 seconds at 2000 rpm at a pressure of 5 to 6 1/2 psi. Should the pump fail to meet these specifications, replace the filters, tighten the suction-side line connections, and retest.

Most pump failures are associated with the diaphragm. Loss of elasticity, tears, and pinhole leaks affect both volume and pressure. Leaks too insignificant to prevent the engine from running can divert fuel into the oil sump. Assuming that the pump can be disassembled, consider the diaphragm guilty until proven innocent by substitution of a known-good one.

Valve failure is usually total and absolute. Check by alternatively blowing and sucking on the valves. As positioned in the pump body, the inlet valve should open under slight negative pressure and seat under positive pressure. The outlet valve works in the reverse manner. After long use, it may be necessary to replace the spring (it determines the output rate and pressure) or the pump arm and its pivot shaft. As these parts wear, the stroke of the pump is shortened. Pack the engine-side cavity with heavy grease before final assembly.

FUEL TANKS

A detachable fuel tank is illustrated in Fig. 4-23. The quick-release filler cap shown here is a convenience, but one that tends to leak unless the gasket is routinely replaced.

Rust is the No. 1 enemy. Tanks can be cleaned with the same compounds used for carburetors, but this is at best an expedient. Once the protective coating has been compromised, the tank quickly rusts again. All gasoline contains some water and dissolved oxygen. Additional water enters by way of condensation out of the air. This problem is particularly severe in hot climates and can be retarded, but not prevented, by keeping the tank topped.

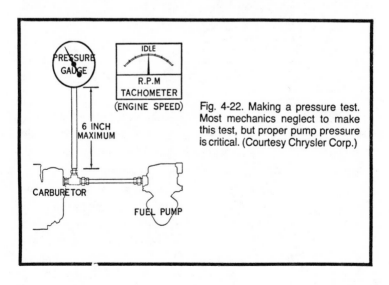

Fig. 4-22. Making a pressure test. Most mechanics neglect to make this test, but proper pump pressure is critical. (Courtesy Chrysler Corp.)

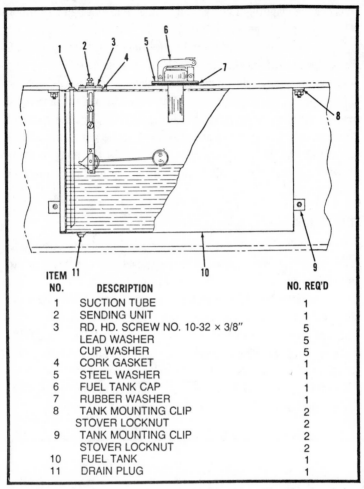

ITEM NO.	DESCRIPTION	NO. REQ'D
1	SUCTION TUBE	1
2	SENDING UNIT	1
3	RD. HD. SCREW NO. 10-32 × 3/8"	5
	LEAD WASHER	5
	CUP WASHER	5
4	CORK GASKET	1
5	STEEL WASHER	1
6	FUEL TANK CAP	1
7	RUBBER WASHER	1
8	TANK MOUNTING CLIP	2
	STOVER LOCKNUT	2
9	TANK MOUNTING CLIP	2
	STOVER LOCKNUT	2
10	FUEL TANK	1
11	DRAIN PLUG	1

Fig. 4-23. Fuel tank with sending unit and quick-release filler. (Courtesy Industrial Truck Div., Eaton Corp.)

Leaks can be repaired in the field although the prognosis is poor. Even if the mechanics are willing to do the work—and lift truck mechanics rush in where some of their brethren would fear to tread—the operation has little chance of long-term success.

The only practical way to repair a leaking tank is to solder it. Epoxy fails more often than it succeeds, and brazing is asking for trouble. Gasoline vapor is, as we all realize, highly explosive when mixed with air. Vapor has been known to linger in an empty tank for years. Steam clean the tank thoroughly, introducing steam at every access port. After you are satisfied that the tank is safe, steam it again for the insurance value. Men who do this kind of work for a living steam tanks for an hour or more before putting a torch to it.

Clean the affected area with sandpaper and a weak solution of muriatic acid. If the tank has holed because of rust, it may be necessary to replace a whole section of the tank. Normally, rust damage tends to localize and it is not too difficult to fix if the edges of the hole are trimmed back to virgin metal. Use acid core solder and only enough heat to make a good bond.

The shop should be cleared during this repair. It is wise for the mechanic to stand clear of the ends of the tank since the ends tend to blow first. However, this precaution is not a guaranteed safeguard—tanks have been known to split at the sides.

GOVERNORS

Sandwich, or velocity, governors are entirely self-contained devices mounted below the carburetor (Fig. 4-24). The governor throttle is sensitive to airstream velocity and manifold vacuum. At a preset combination of the two, it closes and blocks a further increase in engine rpm. The no-load adjustment is by means of the vertical

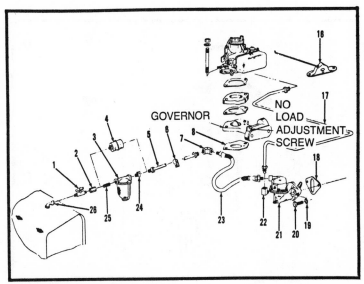

Fig. 4-24. Sandwich type governor, shown in position under carburetor. (Courtesy Industrial Truck Div., Eaton Corp.)

screw shown on the governor body. Diaphragm replacement and other repairs are not possible. If the engine is otherwise in tune, but fails to reach governed speed, replace the unit.

Centrifugal governors are the hallmark of engines that have been designed for industrial purposes. Details vary between makes, but all operate by means of centrifugal weights (Fig. 4-25). As these weights revolve, the spool is cammed down as a result of centrifugal force, causing the throttle to close. The spring shown at the bottom acts against this camming action.

These governors are quite sensitive—the best ones can give 2% speed regulation under widely varying loads—and require some desensitizing to make them practical. Otherwise the engine would be constantly surging as it attempted to catch up with commands from the governor. The antisurge adjustment is the threaded screw shown to the left of the drawing.

The next drawing—Fig. 4-26—illustrates a typical governor linkage. Increasing the tension on the spring with the adjustable eyebolt reduces maximum engine speed; decreasing the tension increases the speed.

When it is necessary to disassemble the governor and its linkage, carefully mark the adjustments. If the adjustment has been

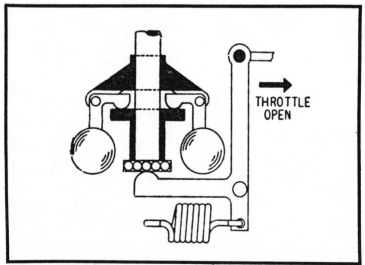

Fig. 4-25. Pictorial diagram of a centrifugal governor as found on some Continental engines.

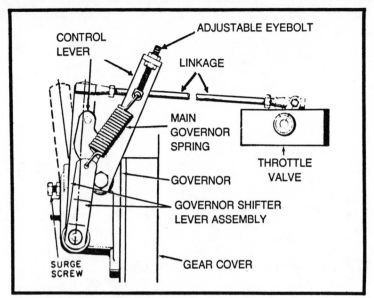

Fig. 4-26. Governor adjustments. This particular setup is that used on Waukesha VR series engines, but is quite typical.

lost, the governor should bias the throttle slightly closed with the engine stopped and the accelerator depressed as far as it will go. Final adjustment is made at the eyebolt with the help of a tachometer.

5

LPG Fuel Systems

Liquified Petroleum Gas (LPG) is a general term that refers to propane, butane, or to a mixture of both. These gases are found in the natural state and are a byproduct of petroleum refining.

The chemical structures of propane and butane are quite simple. Without going very deeply into chemistry, a molecule of propane consists of three atoms of carbon and eight of hydrogen arranged in the structure shown in Fig. 5-1A. Butane has four atoms of carbon and ten of hydrogen. The structure is variable. Ordinary butane forms the pattern shown in Fig. 5-1B. Isobutane (Fig. 5-1C) contains the same number of carbon and hydrogen atoms, but combines them asymmetrically as shown in the final drawing of the series. Isobutane boils at a lower temperature and is sometimes mixed with butane for cold weather use.

GASOLINE VS LPG

In contrast, gasoline is a blend of hydrocarbons, although it is primarily octane, which has eight atoms of carbon and 18 atoms of carbon. Lighter hydrocarbons such as heptane and hexane are added on a seasonal basis, since they vaporize at lower temperatures than octane. Gasoline also contains various additives and impurities. In other words, gasoline is an Irish stew of a fuel that is very difficult for the engine to digest properly. Consequently, the exhaust is polluted with unburnt hydrocarbons (HC), carbon monoxide (CO), and oxides of nitrogen (NO_x). LPG exhausts are by no means free of these pollutants, but they are present only in trace amounts.

Impco, a leading manufacturer of gas carburetors and converters, made a careful comparison of gasoline and propane exhausts. The test vehicle was a large and unsanitized V-8 passenger car. When running on gasoline, the engine spewed out 1.1 grams of HC per mile, more than 19 grams of CO, and 5.2 grams of the family of toxins known as NO_x. Propane cut HC emissions to 0.3 grams, CO to 2 grams, and NO_x to 0.6 grams. In one fell swoop propane allowed this engine to meet 1975 federal emissions standards. With the exception of NO_x—a pollutant that is generated by high combustion temperatures—the engine met 1976 federal standards as well.

In addition, propane promises extended engine life as well as longer intervals between oil changes. While these promises are sometimes unfulfilled, it is known that those unburnt hydrocarbons

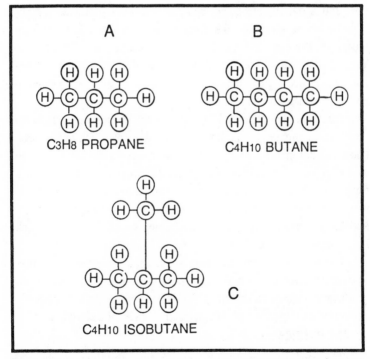

Fig. 5-1. Molecular structure of petroleum gases. Note that butane has two forms.

that remain in the engine eventually puddle in the sump. On their way they wash oil from the cylinder walls and accelerate bore and ring wear. Gasoline is not a good lubricant and it can be expected that gasoline-tainted oil would cause increased bearing wear.

But gasoline has certain advantages of its own. While it is a poor lubricant in the sump, the fuel is wet and does offer better scuff protection than a dry gas. In addition, most gasoline is doped with tetraethyl lead (TEL) at the rate of about 3 cc per gallon of regular grade fuel. The purpose of TEL is to increase the octane rating. But lead, even in the liquid form, is a very good lubricant and has extended exhaust valve life. This is particularly true during the critical break-in period.

LPG has no lubricating qualities and is (or should be) entirely free of oil contamination. Some engines have not taken kindly to this and their manufacturers have been forced to fit upper cylinder oilers. These devices inject minute amounts of oil into the gas stream prior to combustion. But most engines will tolerate LPG without modification. Industrial engines have well-protected valves made of high-nickel content steel and insert-type valve seats. Most of these engines feature positive valve rotation which has the effect of prolonging seat, valve, and (usually) valve guide life. Automotive engines have recently had their valve train uprated in order to tolerate low- and no-lead fuels.

Another advantage of LPG takes a bit of explaining. Internal combustion engines are plagued by a kind of maverick combustion known as detonation. Rather than burn in a controlled manner, the air-fuel mixture explodes at once. Cylinder pressures zoom to 3 or 4 times their normal values. This pressure rise is so violent that it actually rings the piston and head, and is described as ping or spark knock. Very much of this and the piston holes as if it had been struck by an armor-piercing shell.

Unfortunately, detonation occurs at peak power settings. It is characteristic of engines with high compression ratios, advanced spark, and wide-open throttles. All things being equal, an engine's performance depends upon delaying the onset of detonation.

OCTANE RATINGS

This can be done in part by design factors. But the real progress has come about because of chemistry. The measure of a fuel's resistance to detonation is its octane number. Isooctane is one of the family of hydrocarbons found in gasoline. It has a very high threshold of detonation and engineers use it as a reference fuel. Pure octane is rated at 100. Heptane, another hydrocarbon found in gasoline blends, is a horrible fuel with an octane rating of 0. Isooctane and heptane form the boundaries of the octane system. Higher than octane numbers of 100 are assigned according to the amount of TEL added to the fuel.

A fuel to be tested is run through a specially constructed engine. If the fuel in question behaves like pure isooctane, it is rated at 100. If it acts like a 75/25 mixture of isooctane and heptane, the rating is 75. The conditions of the test determine whether the octane rating is by the Research or the Motor method. The Research method is not very meaningful for modern, high-speed engines. The more conservative Motor method is preferred. But both terms are used and fuel suppliers sometimes describe their wares in terms of the Research method.

It should be remembered that octane ratings are only an indirect measure of the fuel's resistance to detonation. No test engine can reproduce the characteristics of an engine in the field. Nor is octane a linear rating. At the high end of the scale, one or two octane numbers take on a tremendous significance. An engine may be reasonably content on 88 octane fuel and detonate itself to pieces on 85 octane.

As you can see from Table 5-1, propane has a Motor octane number octane. Consequently, it is possible to advance the timing and increase the compression ratio with propane and mixtures of butane.

ENERGY CONTENT

Gaseous fuels are less than spectacular in terms of energy content. Heat energy is measured in British Thermal Units (Btu) per gallon. Under laboratory conditions 1 Btu is the amount of energy required to raise the temperature of 1 lb of water 1°F. Table 5-1 lists the heat value of common gaseous fuels together with gasoline and diesel oil. Both gross and net heat values are supplied. The former is the value listed in textbooks and the value that fuel suppliers like to quote. It is not appropriate for engine fuels, because some heat is

Table 5-1. Fuel Characteristics. (Courtesy Kohler of Kohler)

PHYSICAL PROPERTY / 60°F	BUTANE	PROPANE	GASOLINE	DIESEL FUEL
Normal Atmospheric State	Gas	Gas	Liquid	Liquid
Boiling Point (F.)				
Initial	+32°	−44°	+97°	+350°
End	+32°	−44°	+420°	+675°
Heating Value BTU's per:				
Gallon (Net - LHV)	94,670	83,340	116,400	130,300
Gallon (Gross)	102,032	91,547	124,600	139,000
Cubic Foot (Gas)	3264	2516	6390	
Density Cubic feet of Gas Per Gallon (Liquid)	31.26	36.39	19.50	
Weight (Lbs.) Per Gallon Liquid	4.81	4.24	6.16	7.08
Octane Number				
Research	94	110+	82–100	
Motor	90	97	75–90	

lost due to water formation. During combustion, great amounts of energy are given off in the formation of carbon dioxide. But some hydrogen and oxygen atoms combine to form water vapor, and this absorbs energy. The difference between gross and net heat values can be as much as 10–14% with those fuels that are high in hydrogen content suffering the most. Butane, for example, has a gross heat value of 102,032 Btu/gal; its net, or low, heat value is only 94,670 Btu/gal. Gasoline has a net heat value of 116,400 Btu/gal. If all things are equal, a gallon of gasoline will run an engine 19% longer than a gallon of butane. If propane is the fuel, the differential is even greater.

Yet LPG users often claim superior per-hour fuel economy than given by gasoline. Part of the reason is psychological. When one has invested several hundred dollars in an LPG system, it is human enough to exaggerate its benefits. And part of the reason is because of modifications to the engine made possible by the higher octane rating of LPG. More ignition advance and higher compression ratios mean better fuel economy. An additional boost comes by way of blocking the heat riser. It is not necessary to heat LPG to vaporize it, and an engine thrives on cold air.

STORAGE

One of the traditional objections to LPG is that it is difficult to store. And along with this comes the belief that gaseous fuels are extremely hazardous.

LPG must be stored in pressure vessels. The graph in Fig. 5-2 explains why. At any temperature above −40°F propane vaporizes.

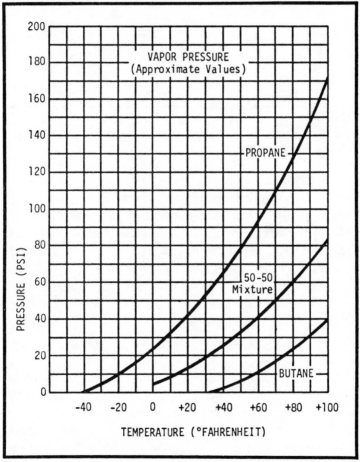

Fig. 5-2. Vapor pressure (the pressure of the vapor above the liquid in the tank) varies directly with temperature. (Courtesy Kohler of Kohler)

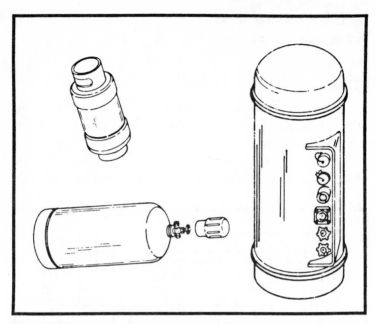

Fig. 5-3. LPG containers. The pair of drawings on the left show the ICC tank in its usual form and armored for vehicular use. An ASME tank is pictured at the right. (Courtesy Kohler of Kohler)

It literally boils. Butane is more inert and does not boil until temperature reaches the freezing point of water, or 32°F. The vapor above the fluid level in the container develops a pressure that is entirely a function of temperature. It has nothing to do with how full the container may be—so long as the container is not topped with liquid. At 100°F the vapor pressure of propane is approximately 172 psi, while butane vapor has a pressure of about 40 psi. Should the tanks be filled completely, so there is no room for vapor boiloff, another set of conditions holds. LPG has a high rate of thermal expansion, and generates pressures that will turn standard tanks into large grenades.

Two vehicle tank types have been approved. The Interstate Commerce Commission bottle-type container has some popularity in the 20 gallon (No. 100) size (Fig. 5-3). These tanks have an internal relief valve (usually set at 375 psi) and an excess-flow check valve in series with the liquid-feed valve. The check valve works something like a fuse in an electrical circuit. When subject to excessive flow, the check valve closes. In addition, these tanks are fitted with a quick-disconnect nipple to speed tank changing. When the nipple is opened, flow automatically ceases.

An American Society of Mechanical Engineers (ASME) container is pictured at the bottom of Fig. 5-3. Made of boiler plate to Department of Transportation (DOT) and ASME standards, these tanks are proofed at 1000 psi. An integral relief valve is an additional safety feature. Both the liquid and vapor feed lines have excess-flow check valves. A vapor-return valve allows vapor generated during filling to be returned to the supply tank, thus balancing pressure between the supply and truck tanks. A fixed gauge guides the filling operation and a second, float-type gauge indicates the tank reserve.

Both ICC and ASME tanks are intended for horizontal mounting, and specifications are in force for the straps. Intelligent design and local regulations insist that an automatic valve be placed between the tank and the converter. This valve closes the circuit when the engine is not running, and may be vacuum or solenoid operated. While it is true that the converter is opened by engine demand, it can fail. The diaphragm can hole or the converter valve fail to seat. Without an automatic shutoff in line, gaseous fuel would escape out of the carburetor air horn.

Hazards with any fuel are intensified when the fuel is stored and particularly when the stores are opened for refueling. LPG comes out better than gasoline on both of these points. The containers are safety-valved pressure vessels that can withstand physical and thermal shocks that would fireball a gasoline tank. Refilling gasoline tanks is all too often a casual process and is carried on within the confines of the plant. Recharging LPG cylinders is often done off-site where the effects of accident would be minimized, and is always performed by trained personnel.

But this does not mean that LPG is completely safe. No fuel is. One study of 18 serious LPG-related accidents tallied 17 injuries and two fatalities. Another, more representative, study included all LPG-related accidents in one plant over a period of 30 years. Some 170 incidents were recorded without any fatalities and only a handful of injuries.

COPING WITH LPG

Butane and propane are colorless and—in the natural state—odorless. Commercial grades are treated with potent aromatics known as mercaptains. (Chemically similar to those aromatics released by excited skunks.) The pungent odor of the gas is absolute evidence of a leak, since mercaptans are destroyed in combustion and therefore cannot escape out the exhaust.

Fuel systems should be inspected for leaks periodically and always after severe impact. With the engine running, daub the lines and castings with a strong solution of soap and water. Bubbles mean escaping gas.

Changing, and particularly refilling, cylinders should be done out of doors. By the same token, the machines should be stored outside. If this is impractical, the storage and tankage areas should be remote from the worksite, furnished with CO_2 or dry-chemical fire extinguishers, and ventilated by mechanical fans at floor level. Service pits and odd corners of the shop can accumulate explosive concentrations of the gas. Before opening the fuel system, close the manual tank valve and run the engine until the lines are dry.

Do not operate a truck that showers sparks from its exhaust or that chronically backfires.

LPG SYSTEMS

A workable LPG system must filter the gas at some point near the tank, reduce its pressure, assure that it is completely vaporized, and deliver a metered amount of fuel through the carburetor. There is some variety in the hardware, but all LPG systems have these components:

- lock valve
- filter
- regulator
- vaporizer
- gas carburetor

Vehicular systems are distinguished from stationary types by virtue of compactness. Primary (field) and secondary regulation is combined in a single unit that may also serve as the vaporizer.

Figure 5-4 is a diagram of the Ensign system used with small air-cooled engines. Liquid is withdrawn from the tank, passes through a wet-gas filter, and goes to the vaporizer. The regulator is a two-stage device and includes the solenoid lock valve. The next

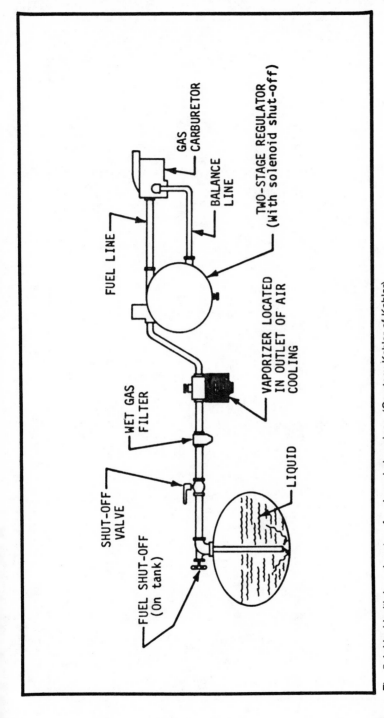

Fig. 5-4. Liquid withdrawal system for air-cooled engines. (Courtesy Kohler of Kohler)

199

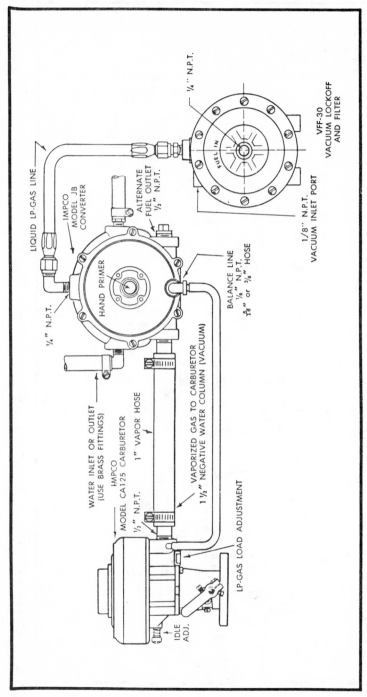

Fig. 5-5. Liquid withdrawal system for water-cooled engines. (Courtesy Impco Carburetion)

200

drawing, Fig. 5-5, illustrates the familiar Impco system. The major difference between it and the Ensign is that the Impco vaporizer is water heated and is in-unit with the regulator. The vacuum-operated lock valve can be replaced by a solenoid type.

Filter

A typical wet filter is illustrated in Fig. 5-6. It is similar in design and appearance to the common gasoline filter, except for the heavy construction needed to withstand tank pressure. The element is serviceable and the sediment bowl should be cleaned periodically.

Vaporizer

The vaporizer or converter (the terms are used interchangeably) heats the fuel to assure complete vaporization. The type shown in Fig. 5-7A is a simple heat exchanger intended for air-cooled engines. It is mounted in the exhaust air stream. The Impco design in Fig. 5-7B is water heated and combines two stages of vaporization

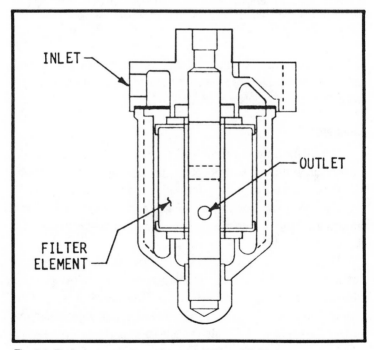

Fig. 5-6. Typical wet-gas filter. (Courtesy Kohler of Kohler)

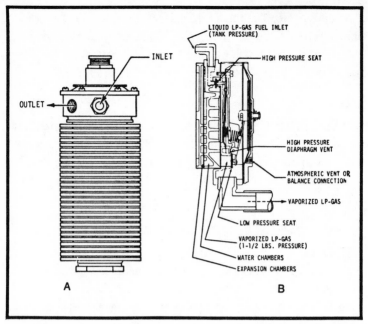

Fig. 5-7. The vaporizer on the left is for air-cooled engines; the one on the right is water heated and incorporates two stages of regulation. (Courtesy Kohler of Kohler)

under a single cover. Fuel at tank pressure enters the top of the unit and is vaporized as it passes over the heated core. Two diaphragm-controlled valves regulate pressure.

Carburetor

Since the carburetor (or mixer) receives fuel that is already in the gaseous state, it does not need to provide further vaporization. Its only function is to adjust air/fuel ratios to engine speed and load.

There are two basic types of gas carburetors: one meters through a venturi and nozzle system, and the other by means of a diaphragm and valve.

The venturi type (Fig. 5-8A) is very similar to a gasoline carburetor. Fuel exits from the discharge nozzle at the point of greatest pressure drop in the venturi. The nozzle is subject to negative pressure that varies with the changing rate of airflow through the venturi. At elevated engine speeds, the airflow velocity is high, and the nozzle discharges large amounts of fuel for a rich

202

mixture. At low speeds, the throttle plate is almost closed, and the airflow through the venturi is reduced to a trickle. Very little vacuum is developed and little fuel is delivered.

The diaphragm type (Fig. 5-8B) is the more popular of the two. The inlet valve is normally held closed by the diaphragm spring. Once the engine is primed and started, airflow pushes the diaphragm down and unseats the valve. The flow through the valve depends upon the velocity of the air stream. The greater the velocity, the further the diaphragm is displaced, and the greater the flow through the valve.

Carburetor Adjustments

The only sure way to make the power adjustment (Fig. 5-9) is with the aid of an accurate exhaust gas analyzer. Approximate adjustments can be made by ear, but cannot give the economy inherent in this fuel.

The power mixture valve and the idle-adjustment screw are shown in Fig. 5-9. A few applications may have the idle-adjustment screw located on the converter/regulator and a separate idle fuel line to the carburetor. In any event, follow this procedure:

- Adjust the idle screw for highest rpm. Use a tachometer.
- Turn the throttle-stop screw in until the engine runs at 1400 rpm.
- Adjust the power mixture valve to give a 12.5:1 reading on the exhaust gas analyzer.
- Back off the stop screw to idle specification.
- Reset the idle screw since power mixture valve adjustments will have upset its calibration.

If an exhaust gas analyzer is not available, you can get the machine into service by the lean-roll/rich-roll method. Make the initial idle adjustment, block the throttle plate open to 1400 rpm, and adjust the power mixture valve midway between lean and rich roll. This method is crude, and for insurance it is a good idea to set the valve slightly on the rich side. (LPG is cheaper than pistons.)

Ignition Timing

Existing timing specifications mean little when an engine has been converted to LPG. The exact timing depends upon engine

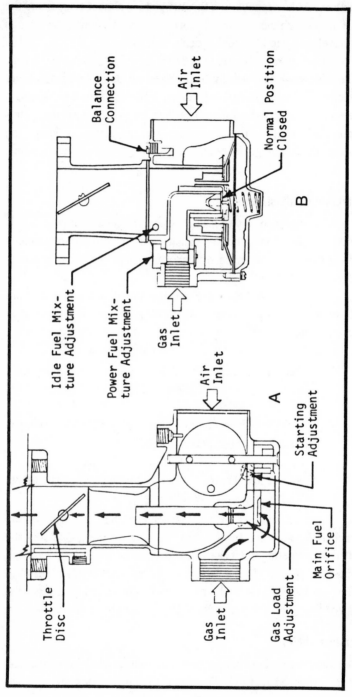

Fig. 5-8. Gas carburetors. View A shows a venturi type and view B the more popular diaphragm type. (Courtesy Kohler of Kohler)

make and other variables, such as the amount of carbon in the chambers and compression. The instructions here are offered only as a guide. Check the timing against actual engine operation. If the engine detonates or the starter labors, the ignition should be slightly retarded. To do this:

- Set the idle stop screw to 1400. Note that this is not the governed top speed.
- Pull off one spark plug wire at a time until engine speed falls to 1000–1100 rpm.
- Rotate the distributor for best rpm. The engine is not particularly sensitive to distributor movement and it will be found that best rpm is in a 5 to 10 degree area. Time to the late edge of this area.

TROUBLESHOOTING

LPG systems are surprisingly troublefree—considering the number of diaphragms and valves present. When problems do arise, the converter/regulator becomes the prime suspect only after ignition, air filter, muffler, PCV valve, and mechanical malfunctions have been ruled out.

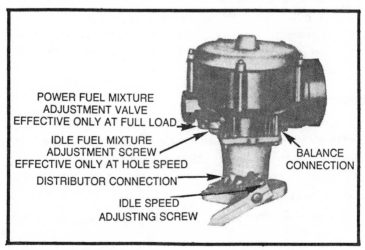

Fig. 5-9. Carburetor adjustments. (Courtesy Waukesha Motor Co.)

No Fuel to the Carburetor

You can verify this condition by disabling the lock valve and removing the hose to the carburetor. Fuel should flow. If it doesn't, make the following checks:

- Fuel level in the tank.
- Excess flow check valve. If the manual valve is opened too quickly, the check valve will seat. If it remains seated with the manual valve closed, a sharp rap with a mallet may be enough to open it. Otherwise replace the tank.
- Quick-disconnect fitting.
- Plugged lines or filter (the area of the obstruction will be cold to the touch and may be frosted).
- Converter.

Insufficient Fuel

Typically, the engine fires a few times and quits. If it can be started, it runs erratically at full throttle. Check the carburetor adjustments described previously. Should the engine continue to balk, or if radically new adjustments are needed, the problem is in the feed system. Check the following:

- Filter and lines for possible obstruction.
- Converter-to-carburetor line for leaks. Some applications use a flexible hose here; others use tubing with a flex joint. The flex joint is the most likely troublespot.
- Converter/regulator. Be on the lookout for a clogged breather vent, a ruptured secondary diaphragm, or binds in the internal valve linkage.

Excess Fuel

Frost on the converter/regulator housing and fumes at the carburetor with the engine stopped are a sure sign of regulator failure. Check the secondary diaphragm and associated hardware. Other converter/regulator failures may only show up when the engine is running and include:

- Excessive primary pressure (10 psi is usually the upper limit).
- Broken primary regulator spring or ruptured diaphragm.

- Secondary regulator lockoff adjustment.
- Broken or weak lockoff spring.
- Secondary regulator diaphragm stretched drum tight.
- Leaking secondary regulator valve seat.
- Binding in the secondary regulator valve mechanism.

Erratic Idle

Check the ignition, compression, PCV, and intake manifold. The engine should pull at least 16 inches of mercury at idle with the timing in sync. Less than figure indicates a leak in the induction tract between the throttle plate and the engine. Check the throttle shaft bushings (some Impco throttle bodies use needle bearings that pretty well eliminate this problem), carburetor and manifold hold-down bolts and gaskets. Numbering among fuel system difficulties are:

- Clogged air filter.
- Clogged idle passage.
- Regulator failure.
- Converter overheating (due to failure in the cooling system).

Lack of Power

This symptom can have many causes, from dragging brakes to a worn hydraulic pump. Verify for yourself that the engine is involved and check ignition, compression, and governor operation before turning to the fuel system. You should bear in mind that LPG-fueled engines are sensitive to temperature, and lose power on hot days. Straight butane or butane mixtures call for richer power settings than does propane.

Converter/Regulator Tests

The converter/regulator under discussion is the popular Impco Model J intended for engines of up to 150 hp (Fig. 5-10). These instructions apply with modifications (obvious in the event) to other Impco types and can serve as a general guide to the products of other manufacturers. This unit combines two stages of regulation together with a water-heated converter section.

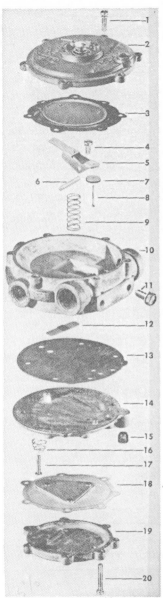

INDEX NO.	DESCRIPTION
1	SCREW, 8-32 x ⅝" SEMS (6)
2	COVER ASSY., SECONDARY: C1-34, P1-10, S2-21, W1-27, S7-1
3	DIAPHRAGM ASSY., SECONDARY: D1-21, P2-27, R2-1(2), P2-28
4	SCREW, 8-32 x ⅜" SEMS
5	LEVER ASSY., SECONDARY REGULATOR: L1-37, S3-23
6	PIN, SECONDARY FULCRUM
7	SEAT, SECONDARY REGULATOR
8	PIN, SECONDARY SEAT
9	SPRING, BLUE SECONDARY
9	SPRING, ORANGE SECONDARY
10	BODY ASSY.: B1-33, J1-7, P3-14
11	SCREW, ¼"-20 x ⅝" SEMS (2)
12	SEAT, PRIMARY REGULATOR
13	GASKET, BODY TO PLATE
14	PLATE, CONVERTER BODY COVER
15	PLUG, ⅛" PIPE
16	SPRING, PRIMARY REGULATOR
17	PIN, PRIMARY VALVE
18	DIAPHRAGM ASSY., PRIMARY: D1-22, P2-29, R2-3(3), L1-36
19	COVER, PRIMARY REGULATOR
20	SCREW, 8-32 x 1" SEMS (7)

CONTENTS		
S1-59	SCREW, 8-32 x ⅝" SEMS	(2)
AD1-21	DIAPHRAGM ASSY., SECONDARY	
S1-42	SCREW, 8-32 x ⅜" SEMS	
S4-17	SEAT, SECONDARY REGULATOR	
P1-9	PIN, SECONDARY SEAT	
G1-85	GASKET, BODY TO PLATE	
P1-14	PIN, PRIMARY VALVE	
S1-10	SCREW, 8-32 x 1" SEMS	(2)
AD1-22	DIAPHRAGM ASSY., PRIMARY	
S4-16	SEAT, PRIMARY REGULATOR	

Fig. 5-10. Impco Model J converter breakdown and overhaul kit.

Primary Regulator. The primary regulator should be tested first, since it controls the action of the secondary. Close the manual valve on the tank and run the system dry. Then:

- Thread a pressure gauge (0–30 psi range) into the test port on the primary chamber.
- Disable the solenoid or vacuum-operated lock valve and slowly open the manual tank valve.
- Most primary regulators are set at approximately 6 psi. If the pressure climbs to a higher value than this, the primary valve or diaphragm has failed.

Secondary Regulator. With the pressure gauge monitoring primary pressure, check the flow to the carburetor. The secondary should lock off under 6 psi and no fuel should flow. If it does, check the secondary diaphragm, valve, and primer.

Bench Tests. Disassemble the primary section of the unit. Inspect the diaphragm for cracks, ruptures, and deformation. Examine the valve seat and nozzle with utmost care, since even the smallest imperfection can cause gas leakage. If the parts appear good, insert a piece of paper between them and snap the seat closed on the nozzle. The trace on the paper should show that the valve is seating square. Replace as necessary.

Check the secondary section by filling its chamber with water and applying low-pressure air to the test plug on the primary side. The secondary should lock off under 10–12 psi. Should it fail to do so, check the secondary valve visually and against paper. Replace the spring if it is corroded or otherwise suspicious. Impco springs are color-coded and should be replaced with one of the same color.

The secondary diaphragm requires special care during assembly. Run all screws through it before starting any. Tighten the cover in a crisscross pattern, stopping to check that the diaphragm is free to move.

Bracket bolts that extend into the gas passages should have their threads coated with pipe sealant.

Frost

Frost on the converter/regulator after the engine has stopped means that the unit is leaking. There are three possibilities. Leaks to

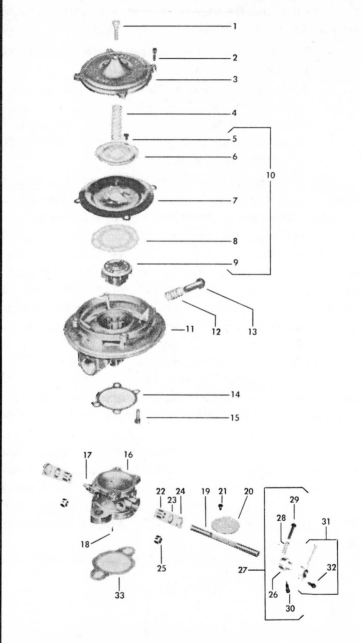

Fig. 5-11. Impco CA125 mixer and throttle bodies.

	DESCRIPTION		LIST PRICE EA.
1	SCREW, 1/4"-20 x 1" SEMS		
2	SCREW, 10-24 x 5/8" SEMS	(4)	
3	COVER, AIR VALVE		
4	SPRING, AIR VALVE		
5	SCREW, 6-32 x 1/4" SEMS	(4)	
6	PLATE, BACKUP		
7	DIAPHRAGM		
8	RING, AIR VALVE		
9	AIR-GAS VALVE ASSEMBLY: V1-14, S4-12, V2-7		
10	VALVE & DIAPHRAGM ASSEMBLY COMPLETE		
11	BODY ASSEMBLY: B1-25, V2-6, W1-12, W1-13, W1-14		
12	SPRING, IDLE SCREW		
13	IDLE SCREW		
14	GASKET, THROAT TO BODY		
15	SCREW, 12-24 x 5/8" SEMS	(4)	
N.S.	GASKET, BODY TO AIR CLEANER ADAPTER		

			1"	1 1/4"-1 1/2"
16	THROAT, 1" FLANGE			
16	THROAT, 1 1/4" & 1 1/2" FLANGE			
17	PIN, THROTTLE STOP	(2)		
18	PLUG, 1/8" PIPE			
19	THROTTLE SHAFT, 1/4" DIA.			
19	THROTTLE SHAFT, 5/16" DIA.			
20	FLY, FOR 1" THROAT			
20	FLY, FOR 1 1/2" THROAT			
21	SCREW, 6-32 x 1/4" SEMS	(2)		
21	SCREW, 8-32 x 5/16" SEMS	(2)		
22	BEARING, OILITE 1/4" I.D.	(2)		
22	BEARING, OILITE 5/16" I.D.	(2)		
23	SEAL, 1/4" SHAFT	(2)		
23	SEAL, 5/16" SHAFT	(2)		
24	RING, SEAL RETAINER	(2)		
25	OPTIONAL NEEDLE BEARING 1/4" I.D.	(2)		
25	OPTIONAL NEEDLE BEARING 5/16" I.D.	(2)		
26	LEVER, THROTTLE STOP 1/4" I.D.			
27	THROTTLE STOP ASSEMBLY: L1-8, S2-15, S1-21, S1-18			
26	LEVER, THROTTLE STOP 5/16" I.D.			
27	THROTTLE STOP ASSEMBLY: L1-8X, S2-15, S1-21, S1-18			
28	SPRING, STOP SCREW			
29	STOP SCREW, 10/32 x 3/4"			
30	PIN SCREW			
31	THROTTLE LEVER w/S1-17			
32	SCREW, 10-24 x 5/8"			
33	GASKET, 1" FLANGE			
33	GASKET, 1 1/4" & 1 1/2" FLANGE			

the carburetor indicate secondary or primary regulator failure; leaks out the secondary vent port mean the secondary diaphragm has ruptured; and leaks into the water jacket point to converter failure. Water-jacket leaks are fairly rare, and can be detected by bubbles or an odor at the radiator header tank.

Frost on the unit while the engine is running is a sign of cooling-system failure. The water level may be below the level of the converter/regulator, the water pump or its drive belt may be defective, or the thermostat may have failed.

Oil Flooding

This was once a rare problem, but is becoming commonplace as inexperienced manufacturers enter the LPG market. Oil plays havoc with regulation and eventually destroys the diaphragms. About all that can be done is to drain and flush the unit, and threaten to change suppliers unless the problem is solved.

CARBURETOR REPAIRS

The Impco carburetor shown in Fig. 5-11 is typical of the breed. The upper or metering section is shown as the mixer (a term that is sometimes used for the whole assembly) and houses the diaphragm and air-gas valve. Overhaul consists of replacing these parts (Nos. 5 through 7 in the photograph) and brushing carbon accumulations from the gas nozzle. Unless the carburetor is very dirty, this work can be done with it mounted on the machine.

Gas carburetors do not take kindly to oil-bath air cleaners. It is not unusual to find oil in the carburetor that has been pulled over from the air-cleaner sump. The problem can be alleviated—if not entirely solved—by underfilling the reservoir with a heavy grade of oil. Bring the level no closer than 1/4 inch to the full line. Of course, the best fix is to replace the air cleaner with a modern paper or polyurethane type.

Diesel Fuel Systems

There are good reasons for the current surge in popularity of diesel trucks. Diesel power offers economy (thermal efficiency can approach 40% as compared to the 25–30% efficiency of gasoline engines), longer stretches between overhaul, and freedom from ignition sytem hassle. As an added bonus, diesel oil is inherently safer than gasoline or LPG.

DIESEL FUEL

Diesel engines can be persuaded to run on almost any hydrocarbon—from alcohol to coal slurry. A few have been converted to LPG, although the advantages of this seem nebulous at best. As a practical matter, diesel fuels are limited to distillates described by the American Society of Testing Materials as suitable for high-speed engines. Fuel specifications are shown in Table 6-1. No. 1-D is for light and medium service and No. 2-D, a somewhat heavier oil, is favored for extreme service and in hot climates.

The terms used by ASTM require some clarification. *Flash point* is the lowest temperature at which the oil releases combustible vapors. It is of more interest to insurance companies and fire marshals than to mechanics, but the fact that No. 1 oil releases explosive vapors when heated to 100°F is a reminder diesel fuel is by no means inert.

Table 6-1. ASTM Specifications for Light Diesel Fuels.

	No. 1-D	No. 2-D
1. Flash pt (°F min)	100	125
2. Cetane No. (min)	40	40
3. Viscosity at 100°F,		
centistokes min:	1.4	2.0
max:	2.5	4.3
4. Water and sediment		
(% by volume, max)	Trace	0.10
5. Sulfur (% max)	0.5	0.5
6. Carbon residue (%)	0.15	0.35
7. Ash (% by wt, max)	0.01	0.02
8. Distillation (°F)		
90% pt, max:	550	640
min:	—	540

The cetane number refers to the fuel's antiknock characteristics. As such, it is probably the most important fuel index. The fuel to be tested is rated against a mixture of two reference hydrocarbons. Cetane discourages detonation because of its rapid combustion and is assigned a rating of 100. Alpha-methyl-naphthalene burns about as slowly as you can pronounce its name and is given a rating of 0. The percentage of cetane in the mixture of these two hydrocarbons is the centane number. A half and half mixture has a cetane number of 50; a one in four mixture has a number of 25.

The oil under examination is injected into a specially constructed test engine with a variable compression head. (Curiously enough, model airplane engines have this same feature.) Injection commences at 13° before top dead center (btdc). The compression ratio is adjusted so that ignition occurs at dc. The percentage of cetane in the *reference* fuel that gives dc ignition under the same compression ratio is the cetane number assigned to the fuel in question.

Diesel detonation occurs early in the combustion process, before normal ignition, which distinguishes it from the gasoline variety. In the gasoline engine, detonation occurs late and involves a sudden explosion of tag ends of the fuel in the cylinder. Diesel detonation is associated with ignition lag, a peculiarity of the engine described by Sir Harry Ricardo some 50 years ago and one that has bedeviled engineers ever since.

Figure 6-1 shows the pressure curve in a typical cylinder. Injection begins early in the compression stroke at point A. Ignition

214

is delayed until point B. The greater the lag, the more fuel is in the chamber and the more sudden is the pressure rise. This explosive form of combustion is a species of detonation, one that is unique to the diesel engine because it occurs before normal combustion commences and not, as in the case of spark-ignition engines, afterwards.

Detonation is normal on startup; the cold block metal quenches the heat of compression, and ignition occurs late. Assuming that the engine is timed and injected correctly, the ignition lag is reduced by increased coolant and air inlet temperature, and increased engine speed.

Viscosity is a measure of how readily the oil flows, or its pourability. As with other petroleum products, viscosity is given in centistokes which is entirely a function of the fluid friction of the oil. To get the complete picture, the density of the oil must also be taken into account. For if the fluid friction of a light and a heavy oil is identical, the heavier oil will flow faster because of gravity. In this same system, water at 68°F has a viscosity of 1.00. Diesel oil has a density of about 0.89; that is, diesel oil is 89% as dense as water. From the table, the minimum viscosity of No. 1-D is 1.4 centistokes. This, multiplied by its density, gives a direct comparison with water. In this case diesel oil has a viscosity of 1.25 or 25% greater than water.

Unfortunately diesel oils contain more sediment and water than lighter hydrocarbons such as gasoline. This is a result of technological limitations in the refining process. No. 1-D oil is allowed a trace of sediments while No. 2-D can have as much as 0.01% of these

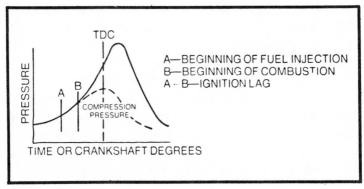

Fig. 6-1. Pressure rise diagram.

contaminants. In both oils, the sulphur content is limited to 0.5%, although some engine manufacturers are more rigorous and insist that the sulphur content be lower than the ASTM standard. Sulphur is corrosive and leaves deposits in the chamber that are difficult for the smaller engines to tolerate. The ash content is determined by burning a sample and weighing the residue. Ash deposits score piston rings and collect on the injector tips where they can distort the spray pattern.

The distillation temperature is a measure of the fuel's volatility. Quite unlike spark ignition engines, diesels fair best on fuels with low volatility.

FUEL SYSTEM

Figure 6-2 illustrates the two basic approaches to the fuel system. View A shows a remote injector pump and view B illustrates unit injectors—each of which has its own integral pump. Remote pumps may be combined with a fuel distributor, so that a single pump element serves all injectors.

In any event, fuel is drawn from the tank, filtered, and filtered again before delivery to the injector pump. Pressure generated by the low-pressure pump never exceeds 20 psi. The injector pump meters and pressurizes fuel for final delivery. At a preset pressure, the injectors trigger and spray atomized fuel into the chambers.

The high-pressure side of the system is as precise as anything our society has been able to put into mass production. This precision is necessary because of the demands put on the injectors and the high-pressure pump. At full throttle, the engine inhales 12,500 units of air to 1 unit of fuel; at idle the ratio is 80,000 to 1. In other words, the pump cylinders must be capable of being throttled down to 1/80,000 of the capacity of the engine cylinders.

This difference of scale is made more critical by the need to inject the fuel against compression. Pump pressures vary with engine type, with most operating in the 2000–6000 psi range. Certain large stationary engines have been built with delivery pressures of 20,000 psi. The injector must open suddenly without anticipation and eject an aimed spray of fuel into the cylinders. Small dislocations that would interfere with the pattern can be disastrous,

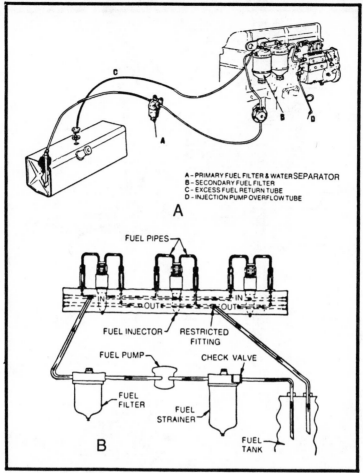

A – PRIMARY FUEL FILTER & WATER SEPARATOR
B – SECONDARY FUEL FILTER
C – EXCESS FUEL RETURN TUBE
D – INJECTION PUMP OVERFLOW TUBE

Fig. 6-2. Fuel systems. (A) System with remote injector pump (Courtesy Ford Industrial Engine & Turbine Operations). (B) System with unit injectors (Courtesy Detroit Diesel Allison).

since liquid fuel must not be allowed to contact with the cylinder walls or pistons. If this happens, the cylinders and pistons melt.

Injector and pump tolerances are on the order of 0.0004 of an inch. If a pump is disassembled and the pistons are placed in sunlight, they can expand enough to refuse entry into the barrels. Since the fuel is the only source of lubrication and the major source of cooling for these precision parts, it is obvious that the fuel supply must be clean. This is why diesel fuel systems have multiple stages of filtration, and why extreme care must be taken during refueling

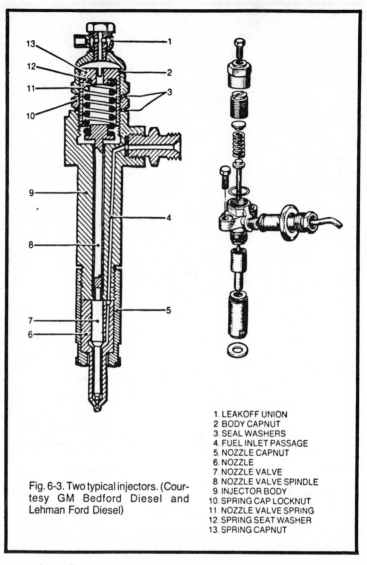

Fig. 6-3. Two typical injectors. (Courtesy GM Bedford Diesel and Lehman Ford Diesel)

1. LEAKOFF UNION
2. BODY CAPNUT
3. SEAL WASHERS
4. FUEL INLET PASSAGE
5. NOZZLE CAPNUT
6. NOZZLE
7. NOZZLE VALVE
8. NOZZLE VALVE SPINDLE
9. INJECTOR BODY
10. SPRING CAP LOCKNUT
11. NOZZLE VALVE SPRING
12. SPRING SEAT WASHER
13. SPRING CAPNUT

operations. Some manufacturers go so far as to suggest that refueling should be accomplished indoors—even rain will contaminate the fuel.

Injectors

Injectors go by many names. In various parts of this country and in England, they are called spray nozzles, spray valves, fuel delivery valves, or atomizers. An injector consists of two major subassemblies. The injector body mounts the unit on the head, carries the fuel inlet and spillage fittings, and on certain designs can mount an individual high-pressure pump. The nozzle and valve subassembly is at the business end of the injector and unseats to deliver a spray of fuel into the cylinder.

Figure 6-3 illustrates two injectors that can serve as patterns for the others. Fuel enters through the large fittings and, at a pressure predetermined by the tension of the spring, unseats the valve. At the end of delivery, the spring snaps the valve closed against falling line pressure. Opening and closing the valve must be abrupt and precise. Early delivery with insufficient pressure available for atomization and after-dribble can both cause detonation.

Both orifice and pintle nozzles are used. Orifice nozzles offer good atomization, but are vulnerable to carbon buildup. Others may have 16 holes or more with diameters as small as 0.0006 of an inch.

Pintle nozzles feature a pintle or pin that retracts out of the orifice during discharge. When retracted it releases a hollow, cone-shaped spray that fans out as much as 60° from the vertical. The pintle nozzle promises reduced maintenance because of the large diameter of the orifice and the self-cleaning action of the pintle as it shuttles back and forth.

A variant is shown in Fig. 6-4. Known as the throttling pintle, this nozzle controls the rate of discharge of fuel into the cylinder by means of its angled face. At the beginning of injection, the valve allows only a small amount of fuel to pass between its face and the

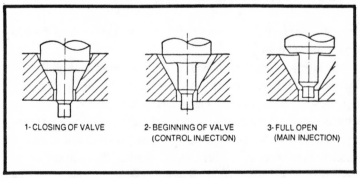

Fig. 6-4. Throttling pintle injector. (Courtesy Marine Engines Div., Chrysler Corp.)

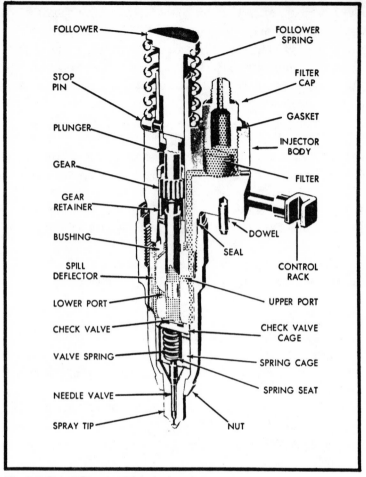

Fig. 6-5. Detroit Diesel unit injector in cutaway.

sides of the orifice. As the pintle retracts, the gap between the two widens for full delivery.

Unit Injectors. Unit injectors are most often seen on Detroit Diesel engines. Each injector has its own pump on the injector body (Fig. 6-5). This approach eliminates the high-pressure plumbing between a remote pump and the injectors and the associated problems. These lines have a tendency to develop small leaks and can suddenly snap because of vibration. In addition, they are subject to pressure waves each time an injector opens and closes. These waves bounce back and forth in the oil column at a rate of 5000 fps. In addition to the toll of physical damage, it is possible for these pressure waves to unseat the injectors of their own accord.

A unit injector combines four functions in a single assembly. It generates the high fuel pressure needed to give the spray pattern penetration, meters and injects the exact amount of fuel required by the load, atomizes the fuel for efficient combustion, and permits continuous fuel flow for cooling and to prevent air bubbles from forming in the lines.

In basic outline, the fuel enters the injector at the filter cap under pressure generated by the transfer pump. This pressure is on the order of 20 psi. Passing through the filter, the fuel goes to the supply chamber—that area between the spill deflector and the plunger bushing and under the plunger in the bushing. These parts are identified in Fig. 6-5. The plunger moves up and down in the bushing. Oil circulates below the plunger by virtue of two funnel-shaped ports in the sides of the bushing.

As the plunger moves down, a portion of the fuel under it is forced into the supply chamber through the lower bushing port. Flow continues until the port is covered by the lower edge of the plunger. At this point, a metered amount of fuel passes through a central passage in the plunger—indicated in Fig. 6-5 by the dotted line passing upward through the plunger—and to the supply chamber through the upper bushing port. The amount of fuel is determined by the relationship between the helical groove in the plunger and the upper port. Once the plunger blocks flow to the supply chamber, oil under it has nowhere to go and is subject to increasing pressures as the plunger falls.

The check valve unseats when sufficient pressure is built up. Fuel in the check-valve cage, spring cage, tip passages, and tip fuel cavity is compressed until the pressure forces the needle valve up and off its seat. At this moment injection commences. Fuel is forced through orifices in the spray tip and enters the chamber as a fine spray.

Injection ceases when the lower land of the plunger uncovers the lower port of the bushing. Pressure below the plunger is relieved and the valve spring closes the needle valve.

The action of the plunger and the relation of its lower edge and spillways to the bushing ports can be better visualized by careful study of Fig. 6-6.

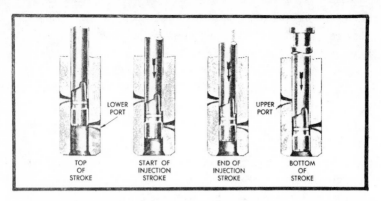

LOWER PORT

UPPER PORT

| TOP OF STROKE | START OF INJECTION STROKE | END OF INJECTION STROKE | BOTTOM OF STROKE |

Fig. 6-6. Plunger operation. (Courtesy Detroit Diesel Allison, Div. of General Motors Corp.)

On the plunger's return stroke, the high-pressure cylinder within the bushing is again filled with fuel entering through the ports. This circulation of fuel from the filter, down low in the injector body, and up to the supply chamber prevents air bubbles that would upset the timing and the consistency of the spray pattern, and also helps to cool the injector.

The stroke of the plunger is fixed by the camshaft and rocker-arm geometry. In order to throttle the engine for different load and speed requirements, it is necessary to vary the amount of fuel entering the chambers. This is done by changing the effective length of the pump stroke.

A helical groove is milled in the side of the plunger. This groove provides an oil flow path between the lower and upper bushing ports. Changing the position of the helices by rotating the plunger advances or retards port closing and the beginning and ending of injection. The plunger is rotated by means of the control rack and gear shown in Fig. 6-5. The free end of the rack is linked to the accelerator and to the governor.

Up and down motion of the plunger is controlled by the follower and follower spring shown on top of the unit. The next illustration, Fig. 6-7, details the drive mechanism and the injector mounting. The follower (No. 9) is driven through a cam (No. 10) and rocker arm (No. 2). Since the example under discussion is a two-cycle, the cam runs at engine speed. There is one injection per cylinder per revolution of the crankshaft.

When the operator wishes to shut down the engine, he pulls the rack full out. At this position the helices are turned to uncover both ports simultaneously (refer to Fig. 6-8).

Remote Injector Pumps. Unit injectors have never been as popular as remote pumps for small engines. In operation of the remote injector pump, the function of the injector is confined to atomizing the fuel. Pressure and metering are handled by a pump, which is mounted on the side of the block. In most cases, the pump is driven from the camshaft.

Two basic types of pumps are used. The *distributor* type employs a single pump element, in which fuel is apportioned to the

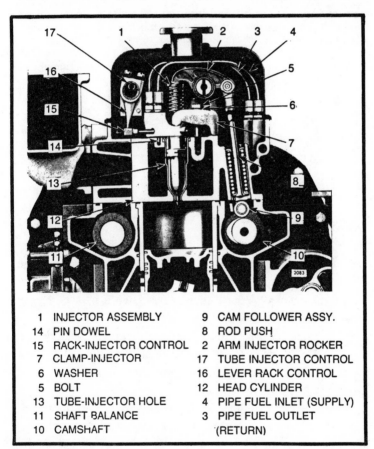

1	INJECTOR ASSEMBLY	9	CAM FOLLOWER ASSY.
14	PIN DOWEL	8	ROD PUSH
15	RACK-INJECTOR CONTROL	2	ARM INJECTOR ROCKER
7	CLAMP-INJECTOR	17	TUBE INJECTOR CONTROL
6	WASHER	16	LEVER RACK CONTROL
5	BOLT	12	HEAD CYLINDER
13	TUBE-INJECTOR HOLE	4	PIPE FUEL INLET (SUPPLY)
11	SHAFT BALANCE	3	PIPE FUEL OUTLET
10	CAMSHAFT		(RETURN)

Fig. 6-7. Unit injector mounting and drive mechanism. (Courtesy Detroit Diesel Allison, Div. of General Motors Corp.)

223

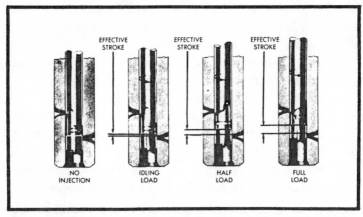

Fig. 6-8. The effective stroke of the plunger can be varied to match fuel delivery with load. (Courtesy Detroit Diesel Allison, Div. of General Motors Corp.)

various cylinders by means or a rotary valve. The attraction of this system is that is promises reduced manufacturing costs and that it gives consistency since pressurization and metering are the same for all cylinders. The *in-line* pump—a legacy of Robert Bosch and the first generation of diesel engineering—provides a pump element for each injector, with the pumps ganged for compactness and drive simplicity. Both distributor and in-line pumps use the fuel for all or part of the lubrication and both require a separate transfer pump.

Distributor Systems

The Roosa Master Model DB pump is shown in Fig. 6-9. Fuel, under transfer pump pressure, is forced through the drilled passage in the hydraulic head and into the annulus. It flows around the annulus to the top of the sleeve and through a passage to the metering valve, and ultimately to the pump element.

The pump is a pair of roller-tipped plungers moving inside of a cam ring. On the charging stroke, the plungers are moved outward by the oil that enters between them. At this time the rollers are in the cam valleys to allow the plungers full movement. But the actual distance they move is a function of the metering valve. At idle the valve allows little fuel to pass and the plungers are barely forced apart; under heavy load the pistons bottom their rollers against the cam depressions. A leaf spring adjustment is provided to limit full power fuel flow.

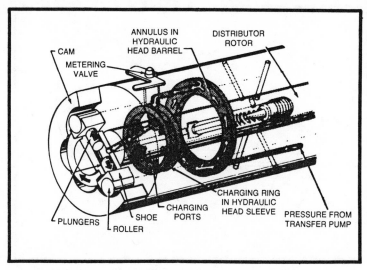

Fig. 6-9. As the pump charges the pistons move outward into "valleys" on the cam. (Courtesy Waukesha Motor Co.)

At the completion of the charging cycle, the rotor moves out of registry with the head port and the pump is sealed. No fuel can enter or leave. Further movement of the rotor aligns the discharge port with an outlet port on the hydraulic head. At the same time the plungers are cammed together, forcing the fuel between the plungers out past the delivery valve and into the appropriate injector line. Figure 6-10 illustrates the discharge cycle.

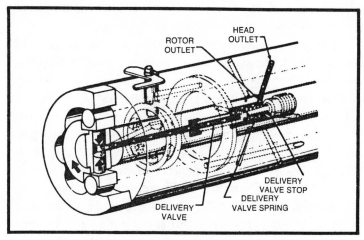

Fig. 6-10. Discharge cycle. (Courtesy Waukesha Motor Co.)

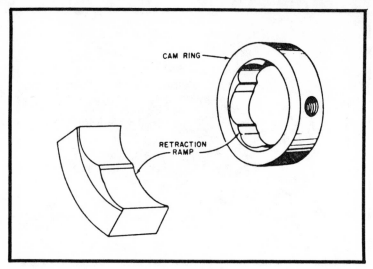

Fig. 6-11. Cam ring with retraction ramps. (Courtesy Waukesha Motor Co.)

The delivery valve is a feature found on a number of distributor and in-line pumps. In this case it takes the form of a spring-loaded slide valve mounted inside of the rotor. Discharge pressure, generated by the cam forcing the pistons together, overcomes the spring tension on the valve and it unseats. At the end of the cycle there is a gradual fall in pressure as the pistons ride over the lobes and settle into the retraction ramps (Fig. 6-11). The discharge valve senses this and closes. As it does, it displaces oil back out of the injector delivery line. Line pressure falls to zero and the injector needle extends, chopping flow in one fell motion.

A section-side leak will introduce air into the circuit. Small amounts of air separate from the oil in the odd corner of the pump, collect, and reenter the oil stream as large bubbles. These bubbles interfere with delivery and, if large enough, destroy the pump's prime. The Roosa pump eliminates most of this with a purge circuit. Some fuel is diverted from the transfer pump side through a passageway running the length of the pump (Fig. 6-12). Oil and the air bubbles collected en route are returned to the tank.

The British CAV system is shown in diagrammatic form in Fig. 6-13. It is distinguished from the Roosa Master by detail differences and by the two low-pressure pumps in conjunction with a second stage of regulation. The pump closest to the tank is known as the feed pump and feeds the vane-type transfer pump. (Most engines have a single low-pressure pump that can be called either a lift or transfer pump.) The legend in the drawing indicates the four pressures at which this system operates. Low pressure is present in the lift pump and return circuits. Transfer pressure is somewhat greater, but always within the limits set by the regulating valve. Some of this pressure is lost across the high-pressure pump head. Highest pressure in the system is present at the injectors.

In-Line Pumps

Figure 6-14 illustrates a typical in-line pump. Each cylinder (in this case six) is fed by its own plunger and delivery valve. The plungers are spring loaded and cam driven through roller tappets. An oil sump supplies lubrication for the camshaft and tappets; the plungers and their bores are lubricated by the fuel.

These pumps are, almost without exception, constant-stroke types. The plungers move the same distance with each revolution of the camshaft. The amount of fuel delivered is determined by the position of the control rod (No. 26 in Fig. 6-14). The rod rotates the plungers to vary the effective stroke. Each plunger has a helical slot running down its outer diameter. When the plunger is at the bottom of its stroke, fuel flows through both ports to fill the interior of the barrel as shown in Fig. 6-15A. As the plunger is cammed upwards,

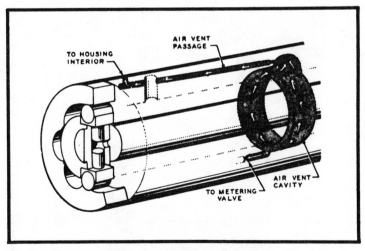

Fig. 6-12. Purge circuit. (Courtesy Waukesha Motor Co.)

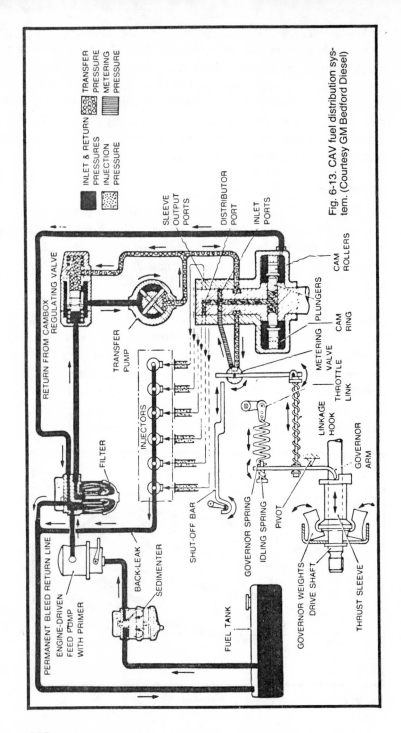

Fig. 6-13. CAV fuel distribution system. (Courtesy GM Bedford Diesel)

TRANSFER PRESSURE
METERING PRESSURE
INLET & RETURN PRESSURES
INJECTION PRESSURE

SLEEVE OUTPUT PORTS
DISTRIBUTOR PORT
INLET PORTS
CAM ROLLERS

RETURN FROM CAMBOX
REGULATING VALVE

TRANSFER PUMP

PLUNGERS
CAM RING

METERING VALVE
THROTTLE LINK

INJECTORS

LINKAGE HOOK
GOVERNOR ARM

SHUT-OFF BAR

GOVERNOR SPRING
IDLING SPRING
PIVOT

BACK-LEAK

PERMANENT BLEED RETURN LINE
ENGINE-DRIVEN FEED PUMP WITH PRIMER

FILTER

SEDIMENTER

FUEL TANK

GOVERNOR WEIGHTS
DRIVE SHAFT

THRUST SLEEVE

228

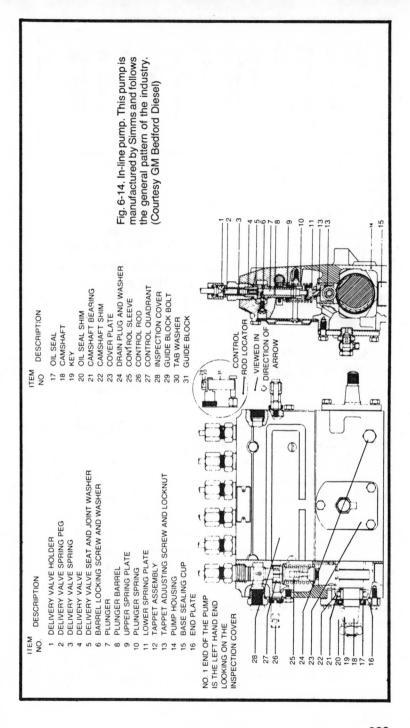

ITEM
NO.   DESCRIPTION
1   DELIVERY VALVE HOLDER
2   DELIVERY VALVE SPRING PEG
3   DELIVERY VALVE SPRING
4   DELIVERY VALVE
5   DELIVERY VALVE SEAT AND JOINT WASHER
6   BARREL LOCKING SCREW AND WASHER
7   PLUNGER
8   PLUNGER BARREL
9   UPPER SPRING PLATE
10   PLUNGER SPRING
11   LOWER SPRING PLATE
12   TAPPET ASSEMBLY
13   TAPPET ADJUSTING SCREW AND LOCKNUT
14   PUMP HOUSING
15   BASE SEALING CUP
16   END PLATE

NO. 1 END OF THE PUMP
IS THE LEFT HAND END
LOOKING ON THE
INSPECTION COVER

ITEM
NO.   DESCRIPTION
17   OIL SEAL
18   CAMSHAFT
19   KEY
20   OIL SEAL SHIM
21   CAMSHAFT BEARING
22   CAMSHAFT SHIM
23   COVER PLATE
24   DRAIN PLUG AND WASHER
25   CONTROL SLEEVE
26   CONTROL ROD
27   CONTROL QUADRANT
28   INSPECTION COVER
29   GUIDE BLOCK BOLT
30   TAB WASHER
31   GUIDE BLOCK

Fig. 6-14. In-line pump. This pump is manufactured by Simms and follows the general pattern of the industry. (Courtesy GM Bedford Diesel)

CONTROL
ROD LOCATOR
VIEWED IN
DIRECTION OF
ARROW

229

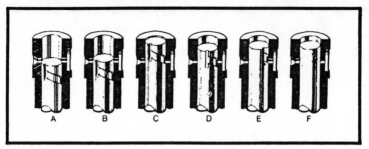

Fig. 6-15. Rotating the plunger varies its effective stroke. (Courtesy GM Bedford Diesel)

some of this fuel is forced out of the ports until the plunger reaches the position shown at B. Further upward movement causes increases in the pressure on the fuel and causes the delivery valve to open the way to the injector. The circuit above the plunger is nearly solid with fuel because of previous operations of the pump. The additional fuel raises line pressure and causes the injector valve to lift off its seat. Fuel discharges into the cylinder.

Injection continues until the edge of the helix uncovers the spill port as shown at C. Fuel in the barrel flows down the vertical recess, into the helix, and out the spill port. Once fuel can escape by any other route than injection, the effective stroke of the pump is over. Fuel delivery begins as soon as the plunger uncovers the spill ports, but is terminated by the helix/spill-port timing. And timing is a function of the rotation of the plunger.

At C the plunger is shown in full-load position, where it delivers a maximum fuel charge. In D the plunger is at half-load; in E it is at idle; and at F the engine is shut-down with no fuel delivery.

Some designs throttle by means of a helix drilled along the pump axis rather than the vertical slot shown in Fig. 6-15.

Most of these pumps employ delivery valves to assure positive injection cutoff. Figure 6-16 illustrates a typical valve. It is threaded into the pump body in series with the injector line. Pump pressure unseats the valve and the pressure loss as the plunger uncovers the spillway causes the valve to close. In closing, the valve displaces some fuel from the injector line. The injector senses this fall in line pressure and closes.

Some pumps incorporate a fuel timer. Ignition delay is relatively constant. It takes about as long for the fuel to ignite at 4000 rpm as it does at idle. High-speed turbulence speeds events somewhat, but not so much as to be significant. A fuel timer advances pump delivery with rpm in the way that a centrifugal advance mechanism advances ignition timing in a gasoline engine. Both are energized by weights that are centrifuged outward and both are sandwiched between the lobe and drive ends of their respective camshafts. Not surprisingly, both mechanisms are constructed on similar lines.

Pump-Supply Circuits

Injector pumps have poor suction ability and must be primed by an external source. The source is variously known as the low-pressure, lift, or transfer pump. Its primary purpose is to supply the injector pump, although a few designs give it some small metering function as well.

The pumps, filters, and other fittings that make up the supply circuit are familiar to lift-truck mechanics. Some components, such as the automotive-type supply pump and first-stage filter, are similar to those used on gasoline trucks. Up-line filtration and gear or vane pumps are functionally no different than those encountered in hydraulic circuits. Further discussion is unnecessary.

FUEL SYSTEM SERVICE

The most critical aspect of fuel system service is preventive maintenance. Dirt and water are responsible for more fuel-system

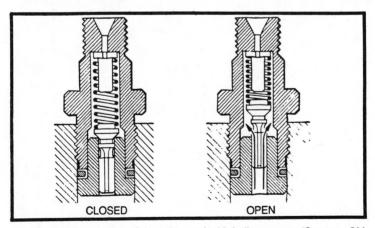

Fig. 6-16. Delivery valve of the type used with in-line pumps (Courtesy GM Bedford Diesel).

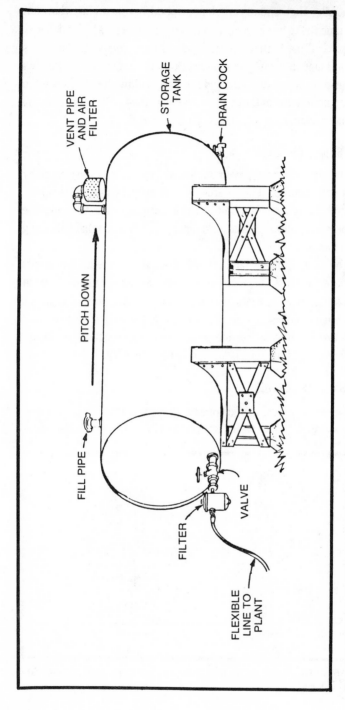

Fig. 6-17. Permanent fuel storage facility. Note the filters at the vent and discharge line, and the provision for sediment drain. (Courtesy Onan)

failures than all other causes put together. Great care must be exercised to keep the fuel clean in storage, during transfer to the vehicle, and once aboard. Since diesel fuel is by no means virginal as it comes from the refinery, the storage tank or drum must be tilted away from the outlet valve as shown in Fig. 6-17. Some fuel is lost in this manner, but the loss will be more than compensated for by the reduced level of sediment in the fuel used. It is strongly suggested that the storage outlet be fitted with a strainer to reduce the load on the truck's filter system.

The fuel filler cap and the transfer equipment should be wiped off and the fuel transferred in a clean environment. Refueling in the open in the rain is emphatically not recommended. The filtration system on the truck is usually adequate as supplied. In almost all cases you will find at least two stages of filtration in collaboration with a sediment bowl. The bowl is necessary to trap water, and should be cleaned periodically. Filter elements must be replaced on schedule or, if you own records indicate the need, ahead of schedule. Figure 6-18 illustrates one common type of filter. It is secured by a central bolt entering from the top. Loosen the bolt enough to disengage and carefully remove the bowl. Clean it in solvent and replace the element. The adjacent bolt is for bleeding.

Bleeding the System

Bleeding (deaerating) is necessary after the system has been opened and assembled. The technique requires priming the system by hand to put a slight pressure on it and cracking one or more bleed screws. The priming mechanism is a manual lever associated with the supply or low-pressure pump. The location of the bleeding screws varies a bit, but will be on the filters and on the injector pump (Fig. 6-18). Wipe off the bleeder screw tops and the adjacent areas to prevent dirt from entering the system. Working from the tank forward, crack the bleeder screws and tighten when fuel discharges in a steady stream. If much air is in the system it may be necessary to open the line fittings at the injectors. Continue to keep pressure up with the primer and crack one union at a time. Hold open until the bubbles disappear. Run the engine for a quarter of an hour to insure complete purging.

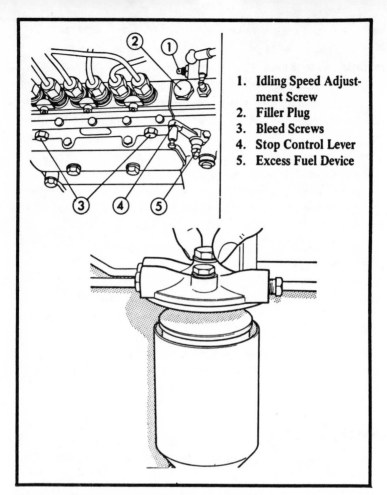

1. Idling Speed Adjustment Screw
2. Filler Plug
3. Bleed Screws
4. Stop Control Lever
5. Excess Fuel Device

Fig. 6-18. Bleeder-screw arrangement for an in-line pump. (Courtesy Ford Engine & Turbine Operations)

Fuel Lines

Check the low-pressure lines as you would any gasoline fuel line. That is, inspect for leaks, abrasions, and periodically snug up the fittings. The high-pressure lines between the remote pump and the injectors are another matter entirely. These lines are constructed of heavy-duty, seamless-steel tubing and appear to be indestructible. Unfortunately, this is not true. The lines grow and swell with each surge of pump pressure and can be permanently distorted by overtightening the fittings (see Fig. 6-19) or by improperly installed hold-down brackets. Untorqued connections will not always leak, but will allow the ferrule to move up and down in its fitting. Eventually the ferrule and the fitting wear and the seal is destroyed. Discard any lines that are damaged in this manner, as well as any that are dented or nicked. Small imperfections act as stress risers.

Injector Tests

The injectors are the most vulnerable elements in the system and should be suspected any time there are problems associated with one or two cylinders. Symptoms include black or white smoke, detonation, and missing under load. Locating the faulty injector is no problem. Unit injectors can be disabled one at a time with a prybar held against the cam follower. Note the rpm drop as each injector is taken out—the injector that has least effect on rpm is faulty. Pump-fed injectors are isolated by cracking their fuel lines enough to relieve pressure. Another method is to remove the exhaust manifold and observe the exhaust flame.

If a special tool is required for injector removal, it should be supplied with the engine. Disconnect the high-pressure fuel line at both ends, remove its hold-down hardware, and cap the line to prevent dirt from entering. Removal of unit injectors involves disassembly of the associated rocker arm and the control rack. Replace

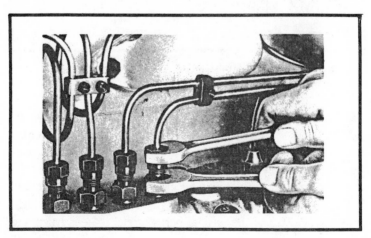

Fig. 6-19. Use a backup wrench on high-pressure fittings. (Courtesy GM Bedford Diesel)

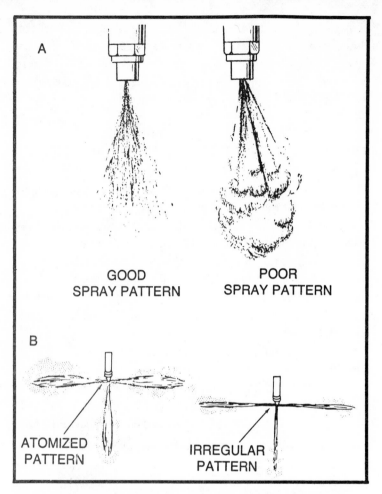

Fig. 6-20. Spray patterns. (A) Pintle nozzle used in Onan engines. (B) 120° multihole Waukesha nozzle.

the injector with a new or known good one. Carefully pull down the flange nuts to seat the injector square. Start the engine and listen for possible air leaks around the injector body. Correct the problem as necessary and test under load.

The spray pattern of pump-fed injectors can be quickly checked by removing the injector from the engine and connecting the high-pressure line. Crank the engine, being careful to keep hands and eyes clear of the oil spray. The pressures involved drive the oil through human tissue.

The desired pattern varies with injector types and with specific applications. Figure 6-20 illustrates correct and faulty patterns for representative pintle and multihole nozzles. Of the two, the pintle pattern is the most used. Multihole nozzles come in many configurations and the correct pattern can vary a great deal from the one shown here. As a general rule, the pattern should be symmetrical and defined. It should be free of oil drops, solid streams, and, at the same time, free of mist that may form in miniature clouds near the outer edges of the pattern.

If there is any choice in the matter, avoid disassembly of a nozzle unless you have access to a tester (Fig. 6-21) and the experience to use it. The tester allows a better fix on the pattern than an engine test, and allows the nozzle to be checked and calibrated for opening pressure. Mount the injector body in the fixture provided and place a cup under the nozzle to contain the spray. Fill the reservoir on the tester with clean diesel oil or, as per manufacturer's specification, kerosene. Pump the handle a few times to bleed the lines. This should be sufficient; if not, raise pressure and crack the bleeder screw on the tester. Close the screw while the system is still pressurized. Once you are satisfied that system is free of air, slowly bring the pressure up. Observe the gauge reading when the nozzle opens. This is, of course, the opening pressure and should be within specification.

Low opening pressure is the most common complaint. It may be caused by a weak valve spring. Most injectors allow some takeup

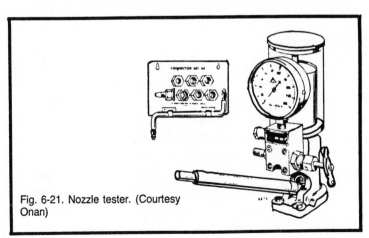

Fig. 6-21. Nozzle tester. (Courtesy Onan)

of spring tension. Bosch, for example, supplies shims while CAV and American Bosch favor an adjustment screw. If a screw is present it will not be possible to accurately assemble the unit without making an opening-pressure test. Another possibility is wear on the valve. Excessive opening pressure is usually caused by carbon accumulations on the nozzle tip.

The nozzle should hold at least 20% of opening pressure without dribble. Failure to do so means that it must be disassembled, cleaned, and have its sealing surfaces lapped.

Injector Repair Facilities

Injector service is serious business. In addition to a nozzle tester, you will need a tool kit designed for injector work (in many instances, for the injector at hand), and a place to work that is isolated from the rest of the shop. Ideally, the work should be carried on in a clean room, fed filtered and dehumidified air at slightly above atmospheric pressure. Tools and the room itself should be spotless and the service people should wear shop coats or overalls, heavily starched to minimize lint. Benches should be covered with linoleum, finished masonite, or varnished hardwood. Soft wood bench tops collect dirt and steel tops can damage dropped parts. Several porcelain or glass trays are needed for fuel oil and solvents. Fit the trays with brass screens supported on 1/2 inch blocks to hold the parts above the sediment. Muzzle vise jaws with copper or fiber inserts, and use paper shop towels as mats upon which the parts can be placed.

Injector Repairs

I will confine my remarks to generalities; specific information about injector breakdown and calibration will be found in your engine manual. It is important to remember that injector parts are not interchangeable. To eliminate the possibility of confusion and subsequent grief, disassemble only one injector at a time.

The purpose of this operation is to inspect the internal parts, smooth out small imperfections, and remove all traces of carbon and gum. Some care must be taken not to scratch or score the injector during cleaning. Treat the lapped surfaces with the greatest respect—if at all possible, do not even touch the lapped parts with your fingers. As a further safeguard against corrosion and to provide starting lubrication, assemble the injector with oil. If the injector is to be stored, charge it with test oil; don't use diesel oil because it sometimes oxidizes and gums.

The injector tool kit consists of a collection of steel and hardwood scrapers (similar to those dentists use to clean teeth), reamers, hardwood burnishing tools, and steel needles. Light heat discolorations and surface scratches are removed with a burnishing stick or a polishing pad dipped in tallow. Scrapers and reamers are used to clear carbon from internal passageways. Pintle-nozzle orifices are polished with tapered hardwood sticks, and needles are used to open multihole nozzles. The needle should be held in a pin vise so that it extends 1/16 inch for the first cleaning operation. As carbon is dislodged, the needle is relocated to extend in increments of 1/8 inch. If the nozzle is frosted over with carbon, flake enough of it off to define the orifice. Extend the needle about 1/32 inch and lightly tap on it with a small mallet. The work goes faster if you soak the nozzle in solvent. If axial holes are present, clean these last since dirt dislodged from the orifices will lodge here.

Some injectors—notably American Bosch—require an assembly sleeve to center the nozzle in the nozzle cap. Torque the cap nut to specification and remove the sleeve.

Brass wire brushes can be used on injector sleeves (the tubular part that mates the injector body to the head) and on the after sections of the injector body. It is not recommended that the tips be wire brushed. Steel and power-driven brushes have no place in this operation.

Injector Pump Repairs

Pump failure can be distinguished from injector failure by the process of elimination. If a new injector does not solve the problem and engine systems (compression, etc.) are okay, the pump must be at fault. Pump performance is verified with a fuel pump test stand (FPTS). These instruments are highly sophisticated—typical specifications call for infinitely variable hydrostatic drives, 60 pound flywheels, built-in oil heaters and coolers, full-pressure lubrication, and a bank of gauges as accurate as any you will find in a laboratory

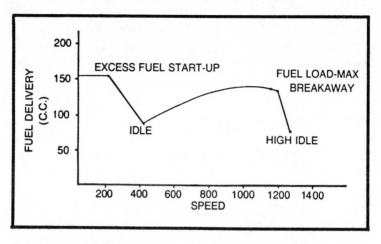

Fig. 6-22. Hypothetical fuel delivery curve. While the values differ the profile of this curve is typical of all diesel engines. (Courtesy Bacharach Instrument Co., Div. of Ambac Industries, Inc.)

Operating a FPTS is a profession in itself, requiring special training and a dedication to precision work.

The purpose of the FPTS is to check pump calibration against its theoretical output curve (Fig. 6-22). This curve differs between engines and is affected by environmental factors. For example, some pumps are so sensitive that a 10° change in oil temperature causes a 7 to 9% change in delivery pressure with a volume change of 2 to 3 cc.

Pump calibration and pump overhaul—one is tantamount to the other—are beyond the average shop. It is much wiser to turn the pump over to specialists for this work.

Prior to pump removal, scrub the pump body and mounting flange with solvent and blow dry. Bar the engine over to identify the timing marks for refitting. Remove the fuel lines and pump oil lines (if so fitted). Cap off all connections and clean the pump a second time now that all surfaces are accessible. The pump must be spotless before it is put on the FPTS.

Timing

The timing drill varies, but the purpose is to synchronize the No. 1 plunger or (in the case of distribution pumps) the No. 1 hydraulic head port with No. 1 cylinder.

There are two reference marks. One mark is on the engine proper and may be found on the harmonic balancer or flywheel. The second is usually in plain sight on the pump. This mark references the position of the plunger at the moment of fuel delivery. Both have to be aligned so that they pass their pointers at the same instant. Most engines have a provision for pump adjustment at the drive coupling; IHC engines with integral pumps fix the adjustment with timing marks.

The usual approaches to timing are limited by injector delay. The pump pressure wave takes approximately 0.0005 second to travel from the plunger to the injector. This delay sounds insignificant, but occupies some 9° of crankshaft rotation at high speed. Engine manufacturers are aware of the problem and advance the timing in an effort to compensate. But the amount of advance must be a compromise.

The way around this is to time the engine with reference to the pressure wave. A strobe light is triggered by a transducer spliced into the injector side of No. 1 fuel line. Signal voltage generated by the transducer switches current from the engine's electrical system or from an external source to the xenon bulb. The bulb fires in sychronization with pressure pulses in No. 1 line. Because it has no afterglow, its beam gives the illusion of stopping motion. The pump drive is adjusted until the engine timing mark aligns with its pointer. Some lights feature a dial-in delay for checking timer operation and a tachometer. It is no longer necessary for a helper to hold a mechanical tachometer against the crankshaft pulley while the mechanic adjusts the governor.

Electrical Systems

Engined trucks have a fairly elaborate electrical system including a starter motor, AC or DC generator, regulator, battery, and in the case of gas and LPG trucks, an ignition system.

IGNITION SYSTEMS

Two systems are in use. Their differences involve the way in which the high-voltage current is generated. Spark plugs, ignition cable, and (with modifications) distributor caps and rotors are shared by both. The conventional battery-and-coil system has sparked engines since the century began and remains the most popular of the two. Solid-state or transistorized ignitions as they are sometimes called have been around for more than twenty years, but have only recently gained mass acceptance. The pure solid-state system that does away entirely with the contact points makes it easier to meet Environmental Protection Agency emissions regulations. Passenger and light-truck engines must remain clean for 50,000 miles with only minor adjustments. Because of the reliability of solid-state components, this is more likely to happen than with the conventional system. In addition, the intense and sudden voltage generated by solid-state ignitions allows spark plugs to be gapped wider for surer ignition. While EPA emissions regulations do not apply to lift trucks, the existence of these high-reliability systems has encouraged lift-truck builders to specify them. The owner benefits from reduced maintenance and less down time.

Spark Plugs

Ignition commences when a spark arcs between the ground or side terminal and the central electrode. The spark must be intense enough to arc against cylinder compression in an atmosphere that is clouded by fuel and varying amounts of oil. The firing tip is swept by gases that can be as hot as 5000°F and alternatively cooled by the fresh charge during the intake stroke. The spark plug must also be mechanically strong enough to withstand combustion pressures and occasional detonation. The metal shell has to hold up under the forces generated during installation and the much greater forces that can be required for removal. It is no wonder that spark plugs are the most vulnerable parts of the system.

Spark-plug malfunctions usually show up as slight missing under load and during acceleration. This symptom is accompanied by hard starting and progressively gets worse as the misfiring plugs become oil and fuel soaked. Eventually the plugs refuse to fire at all.

The brand of spark plug that you use is a matter of personal preference. The major brands are pretty much identical—at least in so far as lift trucks are concerned. But there are other differences. The most obvious is the thread diameter. Most truck heads are tapped for a 14 mm thread; Ford, early Continental, and a few others use 18 mm. Flat seats require a gasket while the tapered variety are intended to make metal-to-metal contact. While I'm on this point, it is possible to repair a stripped out 14 mm port by reaming and tapping the threads to 18 mm. If the other characteristics of the replacement plug match the originals, this expedient will work. However, it is wiser to either replace the head or else install the appropriate Heli-Coil or Tap-Loc insert. These thread renewal inserts are available in all standard inch and metric threads.

The reach is the distance from the end of the threads to the seat. In lift trucks this dimension varies from 3/8 inch to 1 1/4 inches. Using a short-reach plug where a long one is called for wastes fuel and can cause hard starting in the bargain. If the proper plugs are installed later, there is a good chance of stripping the

Fig. 7-1. This spark plug was installed improperly. (Courtesy AC Spark Plug Div., GM Corp.)

threads since the lower threads will be filled over with carbon. Using a plug of excessive reach can mean a shattered piston.

The style of the firing tip is also important. Many modern trucks use plugs with elongated tips extending below the threads.

In recent years extended-tip plugs—with the firing tips protruding beyond the threads—have become popular. These plugs benefit from the scrubbing action of the gases and have a broader heat range than conventional shielded-tip plugs. But check the interchange chart before you substitute one, since the tip adds a quarter inch or so to the reach.

Heat range is another variable and one that is not obvious from merely looking at the plug. The ideal temperature of the firing tip is 900°F. At this temperature the tip is cool enough so that there is no possibility of self-ignition and warm enough to keep most of the carbon burned off. The heat range depends upon the length of the thermal path from the tip to the relatively cold spark-plug seat and upon the shape of the insulator. Full-bodied insulators that take up most of the area above the firing tip provide a broad thermal path and tend to keep tip temperatures down.

A plug that is too cold for the engine in question quickly carbons over. One that is too hot encourages detonation and can, in extreme cases, act as a glow plug and ignite the mixture before the spark.

The heat range is stenciled on the insulator. While each manufacturer has his own code, American made plugs get hotter as the number goes up. An AC 45 is one step hotter than an AC 44. The reverse is true with foreign plugs—the higher the number the colder the plug.

There is only one way to change spark plugs without showering dirt down into the cylinder and without chancing a blowout. The photograph in Fig. 7-1 shows a relatively mild blowout. It is mild because the threads have been spared and the head can be reused. Heat from the spark-plug tip travels up through the insulator and into the shell. It escapes back into the water jacket via the seat. A particle of dirt or a thin film of carbon on the area of the head under the seat can block the heat path. The spark plug progressively gets hotter and, before many ignition cycles, melts with the results shown here. In honesty, blowout is rare even on engines that are casually maintained. But it can happen if this procedure is not followed:

1. Loosen the old plug two or three turns.
2. Blow out the dirt and residue from around the plug with compressed air.
3. Remove the old plug and inspect.
4. Clean the port and seat area before installing a new plug.

It is suggested that you use a thread chaser of the type shown in Fig. 7-2. It will dress the threads and clean the port area in one simple operation.

Assuming that the spark-plug's heat range is correct, the color and texture of deposits on the firing tip reveal a great deal about the engine. Light brown or tan deposits mean that combustion temperatures are normal. It can be confidently supposed that the ignition timing and fuel mixture are correct. Black, fluffy deposits point to

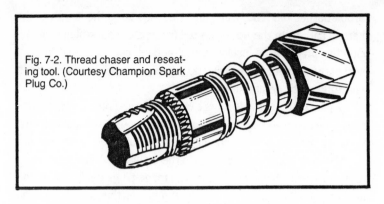

Fig. 7-2. Thread chaser and reseating tool. (Courtesy Champion Spark Plug Co.)

cold combustion and imply that the spark plug has chronically misfired or that the mixture is fuel rich. Wet, oily deposits mean that the chambers are flooded with oil and may indicate that an engine overhaul is in order. The firing tip bleaches white as temperatures rise. In severe cases the firing tip is bone white and the side electrode shows blue temper marks. Check for too much ignition advance, excessively lean fuel mixtures, and intake manifold leaks.

Spark-plug gap varies with the engine make and model, and is normally set wider than original specifications when LPG fuel is used. A spark plug-feeler gauge uses wire elements for accuracy with eroded electrodes and has bending notches in the gauge handle. Insert the side electrode in the appropriate notch and bend until the specified wire just slips between it and the fixed center electrode.

While few lift-truck mechanics bother to torque spark plugs, the additional effort pays for itself in the long run. Overtightened plugs can be a bear to remove and can distort the head enough to affect valve seating. Undertightened plugs tend to overheat and have been known to unthread and eject themselves from the port.

Start the plugs by hand and torque to these specifications:

	Torque (ft-lb)	
Thread	Aluminum Heads	Cast-Iron Heads
14 mm	18 – 22	26 – 30
14 mm (tapered)	10 – 15	10 – 15
18 mm	28 – 34	32 – 38
18 mm (tapered)	15 – 20	15 – 25
7/8 in. × 18	31 – 39	35 – 43

Spark-Plug Cables

From a maintenance standpoint, metal core-cables are preferred over the carbon-film type currently in vogue. The major service problem with "wire wires" is leakage through the insulation and that takes years to become serious. But these wires cause problems in radio communications. Ham radio operators may remember the old spark-gap transmitters. An ignition system is the same thing and metallic wires serve as the broadcast antenna. The signal generated by the spark-plug gap is radiated by the wires, causing static in nearby radios and a blip-blop pattern on television screens.

Carbon-filament wires cut down on broadcast interference because they introduce a certain amount of resistance into the spark gap circuit that dampens radio-frequency oscillations. Typical resistance values for new wire are on the order of 1000 ohms per inch. But this value tends to increase dramatically with age. The plastic filament that serves as a binder for the carbon granules develops hairline cracks in response to engine vibration, temperature extremes, and handling. These cracks are barriers to current flow and enough of them can send resistance readings to infinity.

Metal-core wires are usually checked by ear—the mechanic listens for the telltale crack of a spark arcing outside of the engine. Another way is to run the vehicle in the dark and watch for miniature lightning displays. Conductor failure is rare and usually betrays itself as smoked insulation around the hot spot.

TVRS cable is sold in sets. Metallic-core cable can be purchased in bulk and the terminal crimped on with a tool like the one shown in Fig. 7-3.

The first sign of failure of carbon-filament wires is a periodic interruption blink of the timing light. This interruption is of short duration, but is quite pronounced and cannot be confused with the normal flicker of the strobe light. It may increase in frequency with rpm or can be immune to changes in engine speed. A resistance check can also be helpful, although it is not 100% reliable. Connect the ohmmeter between the terminals and watch the needle while you gently bend the cable. Resistance should remain constant at something less than 15,000 ohms per foot.

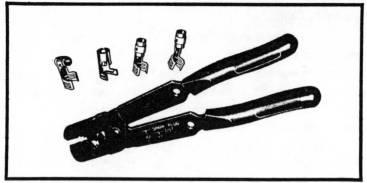

Fig. 7-3. Spark-plug cable crimping tool. (Courtesy American Parts Co., Inc.)

One more point: the most important single wire in the system runs between the coil and the distributor cap. Defects in it are mirrored in all the others.

Conventional Distributors

As far as the mechanic is concerned, the distinguishing mark of conventional distributors is the presence of a contact-point set and a condenser. The contact points are wired in series with the battery (Fig. 7-4). The feed or primary circuit runs from the battery, through the ignition switch, the primary windings of the coil, and to the point contacts to ground. The movable contact is "hot" and the fixed arm contact is the ground return through the distributor plate.

The movable contact is held against the distributor cam by the point spring. The cam rotates at half engine speed (since there is one ignition event every second crankshaft revolution) and has as many lobes as there are cylinders. As the cam turns, it pivots the movable contact away from the fixed contact, breaking the primary circuit.

A little theory is needed to understand how breaking a low-voltage circuit creates a high-voltage spark. The coil is the heart of the matter. It consists of two separate coils of wire wound over a laminated iron form. The primary winding, the winding that is controlled by the points, amounts to a few hundred turns of heavy wire. The secondary winding can have as many as 20,000 turns of wire. One side is grounded internally in the coil and the free end goes out to the high-tension cable. Because very little current flows in the secondary, fine hair-like wire is adequate.

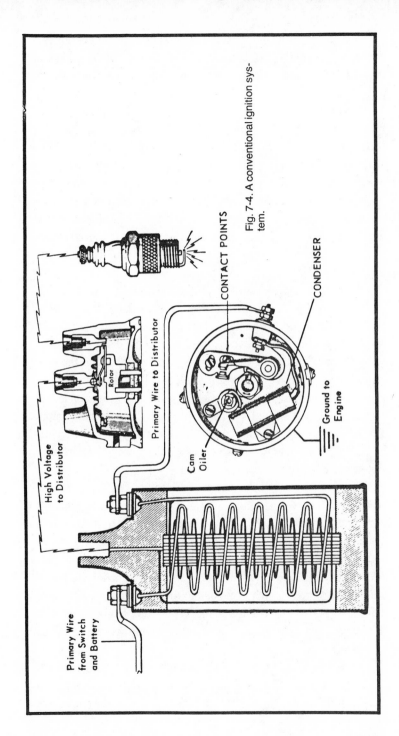

High Voltage
to Distributor

Primary Wire to Distributor

CONTACT POINTS

CONDENSER

Rotor

Ground to
Engine

Cam
Oiler

Primary Wire
from Switch
and Battery

Fig. 7-4. A conventional ignition system.

When the points are closed, the primary winding generates a strong magnetic field inside the coil. This field is the byproduct of current and is intensified by the close proximity of the windings and the iron core. When the points open, the field collapses in upon itself. Magnetic lines of force pass through the secondary windings. Current is generated whenever a conductor is subject to a moving magnetic field. The intensity of the current is a matter of the strength of the field and the rate of its movement. In this case, the field is moderately strong and collapse is almost instantaneous. The voltage generated in the secondary is a function of the voltage of the primary and the turns ratio of the two windings. Typical ignition coils have a primary/secondary turns ratio of 100:1. If the coil were completely efficient, the secondary would generate 100 volts, directly proportional to the turns ratio.

The condenser (known by the electrical trades as a capacitor) is a kind of electrical storage bin. It is wired in parallel with the points; that is, the hot lead to the condenser is connected to the primary circuit and the condenser body is grounded to the distributor plate. Electrons that would arc and melt the point contacts find the condenser a more attractive proposition, and collect there instead.

And by discouraging arcing as the points open, the condenser adds energy to the secondary. This is because the secondary output depends in part upon an abrupt collapse of the primary magnetic field. Without the condenser, the collapse is prolonged, which promotes arcing across the contacts.

Distributor Caps. Corrosion develops on the tower inserts (particularly if they are aluminum instead of copper), at the upper or terminal end, and below where the high-voltage current arcs from the rotor. This corrosion should be removed since it adds resistance to the circuit. Clean the terminal end with a wire brush designed for the purpose, and the lower end with emery cloth or a knife blade. The inserts should be tightly molded to the cap. Play or evidence of collision with the rotor means that the wrong rotor has been installed or that the distributor bearings are excessively worn. Repair as necessary.

Figure 7-5 shows the most common cause of cap failure. Mechanics call these jagged traces "cracks" and blame them on thermal shock or the blind workings of fate. Actually, they are spark

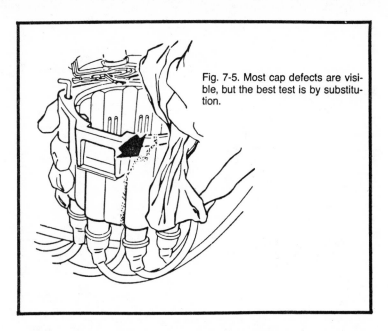

Fig. 7-5. Most cap defects are visible, but the best test is by substitution.

paths and have nothing to do with any failure of the cap material. The origin of these paths is not completely understood, although it is agreed that deposits of metal vaporized from the inserts and rotor tip are involved. At any rate, once these paths appear, the cap is ruined and must be replaced.

Some distributor caps have a carbon button under the center insert. Inspect the button for wear, breakage, and (on the spring-loaded variety) for freedom of movement.

Rotors. The rotor shown in Fig. 7-6A is the type familiar to generations of mechanics. It is secured to the shaft by a spring clip or plastic indent. The Delco Remy shown next to it is a fairly new

Fig. 7-6. View A shows the rotor used in many Continental engines; view B the Delco Remy type used on some Elgin, Hyster, and IHC engines. (Courtesy American Parts Co., Inc.)

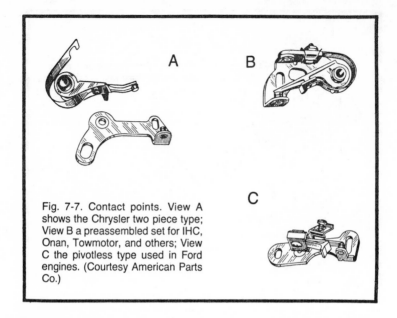

Fig. 7-7. Contact points. View A shows the Chrysler two piece type; View B a preassembled set for IHC, Onan, Towmotor, and others; View C the pivotless type used in Ford engines. (Courtesy American Parts Co.)

design that has had some rather mysterious teething problems. But shaft engagement is positive. The rotor fits over a square and a round peg and is secured by two machine screws.

Rotor failure can cause erratic timing, misfiring, or outright refusal to start. Visual checks are not definitive, but look carefully at the contact spring, the rivet that holds the metal element to the insulator, and the rotor/shaft socket. Error introduced by free movement of the rotor is multiplied by two at the crankshaft.

Contact Points. Aside from the spark plugs, the contact points are the most vulnerable part of the system. And it is no wonder. Assuming that we have a four-cylinder truck that has gone 1000 hours since the last point change and has averaged 1000 rpm over this period, the contacts have opened 120,000,000 times. And, if your mind runs this way, you might like to know that the rubbing block, the phenolic strip that bears against the cam, has traveled some 3000 miles over that 1-inch cam.

Point failure usually involves the contacts (Fig. 7-7). Some arcing and the resultant puddling of the tungsten contacts is inevitable. Each time this happens, a thin film of oxide is formed that floats to the surface. Tungsten oxide is highly resistive, and before very many million arcs the points cease to conduct. Rubbing-block wear gradually closes the contact gap, advancing the ignition as the gap narrows. Eventually, the contacts are so close together that the primary circuit arcs between them. Spring failure is fairly rare (at least on factory original parts) but is by no means unknown. The spring may break or simply grow fatigued and lose tension. When this happens, the points "float" on the cam and miss a lobe or so at high speed.

Before installing a point set, wipe the distributor plate clean. A film of oil or, for that matter, a greasy fingerprint is enough to defeat primary current. Handle the replacement point set with care and do not touch the tungsten contacts. Temporarily tighten the hold-down screw and check the contact alignment. The contacts should meet squarely and across their full width. Bend the movable arm as necessary.

Crank the engine to bring the rubbing block up on the highest part of the cam lobe. In this position, the points are separated to their fullest extent. Slightly loosen the mounting screw and move the fixed arm until a specified feeler gauge just passes through the gap. Figure 7-8 shows this operation. Note the use of a round gauge. Besides speeding the work, a round gauge is less liable than the flat type to contaminate the contacts. This particular point set is notched for a screwdriver; earlier types often employed a cam. Be sure to recheck the gap after you tighten the hold-down screw.

Condenser. Condenser failure has several symptoms. A shorted or open condenser will cause excessive point arcing and

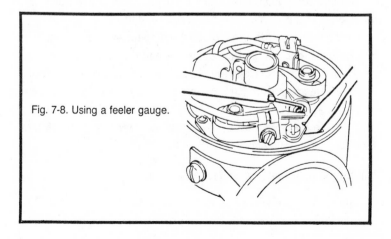

Fig. 7-8. Using a feeler gauge.

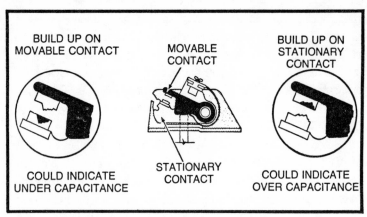

Fig. 7-9. Effects of over- and under-capacitance on point contacts. (Courtesy Kohler of Kohler)

rapid failure of the contacts. With the condenser completely out, one or two cam revolutions is enough to vaporize the contacts. Excessive or insufficient condenser capacity causes metal to migrate from one contact to the other. Under-capacitance is shown by buildup on the movable or hot contact; over-capacitance by buildup on the grounded contact (Fig. 7-9).

Because condenser operation and point life are so intimately related, most mechanics change both components together. While this may offer some insurance (particularly if name-brand condensers are used), it is wasteful since a condenser lasts five or six times longer than the typical point set.

Before replacing the condenser, check it with a tester (it'll pay for itself). Three checks are required: condenser capacity (many new condensers fail this), leakage (the amount of current that can leak between one side of the condenser and the other), and series resistance (the resistance in the pigtail lead and the ground circuit).

One thing to watch for: when installing a Continental condenser, make sure the spaghetti is there (it may be missing) and in place on the condenser strap. Do not allow this strap to touch the distributor plate and short out. (See Fig. 7-10.)

Solid-State Distribution Systems

Solid-state systems differ from battery-and-coil systems in the way the primary (low-voltage) current is switched. The high-voltage circuit together with the vacuum and centrifugal advance mechanisms remains unchanged, and the coils are essentially the same.

Instead of contact points and condenser, lift-truck versions of these systems switch by means of a toothed *reluctor* (armature) and a magnetic pickup coil (Fig. 7-11). The reluctor is mounted on the distributor shaft and rotates with it. It has as many teeth as the engine has cylinders. The pickup coil is located on the distributor plate and consists of a coil of fine wire around a permanent magnet. The shape of the magnet varies: Delco's version has a pair of teeth that match the reluctor teeth; Ford and Prestolite magnets are in the form of the letter *C* with the open end toward the reluctor.

So long as it is undisturbed, the magnetic field remains stable. It makes a circuit through the magnet (and the pickup coil) and across an air gap. This gap is defined by the tooth-like projections on the Delco version or by the break in the others. In this stable condition the pickup coil can generate no voltage. For voltage to appear, the coil must be subjected to a changing magnetic field.

Operation. Figure 7-12 illustrates the operation of a typical unit. In view A, the reluctor has turned so that a tooth begins to enter the magnetic field. The field distorts to include the reluctor in its circuit. The distortion of the field increases the intensity of the magnetic field surrounding the coil windings, so a small voltage is generated. As the reluctor continues to turn, the tooth comes into perfect alignment (view B) with the center of the magnet, and the magnetic field stops increasing. As the tooth continues to turn (view C), the magnetic field rapidly decreases, inducing a voltage of opposite polarity in the pickup coil. It is at the point of alignment (view B), when the voltage falls to zero as it is reversing polarity, that the module is triggered to chop the primary current through the ignition

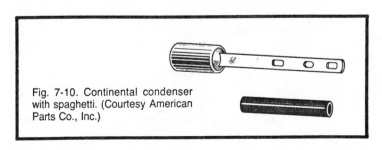

Fig. 7-10. Continental condenser with spaghetti. (Courtesy American Parts Co., Inc.)

255

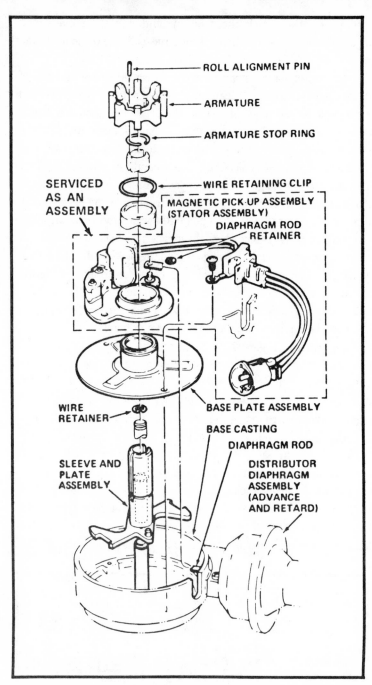

ROLL ALIGNMENT PIN

ARMATURE

ARMATURE STOP RING

WIRE RETAINING CLIP

SERVICED AS AN ASSEMBLY

MAGNETIC PICK-UP ASSEMBLY (STATOR ASSEMBLY)

DIAPHRAGM ROD RETAINER

BASE PLATE ASSEMBLY

WIRE RETAINER

BASE CASTING

DIAPHRAGM ROD

SLEEVE AND PLATE ASSEMBLY

DISTRIBUTOR DIAPHRAGM ASSEMBLY (ADVANCE AND RETARD)

Fig. 7-11. The Ford version of the solid state ignition.

coil. As with conventional systems, interruption of the primary current induces a high voltage in the coil's secondary winding.

While the voltage is generated mechanically by rotation of the reluctor, the zero or null point is defined electrically. Signal polarity reverses as the reluctor swings into and then away from the magnet. The null point is the instant that the direction of current (polarity) reverses.

The module is an electronic switch that controls current flow to the coil. It is sealed in epoxy and may be finned for heat dissipation. On most applications, the module is mounted on the forward engine-compartment bulkhead, although it can be integral with the distributor. The circuit is fairly complex and is, at any rate, non-repairable.

Troubleshooting. As far as the primary side of the system is concerned, there is little that a technician can do other than to replace defective components. Test procedures require an ohmmeter and, in some cases, a low-range voltmeter. These procedures

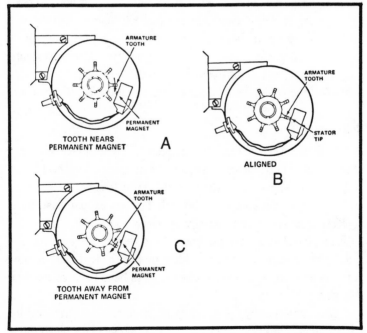

Fig. 7-12. Reluctor movement triggers switches primary current. (Courtesy Ford Customer Service Div.)

Fig. 7-13. A somewhat atypical ignition coil found on 6V IHC engines. (Courtesy American Parts Co., Inc.)

are detailed in the mechanism's service literature. Follow these cautions:

1. Never run the engine with any part of the system—including the battery—out of the circuit.
2. Make voltage checks with a voltmeter and not a screwdriver. Grounding a hot terminal will destroy the module.
3. Remove the battery from the vehicle before charging.
4. Pay careful attention to battery polarity. Most solid-state systems cannot tolerate reversed polarity.
5. Disconnect the solid-state components before arc welding.

Coils

Coil failure can be difficult to diagnose. It may appear as a miss under acceleration (sometimes coupled with spitback and backfire at high rpm) or as a refusal to start. The best way to check a coil is with an automotive oscilloscope, although few shops purchase such sophisticated equipment. Relatively inexpensive coil testers are available, but they are temperamental and require frequent recalibration against known good coils. Most mechanics test coils by substitution after all other system components have been checked or changed.

Like most purely electrical parts, coils can be purchased by specification. The critical differences are the type of terminals (note the male high tension terminal in the IHC coil shown in Fig. 7-13),

258

the battery voltage, and whether or not the coil is internally ballasted. Ford and Chrysler engines require an external ballast resistor while Continental and most others have the ballast built into the coil.

The primary terminals are marked positive (+) and negative (−). It is important that these connections be made correctly. Crossing them will reverse the output polarity. Instead of electronics moving from the hot center electrode of the spark plugs, they will travel from the side electrode. Since electrons do not like to move against heat, the voltage required to fire the plugs will increase as much as 40% and timing may be affected.

An oscilloscope shows reversed polarity by displaying the first coil oscillation upside down. Spark-gap coil testers peg their meters on zero. But an ordinary lead pencil and a pair of nylon ignition pliers will also indicate polarity. Disconnect one of the cables at the spark plug and insert the pencil in the spark path as shown in Fig. 7-14. The arc should splatter on the spark plug side of the pencil-lead tip, regardless of the polarity of the vehicle's electrical system.

Vacuum Advance

High vacuum develops at part throttle in the intake manifold and a small amount of air enters the cylinder. Under these high-turbulence conditions the engine will accept more than usual advance and be happier for it. The vacuum advance mechanism (Fig. 7-15) senses manifold vacuum and dials in additional advance.

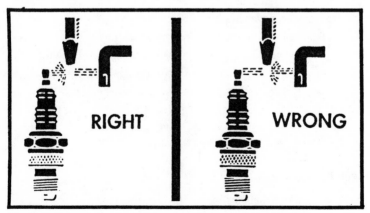

Fig. 7-14. Coil polarity check. (Courtesy Champion Spark Plug Co.)

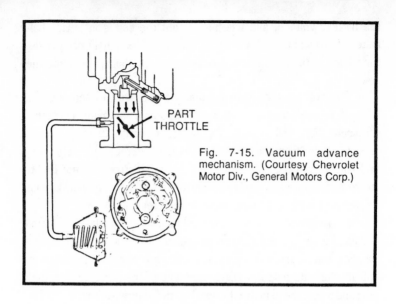

Fig. 7-15. Vacuum advance mechanism. (Courtesy Chevrolet Motor Div., General Motors Corp.)

It consists of a spring-loaded diaphragm connected by a linkage to the distributor plate. The spring-loaded side of the diaphragm is air tight, and is connected by a line to a vacuum port on the side of the carburetor. This port is located slightly above the throttle plate so that it is blocked during idle. As the plate swings open, the port is uncovered and manifold vacuum is applied to the diaphragm. The diaphragm moves toward the vacuum source and pivots the distributor plate against the direction of cam rotation. Since the contact points are mounted on the plate, the points open earlier and the spark advances. At near full throttle, manifold vacuum decreases and the vacuum advance phases out.

Failures of the vacuum advance often go undetected, because the only symptom is an increase in fuel consumption coupled with a "flat spot" during acceleration. A distributor machine is required to check the mechanism completely, but a quick check can be made with a timing light. Connect the light to No. 1 spark-plug cable and rev the engine. The light should register a sudden advance that stabilizes and falls off as engine speed reaches an rpm plateau.

Centrifugal Advance

An engine is happiest when the piston crown is exposed to maximum combustion pressure at 10 to 15 degrees past top dead center. Pressures peak at about 0.003 of a second after ignition, regardless of engine rpm. Thus, if an engine is timed for best power at idle, it will be late at high speed since the piston outruns combustion.

The centrifugal advance mechanism compensates by advancing the ignition at high speed (Fig. 7-16). The distributor cam turns with the distributor shaft, but is free to move a few degrees in advance of shaft rotation. This additional movement is controlled by a pair of spring-loaded weights. These weights revolve with the distributor shaft and, as they turn, centrifugal force pivots them outward. This movement is transferred to the distributor cam and advances the moment of point opening.

A timing light is no substitute for a distributor machine, but will detect gross malfunctions. The ignition should advance smoothly with rpm. If the marks remain stationary or jitter, check the advance mechanism. It should move freely, and show no more than light wear at the pivots. Do not detach the springs unless necessary, since handling can stretch them and allow excessive advance.

Ignition Timing

Timing marks are located on the harmonic balancer (crankshaft pulley) or on the flywheel. The marks may be indexed to show

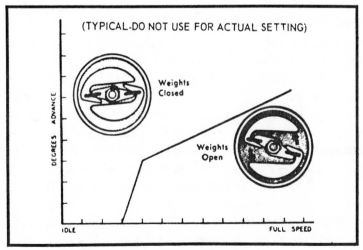

Fig. 7-16. Centrifugal advance mechanism and typical curve. (Courtesy Waukesha Motor Co.)

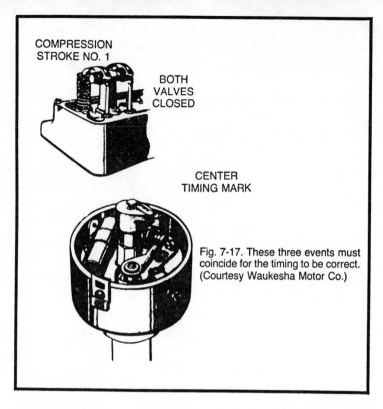

COMPRESSION
STROKE NO. 1

BOTH
VALVES
CLOSED

CENTER
TIMING MARK

Fig. 7-17. These three events must coincide for the timing to be correct. (Courtesy Waukesha Motor Co.)

degrees of flywheel rotation relative to 0 or top dead center, or they may be innocent of any clue as to what they mean. If a single mark is present (as in the case of early Continentals), there is no possibility of confusion. Time to that mark. In a cluster of two or more marks, the first one is always top dead center.

Battery-and-coil ignitions can be timed statically. While mechanics tend to look askance at this procedure, it is as accurate as any other and can be used in conjunction with dynamic timing to detect timing chain stretch. Figure 7-17 illustrates the drill. The crankshaft is rotated until both valves for No. 1 cylinder—the reference cylinder—are closed and the timing mark aligned with its pointer. A test lamp is connected in series with the distributor primary terminal and the battery. The pinch bolt at the base of the distributor is loosened and the distributor body turned by hand until the light flickers out. The points have opened and No. 1 piston is in its firing position.

The only difficulty with this approach is that it is possible to time to the wrong flank of the cam. The initial movement of the distributor body should be *against* the direction of cam rotation.

Dynamic timing requires that the initial timing be close enough for the engine to start. Since the timing specification does not include vacuum or centrifugal advance, both of these mechanisms must be temporarily defeated. The vacuum line to the distributor is disconnected and plugged, and the idle set as low as the engine will tolerate without balking. A strobe light is connected to No. 1 spark-plug cable and the engine is run long enough to reach operating temperature. Flywheel marks on very old engines are sometimes masked by grease. These marks can be made visible by holding a rag against the revolving wheel with a screwdriver. Keep your fingers clear. Turn the distributor until the marks align and recheck after tightening the pinch bolt (most distributors creep).

BATTERY

Battery failure is expensive enough when it is limited to the battery itself, but a battery that limps along with an occasional assist from the charger can damage other components. The first to go is the starter motor. The motor compensates for low input voltage by demanding more current. Even a very weak battery, one that just makes the starter groan, can fry the motor with a burst of current. And a weak battery will cause the alternator to work overtime, shortening its life and wasting fuel in the process.

Charge Tests

It is not easy to determine the state of the charge in a battery. No-load voltage readings are misleading, since a battery on the verge of extinction can show full voltage across the terminals. Nor is it helpful to discharge a battery to see how much current was released.

But there is one physical characteristic that bears directly on the state of charge. The weight, or more exactly the specific gravity, of the electrolyte changes with the charge. Electrolyte is a solution of sulfuric acid and water. When the battery is fully charged it has a specific gravity of approximately 1.280; that is, there is enough acid present to make the electrolyte 1.28 times heavier than water. As

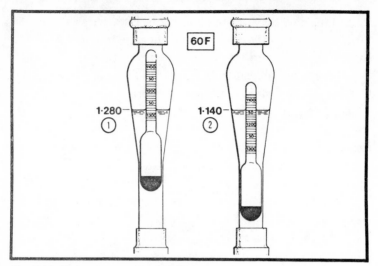

Fig. 7-18. Hydrometer readings of electrolyte (1) fully charged, and (2) discharged. (Courtesy Lansing Bagnall Ltd.)

the battery discharges, the acid molecules break apart and the electrolyte becomes more watery. If it were possible to completely drain the battery, the electrolyte would be transformed into pure water. As a practical matter, a battery is functionally dead when the specific gravity drops to 1.140.

Specific gravity readings should be made with a hydrometer reserved for this purpose, because a hydrometer that has been used to check antifreeze will contaminate the electrolyte. Ideally, the reading should be made prior to morning startup and several running hours after water has been added to the cells. Insert the tip of the tube in the cell and withdraw enough electrolyte to launch the float. Hold the hydrometer upright with the float centered in its chamber. Sight across the liquid level (Fig. 7-18). The portion of the electrolyte that clings to the float tang and sides of the chamber has no significance whatsoever.

American hydrometers are calibrated to be accurate with an electrolyte temperature of 80°F. European makes are accurate at 68°F, while the English (perhaps out of deference to their cold winters) calibrate theirs at 60°F. For each 2.5°F above the calibration point, add 0.001 to the reading; for each 2.5°F below it, subtract 0.001.

You can roughly translate from specific gravity to charge as follows:

100% charge	1.240–1.280
50% charge	1.220–1.230
25% charge	1.100 or less

Some variation between the individual cells is normal, but none should be 5 points (0.005) lower than the average of the others.

Hydrometer tests are fast and usually adequate by themselves. But the chemical condition of the battery is, in the last analysis, only a mark of potential. A broken strap, holed plates, or other internal faults can severely limit the amount of current delivered. And current is what we are after.

Capacity Tests

The true capacity test requires a variable load (a rheostat or carbon pile) and a pair of meters to monitor terminal voltage and output. The load is adjusted to draw three times the battery's ampere-hour capacity. An 80 ampere-hour battery is loaded to draw 160 amps. The load is applied for 15 seconds. A healthy battery will maintain a terminal voltage of more than 9.6V.

A variable load is an expensive piece of equipment. It is possible to use the vehicle's starter motor instead, although results are not absolutely conclusive.

Disable the ignition by disconnecting the switch-to-coil lead or by grounding the coil's high-tension cable. If you go the cable route, take the trouble to fix the distributor side terminal to the block; otherwise high-voltage flashover could damage the coil. Connect a voltmeter across the battery terminals, and crank the engine for 15 seconds. A fully charged battery that drops to 9.6V or less can be considered defective; if the reading dips to 8V the battery is dead and, in all likelihood, the starter as well.

STARTING SYSTEMS

If the starter motor refuses to budge, bar the engine over by hand. Things that hardly bear thinking about could have happened since the engine was last started. Coolant could have leaked into the chambers and bound the pistons or leaked into the sump and turned

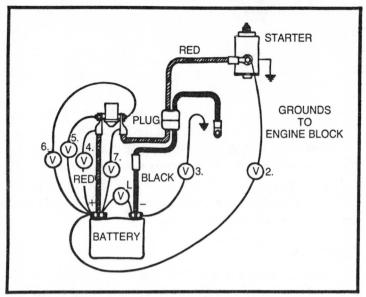

Fig. 7-19. High-current circuit tests are valid only if the battery is fully charged.

the oil into glue. Or the bearings could have seized. And all of this means engine overhaul (Chapter 9), or replacement. However, once you are satisfied that the engine turns over, check the state of charge of the battery, the condition of the battery terminals, and for the telltale click that means the electromagnetic side of the solenoid is functional. Silence when the switch is closed means that either the solenoid, switch, or related circuitry is at fault. If the solenoid responds to switch commands, shunt it out of the circuit since its switching function may be impaired. A quick way to do this is to bridge its cable terminals with a screwdriver. If the starter works, the solenoid is defective and should be replaced. If not, check the cables by connecting a jumper between the battery positive terminal and the motor terminal. If the motor still refuses to work, check the brushes for wear and for contact with the commutator. If the motor still refuses to work, remove the inspection band and check the brushes for proper length and for good contact. Sometimes a nudge with a screwdriver is enough to seat the brushes and restore operation. Otherwise the starter will have to be dismantled.

The series of tests illustrated in Fig. 7-19 are handy when cranking is sluggish and you are not certain which component is at fault. In test 1, the meter is connected between the battery terminals. This test establishes the baseline. Battery voltage should not drop below 10–11V during brief (3–5 seconds) bouts of cranking. If it does, replace the battery with a known-good one and repeat the rest. A second failure means that current draw is excessive. Visually inspect the cables for burnt insulation, crystallized conductor and other evidence of massive hemorrhage. If the cables appear okay and the solenoid is cool to the touch, remove the starter motor for bench tests.

Test 2 includes all of the hot-side circuit. The meter is connected between the battery and the starter-motor terminal. With the switch off, the voltage should be the same as battery voltage. During cranking the meter should show 1V or less. This last named voltage represents voltage lost to the motor because of circuit resistance.

Test 3 is a repeat of 2 on the ground return circuit. There should be 0V with the switch off and not more than 1V cranking. If the drop is greater than this, open and scrape the ground-side connection, with particular attention paid to the battery-cable terminals. Usually this is enough since most problems are caused by simple corrosion. But it is possible for the difficulty to be at the starter-motor/bellhousing interface. A thin layer of oil here is enough to cripple the circuit.

Tests 4 and 5 check respectively the battery cable and the solenoid terminal. There should be no current in the circuit with the switch off. Voltage means that the solenoid is shorting and depending upon the route to ground, can keep the starter motor engaged after the switch is opened or, worse, cause the motor to engage itself with the engine running.

Test 7 is between the battery and the leeward side of the solenoid. Because the starter is grounded, the meter should indicate full battery voltage with the switch open. No more than 1V should be deflected during cranking.

Relays and Solenoids

Figure 7-20 illustrates a typical relay. In series with the battery and starter, the relay is an electromechanical switch. With the starter switch on and (on some machines) the neutral interlock

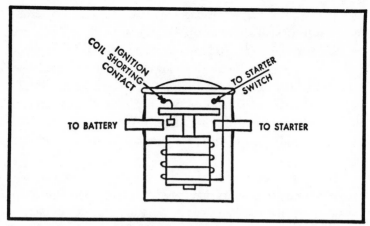

Fig. 7-20. A typical relay. The "ignition coil shorting contact" shunts the ballast resistor. (Courtesy Chrysler-Nissan)

conducting, current flows to the relay windings. These windings generate a magnetic field that attracts the relay plunger. Movement of the plunger closes a pair of contacts and completes the battery-to-starter circuit.

A solenoid is a relay with a second function. Besides switching starter motor current, the solenoid engages the starter pinion-gear with the flywheel ring-gear. A solenoid is both a relay and a linear motor.

One glance is enough to distinguish the two. A relay is mounted in isolation, usually on an engine-compartment bulkhead. It has two large terminals for battery cables and at least one small terminal for signal current. Some relays have a second small terminal to provide an external ground for the windings. A solenoid is mounted piggyback on the top of the starter motor. It is connected to a single cable from the battery and to the control circuit. A lead from the control terminal may be connected to the ignition coil in order to bypass an external ballast resistor during cranking.

The solenoid pictured in Fig. 7-21 has two windings in the best modern practice. The pull-in winding engages the pinion with the flywheel. Since it must overcome pinion inertia and must be strong to force the issue if the teeth do not meet cleanly, the pull-in winding draws heavy current. Some require more than 50A. Once engaged, the lighter hold-in winding is adequate to keep the pinion in mesh.

The pull-in winding is disconnected so maximum current is available for starting.

The next drawing, Fig. 7-22, is a pictorial diagram of an interesting variation in solenoids. The C.A.V. unit was designed with an eye to reducing shock loads on the starter motor. Initially the first set of contacts close and send current to the motor through a limiting resistor (shown in shunt with the second pair of contacts). The starter begins to accelerate while, at the same time, a solenoid-operated plunger moves the pinion toward the flywheel (not shown). Just before engagement, the pinion collar unlatches the first set of contacts. The plunger then closes the second set for full battery current to the starter.

Relay and solenoid failures are signaled by a refusal to close, to remain closed (in which case the device will chatter), or by a refusal to open. The latter is rare and fortunately so, since it can mean the destruction of the starter.

While it is possible to check point resistance and current draw, these tests are academic. Modern relays and solenoids are not in any real sense of the word repairable. Chrysler Delco Remy types are partial exceptions to this statement. The contact bridge can be replaced or reversed to expose a new surface to the contacts.

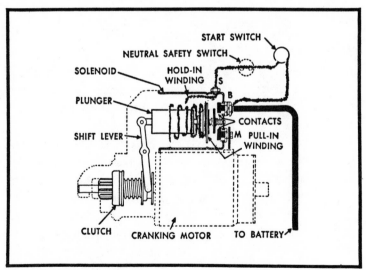

Fig. 7-21. A solenoid with pull-in and hold-in windings. (Courtesy Delco Remy Div., General Motors Corp.)

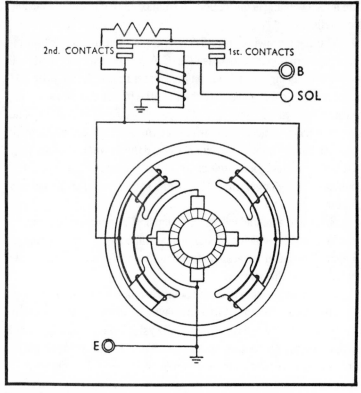

Figl 7-22. C.A.V. starter motor diagram. (Courtesy GM Bedford Diesel)

Starter Drives

The Bendix drive has been around since 1914 and remains popular. (A measure of its popularity is that mechanics routinely use the term "Bendix" to refer to all starter drives, regardless of manufacturer.)

The drive pinion is loosely threaded on the armature shaft (Fig. 7-23A) and is counterweighted. The loose thread and counterweight cause it to lag behind armature rotation and move forward on the shaft. The mechanism is similar to the clutch assembly used on bicycle coaster brakes. Once the engine starts, the differential between flywheel rpm and armature rpm reverses the action and the pinion retracts.

The heavy spring behind the pinion absorbs shock if the teeth happen to mesh on point. The light spring in front of it is a stabilizer to keep the pinion from drifting into engagement with the engine running. Most Bendix drives include a detent mechanism in the pinion assembly. The detent allows the engine to catch momentarily without disengaging the pinion.

The overruning clutch or solenoid-shifted drive is conceptually simpler than the Bendix, although by no means as elegantly compact (Fig. 7-23B). It is moved into engagement by the solenoid lever and yoke mechanism. The pinion rotates on a spiral thread as it is thrust forward to make a wiping contact with the ring-gear teeth. The yoke holds it in place and cranking torque is transmitted by the spiral thread. Once the engine catches, a roller and ramp assembly between the pinion and its cover allows the pinion to turn faster than, or override, the armature. Some designs feature a detent to keep the pinion solidly in mesh during false starts. As soon as the solenoid is no longer energized, the plunger spring retracts the shift lever and pinion.

The common type of failure is refusal to engage. The starter spins merrily without having any effect upon the flywheel. In Bendix units this can be caused by a broken drive spring (the large coil to the left of the pinion in Fig. 7-23A), dirt or grease on the armature threads, or malfunctions of the detent mechanism. Bendix units are sealed and, with the exception of drive spring and antirattle spring replacement, are not repairable.

Refusal of solenoid-shifted types to engage is usually the fault of the overruning clutch. The pinion should lock when turned by hand into the direction of armature rotation. If it doesn't, replace the unit. Another possibility is excessive clearance between the pinion and stop (Fig. 7-23B). This specification is critical and should be checked each time the starter is detached from the engine. Disable the motor by disconnecting the solenoid-to-field strap and energize the solenoid. Insert the specified feeler gauge between the pinion and stop. Insufficient clearance means incorrect assembly or illegitimate replacement parts; excessive clearance can defeat the shifter and points to a worn or warped shift lever.

Refusal to overrun can only mean the clutch. This problem is rare—unless a mechanic has inadvertently washed the lubrication from the clutch assembly. These parts are prelubricated and do not take kindly to solvent.

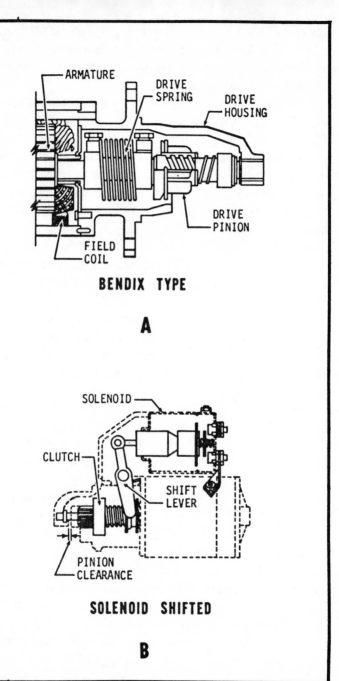

Fig. 7-23. Starter drives. (Courtesy Kohler of Kohler)

272

Starter Motors

Unless you are dealing with very large, outdoor trucks or single-cylinder puttabouts, the starter motor has four magentic poles and four brushes. The field consists of four windings wrapped over iron cores and arranged symmetrically around the armature. Current passes through the windings and through the armature on its way to ground. For maximum longevity four brushes, two hot and two grounded, are used.

In basic arrangement the fields are in series with the armature. Starter motors are series wound machines. However, there are a number of variations on this theme. The C.A.V. approach is to pair the fields and to connect them in parallel (Fig. 7-22). Other manufacturers connect each field in series to provide a single current path through them. Occasionally you will find a starter with three field coils in series with each other and with the armature and the fourth in shunt. The field in parallel brakes the armature and limits its no load speed.

The Chrysler geared motor is shown in Fig. 7-24. With the exception of the gear train, it is quite like the others. The basic package consists of an armature, field frame assembly, brush assembly, and endhead.

The armature is the most complex (and least repairable) part of the motor. It consists of a bundle of heavy copper coils wound over a form. The shaft is an integral part of the assembly. In this case, the free end of the shaft serves as a gear. Other starter shafts terminate in a helical thread for the clutch assembly. The shaft is supported on bearings and located by the endcap and field-frame assembly.

Servicing

As mentioned earlier in this chapter, it is always wise to bar the engine over when a starter problem is suspected. Then check the state of charge of the battery with a hydrometer. The corrected reading should be no lower than 1.220–1.230 for a 50% or better charge. Next run a jumper directly to the motor terminal. A healthy starter with a Bendix drive will engage; a solenoid-shifted starter should spin merrily at its no load speed of 6000 rpm or so.

No response with a jumper or a sluggish response points to a motor fault. Remove the dust cover and check the brushes for wear

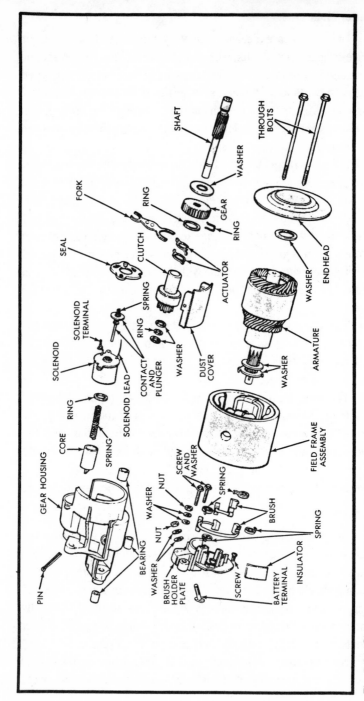

Fig. 7-24. Chrysler geared starter in exploded view.

(they should be replaced when worn down to half of the original length), the springs for tension, and the condition of the commutator. Some discoloration of the copper segments is normal, but a bluish-black patina means that the starter should be dismounted and the commutator cleaned. In an emergency—and lift-truck repairs usually are on an emergency basis—you can get the machine going by polishing the commutator with No. 400 wet or dry paper.

Some starters employ flange shims (Fig. 7-25). Note their location for proper assembly. Otherwise the gear lash will be wrong and the pinion may bind or even strip the flywheel ring.

While most mechanics save starter motor tests for last (if even then), testing the motor before it is disassembled can save time. You will need a brake, a high-range ammeter, and a voltmeter (Fig. 7-26). The test should be continued just long enough to get a torque reading.

Symptom	Possible Cause
Low free speed, high current draw.	Bad bearings (tight, dirty, or worn), bent shaft, loose pole shoe screws, shorted or grounded armature, shorted field.
Won't run, high current draw.	Short in field or frozen shaft bearings.
Won't run, no current draw.	Open field circuit, open armature coils, broken or weakened brush springs, worn brushes.
Low free speed, low torque, low current.	Open field, high resistance at brushes or internal connections, dirty commutator.
High free speed, low torque, high current.	Shorted field windings. Check by substitution.

Clean the external surfaces with solvent and blow dry. Not all endcaps are indexed. Before you remove the through bolts, punch mark the cap and frame as a reference. Lift the brush-side cap clear and spend some time cleaning the internals with trichloroethylene,

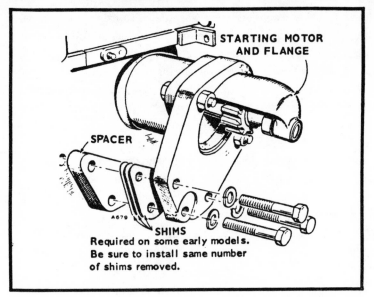

STARTING MOTOR
AND FLANGE

SPACER

A679

SHIMS
Required on some early models.
Be sure to install same number
of shims removed.

Fig. 7-25. Note the presence of shims on some mounting flanges. (Courtesy Onan)

MEK, or some other solvent approved for electrical machines. Petroleum-based solvents—lacquer thinner, kerosene, Varsol, and the like—attack insulation and should be avoided. Carbon tetrachloride is not approved because its fumes cause liver damage. In a pinch you can use TV tuner cleaner or Freon. Both of these solvents are excellent, but expensive.

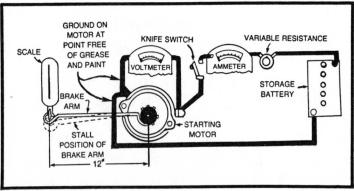

GROUND ON
MOTOR AT
POINT FREE
OF GREASE
AND PAINT

KNIFE SWITCH

VARIABLE RESISTANCE

SCALE

VOLTMETER

AMMETER

STORAGE
BATTERY

BRAKE
ARM

STALL
POSITION OF
BRAKE ARM
12"

STARTING
MOTOR

Fig. 7-26. A stall test requires specialized equipment, but is the most definitive of all start tests. (Courtesy Onan).

Withdraw the brushes from their holders and check for wear and cracks, and for splintering at the rubbing edges. Two brushes should be grounded and two insulated from each other and the frame. The holders, usually riveted to the frame, should be secure.

Some shaft wear can be tolerated, but scores or deep scratches mean that the armature assembly and brush-side bearing must be replaced. The bearing can be removed by chiseling a channel down one side and carefully collapsing it inward.

Inspect the commutator very closely. Most starter defects originate, or at least leave their telltale signatures, here. Puddled solder on the connections between the segments and windings means that the motor has overheated. Starter motors are intended for intermittent use with long cool-down periods between bouts of cranking. Erosion along the edges of the commutator bars means that the armature windings are shorted.

Initial tests require a 120V lamp fitted with probes (Fig. 7-27). Treat this apparatus with respect. Should you get between the

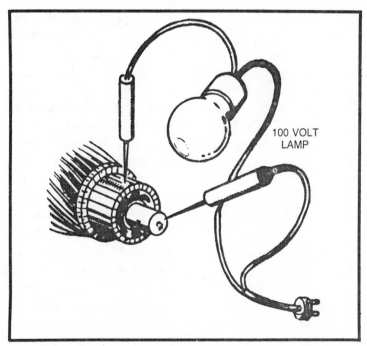

100 VOLT
LAMP

Fig. 7-27. Adjacent commutator segments should be insulated from each other and from the motor shaft. (Courtesy Onan)

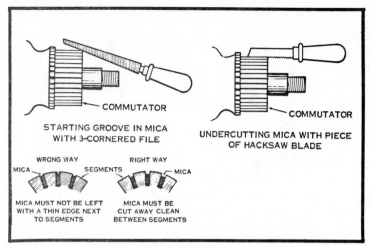

Fig. 7-28. Undercutting the insulation. (Courtesy Harley-Davidson)

probes you will get a shock that travels through the central nervous system. As a further precaution, insulate yourself from the floor and place the motor on a wooden bench.

The lamp should show that adjacent bars are insulated from each other and that all bars are insulated from the motor shaft. Paired bars—distributed approximately 30° apart around the commutator—share the same armature winding and should conduct.

Undercut the insulation (called mica because that was the material formerly used) between the commutator bars. This operation is illustrated in Fig. 7-28. Make the initial cut with a triangular file and use a hacksaw blade to square the edges. Remove burrs with fine emery cloth, and use compressed air to blow the filings from between the segments.

In many cases this is all that is required to put the motor back into operation. Further disassembly requires that the front cover be removed. Disassemble the solenoid, disengage the shift lever from the pinion yoke, and withdraw the armature and clutch assembly as a unit. Note the number and sequence of spacer washers.

Clean the armature and frame cavity with approved solvent. Some discoloration of the windings is normal; brittle or carbonized insulation mean that the windings are shorted. Wear marks on the large diameter of the armature are the result of worn bearings, a bent shaft, or loose pole-shoe screws. Another possibility is a warped end plate. White metal end plates cannot always contain the torque.

The bearings should be replaced as a matter of course. (Replacement bearings should be soaked in oil for several days before use.) The outboard bearing offers no difficulty—it can be popped out with a drift. The one on the brush side is in a blind (closed) boss and can be a bit frustrating. The best way to remove it is with an old motor shaft or a bar that matches the shaft diameter. Pack the boss with heavy grease and drive the shaft into the bearing with a sharp hammer blow. The ram effect will send grease under the bushing and drive it out. Install with a suitable driver or press into place with the help of a soft-jawed vise.

Loose pole-shoe screws are not difficult to detect. But getting them tight enough to prevent subsequent loosening is another matter entirely. Most are Phillips screws and tend to burrow out when torqued. The best approach is to use a hammer impact driver. The impact of the hammer seats the bit while at the same time turning it. Another technique is to mount the starter under a drill press and apply vertical pressure on the screwdriver with the machine.

A test lamp can be used to test the fields for continuity, although you should have access to an internal wiring diagram for the starter before you make any positive determinations. As noted earlier, some fields are paired and others are wired in series/parallel combinations. Winding-to-winding internal shorts are difficult to detect with ordinary shop meters. Resistances are very low and one or two windings shorted together make only the most minuscule difference. The best approach is to save field-coil tests for last. After everything is checked and the starter torque is still low, substitute new coils.

Now that the armature is out it can be tested on a growler—an electromagnet powered by the AC line. Place the armature between the poles and rotate it slowly while holding a hacksaw blade over the windings (Fig. 7-29). A shorted winding will attract and release the blade 60 times a second.

CHARGING SYSTEMS

The charging circuit includes the generator or alternator, voltage regulator, charge indicator (a warning lamp or ammeter), and, in most cases, a fuse block or fusible link (Fig. 7-30). Generator

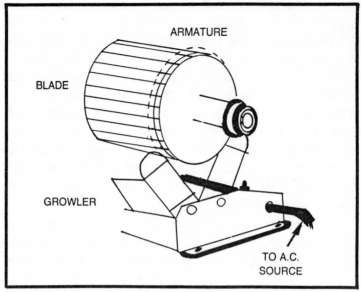

Fig. 7-29. Using a growler. (Courtesy Onan)

output is in parallel with the main circuitry and can enter at any point. This particular setup uses the solenoid as a convenient tiepoint. Others run a heavy wire directly to the hot side of the battery.

Generators

Although obsolete more than a decade, direct-current generators are still very much with us. Functionally, a generator is the mirror image of a starter motor. The motor is fed current and delivers torque; the generator is fed torque and delivers current. Some Chrysler outboard motors and Japanese motorcycles of a decade back combined both functions in a single armature. During cranking, the device acted as a starter motor. Once the engine started it became a fairly efficient generator.

But there are some differences. Generator windings are made of finer wire than those used for starters, and generators normally have only two poles and two brushes. Figure 7-31 shows a popular Delco Remy generator in exploded view.

Most generators have externally grounded fields at the voltage regulator (Fig. 7-32). Certain Lucas machines and, going back many years, Autolite generators fitted to Ford flathead V-8s have the fields grounded inside the frame. The first and most common approach is known as the type A configuration. The second is type B.

Testing Type A Generators. To test type A generators, disconnect the field lead at the generator or regulator. This is the smaller of the two leads from the generator, and in any event, the regulator field terminal is marked. Connect a voltmeter between the output and ground. Switch all accessories off and run the engine up to 3000 rpm or so. Unless the fields have shorted to ground, there should be no output at this stage of the test. Now ground the field lead to the block. Output should be treble normal voltage.

Testing Type B Generators. Type B machines are tested a little differently. Disconnect the field lead at the alternator. With accessories off and the engine turning 3000 rpm, there should be zero output. Momentarily touch the field lead to the armature terminal. This terminal is marked *B, Batt,* or *A*. Output should jump to at least three times the rated voltage.

At the beginning of the charge cycle, the generator sort of lifts itself by its own bootstraps. Output depends upon the magnetic interaction between the field windings and the armature. Initially, the field windings are dead because no current is available from the armature to magnetize them. But there is enough residual magnetism lurking in the pole shoes to get the reaction started. Once begun, some of the armature output is bled back through the voltage regulator to the fields.

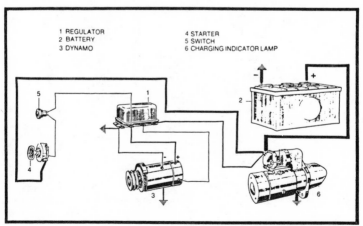

1 REGULATOR   4 STARTER
2 BATTERY   5 SWITCH
3 DYNAMO   6 CHARGING INDICATOR LAMP

Fig. 7-30. A typical DC charging circuit. (Courtesy Teledyne Wisconsin Motor)

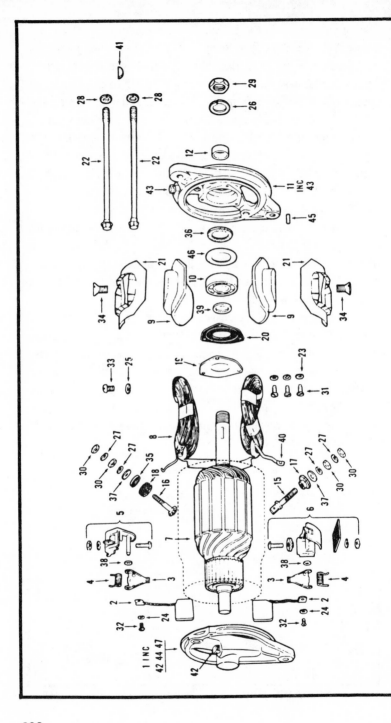

FRAME, commutator end
Includes: Ref. Nos. 42, 44, 47, 48.
BRUSH
BRUSH ARM
BRUSH SPRING
GROUND BRUSH HOLDER PKG.
INSULATED BRUSH HOLDER PKG.
ARMATURE
FIELD COIL SET
Includes: Ref. Nos. 16 and 40.
POLE SHOE
BALL BEARING, D.E.

FRAME, D.E., Includes: Ref. 43
COLLAR, D.E.
STUD, armature terminal
STUD, field terminal (to brush)
BUSHING, armature terminal
BUSHING, field terminal
PLATE, bearing retainer, D.E.
GASKET, bearing retainer plate
INSULATION, field coil
THRU BOLT
LOCKWASHER, bearing ret. plate
LOCKWASHER, brush lead screw

LOCKWASHER (top of field frame)
LOCKWASHER, shaft nut, D.E.
LOCKWASHER, terminal stud
LOCKWASHER, thru bolt
NUT, shaft, D.E.
NUT, terminal stud
SCREW, bearing retainer plate
SCREW, brush lead
SCREW (top of field frame)
SCREW, pole shoe
WASHER, insulating, field term
WASHER, felt, D.E.
WASHER, plain, terminal stud

WASHER, brush arm spacer
WASHER, spacer, D.E.
TERMINAL CLIP
WOODRUFF KEY, D.E.
OILER, C.E.
OILER, D.E.
WICK, D.E. (not illustrated)
DOWEL PIN, C.E.
DOWEL PIN, D.E.
PLATE, felt washer retainer, D.E.
OIL WICK, C.E.
PLUG, C.E. (not illustrated)

Fig. 7-31. Delco Remy 12V generator. (Courtesy Teledyne Wisconsin Motor)

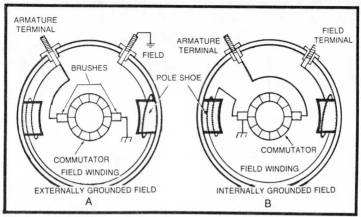

Fig. 7-32. Externally grounded (type A) and internally grounded (type B) fields.

If the generator is bounced about, subjected to hammering and other shocks associated with repair work, or stored near an AC line, it is probable that the residual magnetism will be lost. The generator must be repolarized.

On type A machines, quickly touch the armature lead (identified at the regulator terminal as A, Arm or D) to the battery (B) terminal. Touch the field lead to the battery for type B generators.

Alternators

Alternators have several advantages over direct-current generators. An alternator will deliver 10A or so at idle while a generator is hard-pressed to supply the ignition system at anything under 2000 rpm. Because the generator frame is part of the magnetic circuit, it must be made of cast iron. Couple this weight with the weight of the iron and copper armature and the fields, and we have a very heavy piece of equipment. Alternator windings are lighter than those used in generators, and the covers (the parts that roughly coincide with the frame) are cast in light metal. And while automotive alternators still carry brushes, the current load is such that the brushes cause few problems.

Perhaps the major drawback of the alternator is the need for diodes.

Current output is alternating—it peaks in one direction, drops to zero, then peaks in the other direction. AC is less than useless for battery charging and death to horn relays and other components. A bank of diodes mounted under the rear cover of the alternator converts current flow to pulsating DC. Diodes seem to last forever—so long as the environment is stable. But vibration, excessive heat, reversed battery polarity, voltage spikes, and random voltages introduced with an arc welder or a high-range ohmmeter destroy them.

Take these precautions:

- Remove the battery from the vehicle for recharging.
- Observe correct polarity (almost all alternator-equipped machines are negative ground) when connecting the battery and when using jumper cables.
- Never run the engine with the battery or alternator disconnected.
- Electrically isolate the alternator when arc welding anywhere on the vehicle, and when making resistance tests.
- Use the proper tools to remove and install diodes.

On-Truck Tests. Begin by checking the resistance of the charging circuit. Load the battery with a rheostat or carbon pile adjusted for a 20A draw. Connect a voltmeter between the *B* terminal of the alternator (the terminal with the heaviest wire) and the positive, or hot, battery terminal. Operate the engine at a fast idle and observe the meter. Repeat the test on the grounded side. A reading of more than 0.2V for either branch of the circuit at 1200 rpm means excessive resistance. Loose grounds and corroded quick-disconnects are the usual culprits.

Next check system performance with a fully charged battery in the circuit. Connect a test ammeter in series with the alternator output and connect a voltmeter between the output and a good ground. Turn on the vehicle lights. Start the engine, and block the throttle to give a fast idle. The ammeter should register 10A or more and the voltmeter should hover just under 14V (at 80°F). Switch off the lights. If everything is working properly the voltage will remain constant while current falls to 3–5A.

If the results are inconclusive—they will be affected by how much current was expended in cranking, the draw of the lights, and engine rpm—it will be necessary to make a more thorough check.

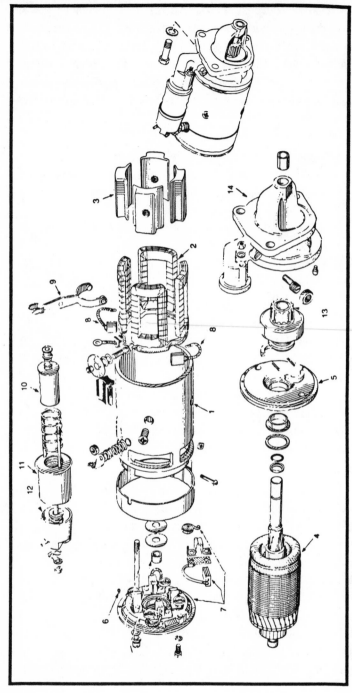

Fig. 7-33. When troubleshooting a charging circuit, the first step is to make resistance tests.

Isolate the regulator so the alternator will give full rated output. Late-production Delco Remy alternators feature a built-in solid-state regulator. It is isolated by grounding the test tab with a screwdriver (Fig. 7-33). The tab is located approximately 1/2 inch below the end cover. Do not force the screwdriver deeper than this. Other regulators are isolated by disconnecting the field lead and grounding the field terminal at the regulator.

Connect the test meters and dummy load as shown in Fig. 7-34. Slowly bring the engine up to 1250 rpm while keeping an eye on the voltmeter. Adjust the load to limit output to 15V. Under no circumstances should the voltage be allowed to climb to 16V. The alternator should deliver its rated amperage (found stamped on the cover) at 1250 engine rpm, less temperature variation and ignition system losses. That is, a 60A machine in good condition will deliver 60A± 3A depending upon the temperature. On a cold day the output will be on the plus side. Subtract 5A for system losses.

Bench Tests. Disconnect the battery and alternator wiring. If there is any chance of confusion, mark the wires. Remove the alternator at the bracket and belt-tensioning bolts. Most covers are

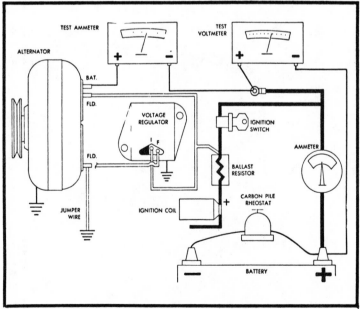

Fig. 7-34. Alternator output test. (Courtesy Chrysler Corp.)

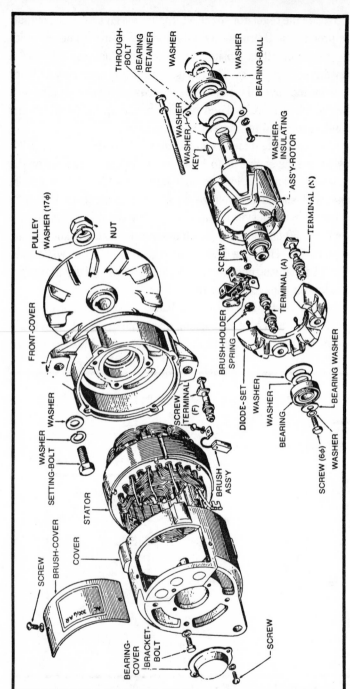

Fig. 7-35. A typical alternator in exploded view. (Courtesy Datsun)

indexed. If the one at hand isn't, punch mark both covers as an assembly guide. Remove the through bolts and detach the brush-side cover. It may be necessary to use a soft mallet to part the covers.

The brushes must be in their holders (Fig. 7-35). Some manufacturers provide a wear limit line on the brushes; otherwise replace if worn down to half of their original length. Inspect the slip rings. The rubbing surface should be dead smooth. Eccentricity should not exceed 0.002 inch for best brush life. Badly scored or egg-shaped rings can sometimes be replaced without purchasing a new rotor and shaft assembly. Check with your parts supplier.

Using an ohmmeter, check for continuity between the slip rings (Fig. 7-36). The rings and rotor windings should be insulated from the shaft.

The rotor and drive-side cover are held by the pulley. The rotor must be prevented from turning when the pulley nut is loosened. On some alternators this can be achieved by blocking the fan; others have the rotor shaft indexed for an Allen wrench; and others,

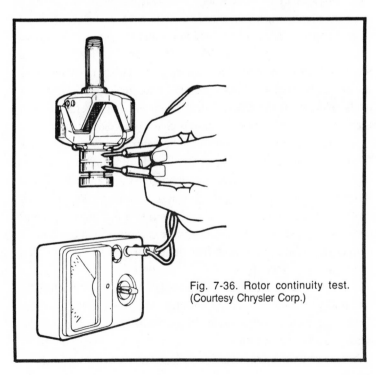

Fig. 7-36. Rotor continuity test. (Courtesy Chrysler Corp.)

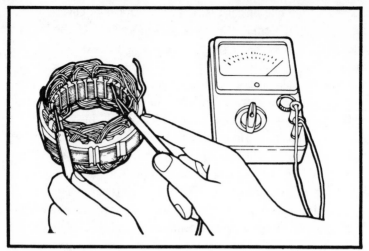

Fig. 7-37. Stator coil continuity test. Check each of the three windings against the neutral (ground) lead. (Courtesy Chrysler Corp.)

borrowed from automotive sources, require a special holding fixture. Do not on any account lock the shaft in a vise.

The stator consists of three independent windings spaced 120 degrees apart. Failure of one will not affect the others but will, of course, reduce output by one third. There are four leads from the stator—three to the diodes and one to ground. American machines are generally fitted with lugged terminals; foreign types have the hot leads soldered to the diodes. Mark the leads and carefully detach them, doing as little violence as possible to the diode bank.

Connect an ohmmeter between the neutral lead and each of the three hot leads in turn (Fig. 7-37). Each winding should show continuity. No winding should be grounded to the stator (Fig. 7-38). Internal, winding-to-winding shorts can sometimes be detected with a very accurate ohmmeter. Connect the meter as before and compare the readings between windings. A difference of a tenth of an ohm is significant, and means that the stator should be taken to a specialist for further tests.

Next on the order of business is to check the diodes. Each of the six should pass current in one direction and block it in the other. Take a careful look at the diode circuit. Some are wired so that the diodes can be tested without isolating them from the larger circuit. Others must be snipped out and resoldered when the test is finished.

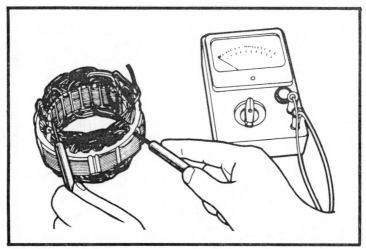

Fig. 7-38. Stator coil ground test. Each winding should be insulated from the laminations. (Courtesy Chrysler Corp.)

Use a low-range ohmmeter as shown in Fig. 7-39. Connect one probe to the diode lead and the other to ground. Note the reading and reverse the meter polarity. You should have nearly zero resistance in one direction and almost infinite resistance in the other. Depending upon construction, a failed diode may be replaced individually or

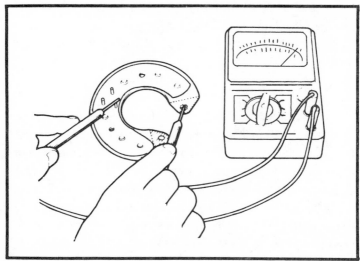

Fig. 7-39. Diode test. Reverse the leads for each diode. It should conduct in one direction and have very high resistance in the other. (Courtesy Chrysler Corp.)

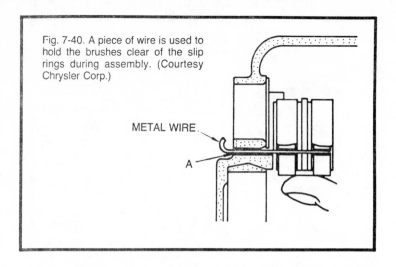

Fig. 7-40. A piece of wire is used to hold the brushes clear of the slip rings during assembly. (Courtesy Chrysler Corp.)

METAL WIRE

A

as part of the whole cluster. Individual diodes require a special tool to press them into their sockets without crushing them. Do not attempt the job without the proper tool.

Diodes do not tolerate much heat. Their crystalline structure disintegrates at 400°F, and any self-respecting soldering gun develops over 700 degrees at the tip. The diode must be protected by a heat sink below the connection. A pair of long-nosed pliers held closed by a rubber band is adequate, although commercial heat sinks are available for people who do much of this work. Use 60/40 rosin-core solder since it has a low melting point of approximately 400°F. Use the tiniest amount of solder possible to fill the joint and remove the gun as soon as the solder melts and flows freely. Overheating the connection endangers the diode and crystallizes the solder, increasing its electrical resistance.

Sealed antifriction (ball or roller) bearings support the armature. Unless the alternator is to be rebuilt as a preventive measure, the bearings are left in place. The symptoms of bearing failure include roughness (detected by turning the inner race with your finger), noise, and pronounced grease leaks around the seal. Bearing noise begins as a low rumble and ends as a shriek as the grease carbonizes. This noise should not be confused with the low-pitched hum that some alternators normally give off.

The old bearings are pressed off and new ones are pressed into place. Be sure to adequately support the end covers and use an arbor

292

that makes flat contact with the outer race. Install the bearings with the numbered sides next to the arbor.

Lock the brushes in their holders with a length of stiff wire (Fig. 7-40). Slip the cover on and withdraw the wire. Turn the shaft a few revolutions to seat the brushes on the slip rings.

DC REGULATION

Most DC systems employ mechanical, vibrating-reed regulators. The typical regulator consists of two or more resistors and three relays; the cutout, the voltage-sensitive, and the current-sensitive relays.

The cutout relay is double wound (Fig. 7-41). One winding is in parallel and the other in series with the armature output. As the generator comes up to speed, its output is diverted through both windings and their combined magnetic fields attract the point armature, closing the points and switching output into the larger circuit. At low speeds the contact points open to isolate the generator (and its ground) from the battery. Otherwise the battery would discharge through the grounded generator brush. Current flow from the battery goes through the series winding. Since magnetic polarity for a given winding depends upon the direction of flow, reverse flow from the battery neutralizes the field generated by the parallel winding, allowing the contacts to open. The generator and its ground remains isolated from the battery until the generator reaches operating speed.

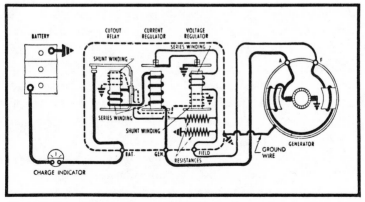

Fig. 7-41. Type A (externally grounded) DC charging system.

The voltage-sensitive relay is wound in parallel with the output. It is distinguished by its fine, hairlike wire used to make the winding. The winding is energized by the armature; the point contacts are in series with the field. Normally, the contacts are closed and the field circuit is completed through them. At a predetermined voltage, the windings generate enough magnetic force to pull the contacts apart. The field is now completed through a resistor. Since the resistor burns off current in the form of heat, less amperage is available to the generator field. Output depends upon the interaction of the field and the armature. The less current available to the field, the weaker its magnetic potential and the less output from the armature.

The current-sensitive winding consists of a few turns of heavy wire in series with the output. At a preset current level, the contacts open and the field is throttled by a resistor.

As temperature climbs, the battery becomes more active. Less current is needed for charging. Regulators sense temperature changes and adjust for them. One approach is to use bimetallic relay springs whose tension decreases with heat. On a warm day the field-limiting resistors are in the circuit more than they would be in the winter months. Other regulators incorporate magnetic "bleeds" to shunt the fields when temperatures are low. And still other relays employ temperature-sensitive resistors whose values increase as they are warmed.

Adjustment

Like all precision mechanisms, regulators require occasional attention. Perhaps the most frequent chore is to adjust output levels to match battery characteristics and changes in the use cycle of the machine. Output would, for example, be boosted to keep a tired battery in service and when a machine is retired from full-time duty. Provisions for adjustment vary. Some manufacturers prefer to adjust armature-spring tension by means of screws. Others specify that the armature hinges be repositioned in their elongated mounts. A few call for bending the stationary contact point.

The cutout relay should close at about 13V for 12V systems and at approximately 26.8V or 24V systems. Connect a voltmeter between the output (A or D) regulator terminal and ground. Put a 10A load on the battery and slowly bring the generator on line. The meter needle will twitch when the contacts close.

The voltage relay is usually adjusted with reference to a voltage reading taken between the battery terminals. While this method is adequate, precise adjustment requires that you remove the regulator cover and insert a piece of paper between the cutout contacts. This isolates the generator from the battery and will allow some very high voltages to develop if you overspeed the generator. Connect a voltmeter between the armature output and ground and slowly open the throttle. The needle should flick at 13.8V for 12V systems and 28V for 24V systems at room temperature or 80°F.

Current adjustment requires an accurate ammeter in series with the armature and battery, and a factory spec sheet. If specifications are not available or if additional circuitry has been added to the system, determine the draw on the battery and add 25–40% to compensate for battery inefficiency.

The final adjustment is to set the air or core gap to specification (Fig. 7-42). This adjustment requires an appropriate gauge and must be made with great accuracy.

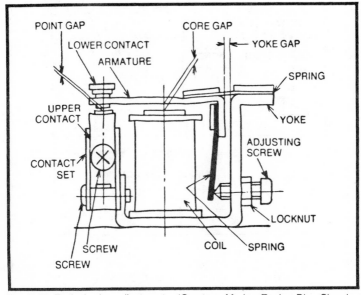

Fig. 7-42. Typical relay adjustments. (Courtesy Marine Engine Div., Chrysler Corp.)

Service

Dress oxidized contacts with a riffle file. Do not use sandpaper or emery cloth, since abrasives imbed themselves in the contact metal and encourage arcing.

Regulators eventually fail. Armature windings short or open, field resistors increase in value, contacts erode to base metal, hinges fatigue and snap. The cause of failure may be entirely within the regulator itself or it can be elsewhere in the charging circuit. Excessive heat, evidenced by burnt windings, severely vaporized contacts, and discolored springs on the voltage and cutout relays, means a bad regulator ground or a high resistance in the charging circuit. If the damage is limited to the current relay, some element in the charging circuit is shorted. Burnt points or discolored springs on the cutout alone means that the generator was not polarized.

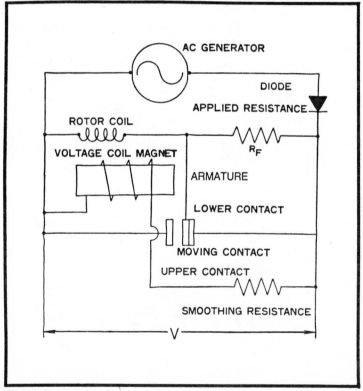

Fig. 7-43. Mechanical voltage regulator in an alternator circuit. (Courtesy Marine Engine Div., Chrysler Corp.)

Fig. 7-44. C.A.V. solid state regulator. (Courtesy GM Bedford Diesel)

AC REGULATION

A single voltage-sensitive relay is usually adequate for AC regulation (Fig. 7-43). Current output is almost linear as speed increases. The slow rise in the amperage curve can easily be flattened by limiting voltage. The bank of diodes prevents battery discharge through the alternator.

Sometimes you will find a second relay under the regulator cover. This relay is normally closed, completing the circuit to the charge indicator bulb. When the alternator's output reaches some 80% of battery voltage the contacts open the circuit and the lamp blinks out.

Most late model machines use solid state regulators (Fig. 7-44). Interestingly enough, these regulators have been more successful in lift trucks than in automobiles. Automotive circuits are complex and convoluted. Switching circuits in and out can give a kind of coil effect and produce momentary voltage peaks that swamp the regulator. While this effect is not absent in lift truck circuits, it is not serious enough to do damage.

Test these regulators by elimination. Determine the resistance of the charging circuit. If it is within specifications (no more than 0.2V drop on the hot and grounded sides), check the unregulated output of the alternator. This test is described under On-Truck Tests. Should the alternator perform as intended, the regulator is, by definition, at fault. Repair attempts are a waste of time; replace with another sealed assembly.

Cooling Systems

An internal combustion engine uses about 10% of the heat energy of its fuel overcoming internal friction. Another 30% escapes out of the exhaust or is radiated from the block. About 30% of the heat is extracted as useful work. The remaining 30% must be dissipated by the cooling system.

Gas temperatures in spark-ignition and diesel engines peak as the piston comes over top dead center. These temperatures can reach 5000°F under normal service. Temperatures can go even higher if the engine is lugged.

The temperature of the fire deck—the interface between the cylinder head and the block—should not be allowed to exceed 400°F. If it does, the pistons will gall and possibly seize. At more than 650–700°F, the valves can seize in their guides and may very well burn. Aluminum alloy piston crowns cannot tolerate more than 500°F before collapse.

Runaway temperatures have a dynamic force of their own. As the parts overheat they expand. The combination of heat and greater rubbing pressures carbonizes the oil into hard granules. More heat and more friction is generated. Overheated chambers cause preignition. The exhaust valve edges, a partially detached carbon flake, or the spark plug itself becomes the source of early ignition. The piston is caught between the inertia of the crankshaft and flywheel, and

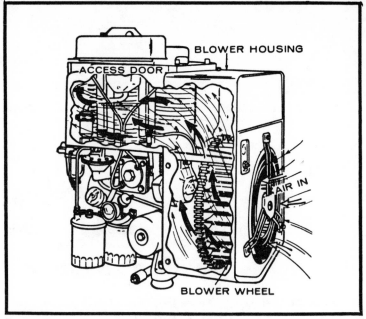

Fig. 8-1. The cooling air circuit on an Onan engine. Air enters at the flywheel hub and is ducted over the cylinder and head fins.

combustion pressures. It grows hotter with each revolution and, before long, the center of the crown softens and blows out.

Overcooling is also destructive, although its effects take longer to make themselves known. Oil congeals and friction increases. Gasoline engines have difficulty vaporizing their fuel—the flame is quenched by raw gasoline that collects between cycles and washes the oil from the upper bore. Ultimately the rings wear out.

AIR COOLING

A few small trucks are powered by fan-cooled engines. The fan is cast as part of the flywheel. Air enters the center of the hub and is expelled along the edges. Shrouds direct the flow over the cylinder barrel and head fins. This system is recommended by its simplicity—there is no radiator, water pump, drive belt, or hoses. Figure 8-1 shows a cutaway view of such a system. Only a tiny minority of these engines employ a thermostat. Another plus is that the engine comes up to operating temperature within a minute or so of starting.

But air is a very poor cooling medium. Approximately 1000 times more air than water must be circulated for the same cooling effect. Nor is the fixed-pitch fan entirely a blessing. Power is required to turn it and it is impossible to adjust the air flow for different operating conditions. At high speed under light load the engine will be overcooled. It will be undercooled when crankshaft speed drops under heavy load. The problem is complicated by an unfortunate characteristic of centrifugal fans. At high-speed efficiency approaches 100%, all of the air that enters is flung off the blades and into the shrouding. But at low speeds most of the output is lost as it slips between the outer edge of the blades and the cowling. The fan flails about uselessly.

Some maintenance is required even on such a simple arrangement as this. The shrouds should be periodically removed (every six months, according to the Army) and the fins cleaned. It is not unusual to find the fins packed solid with debris. Keep the inlet screen clean and occasionally check the shrouds for fit and possible leakage.

LIQUID COOLING

Most lift-truck engines are liquid cooled. Water or a mixture of water and ethylene glycol is a much better medium of heat transfer than air, and it's much easier to control. Another advantage is that liquid-cooled engines are inherently quieter than air-cooled types. The double-wall construction and the smooth outer surfaces of the engine muffle sound.

Figure 8-2 shows the basic circuit. It consists of a pump, thermostat, a pair of hoses, and water passages around the upper cylinder bores and through the head.

Flow takes advantage of the thermosiphon principle. Heated water expands and rises in a closed system. Relatively cool water enters the pump chamber from the lower radiator tank and is forced through the water jacket surrounding the cylinders. It rises to fill the cored passageways in the head where it is circulated around the valves and spark plugs (or injector sleeves). By this time the water is heated and it flows up, past the thermostat and into the radiator header tank.

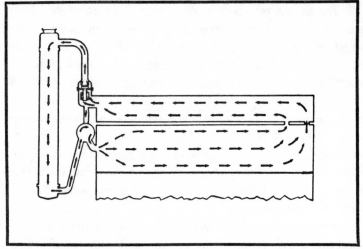

Fig. 8-2. The water circuit on a Bedford engine. Cool water from the lower radiator header tank is pumped through the jacket and cored head, past the open thermostat and into the upper header tank.

The thermostat is a heat-sensitive valve. When the coolant is cold, as in the case of an engine that has just started, the thermostat is closed. The radiator is blocked and the only circulation is back through the engine by means of the bypass hose or port. At a predetermined temperature the thermostat opens and allows some flow to the radiator. Full circulation is restored when coolant temperature reaches 180°F or so.

System Checks

Overheating is endemic in lift trucks and particularly so as they age. While no checklist can anticipate all problems, this checklist modeled after one devised by IHC, has proved to be useful.

- Check the radiator, pump, hoses, and connections for leaks while the engine is running.
- Check for dirt or dust in the radiator core, damaged fan blades, worn out belts and pulleys.
- Check the pressure cap. Use a tester to verify that it holds the pressure stamped on it.
- Check that the radiator overflow tube is clear.
- Check for compression leaks. You will be able to detect them as bubbles in the header tank.

- Check the antifreeze content for the lowest anticipated temperature. If more is needed, use the same brand.
- Check the idle speed to see that the engine is turning freely.
- Check ignition timing and, on diesel engines, fuel-pump timing. Timing errors can cause overheating.
- Check the pump for possible vapor lock. While rare, this can happen if the engine has been run under a heavy load and suddenly shut down.
- As a last resort, take the truck out on the floor and verify that it is overheating. Operators have been known to deliberately overheat trucks when they felt the need of a small vacation.

Water Pump

Figure 8-3 shows a heavy duty water pump in cutaway. The shaft is supported on two ball bearings with grease seals at their outboard sides. A cast-iron impellor is pressed over the end of the shaft and rides against a spring-loaded water seal. The back plate that caps the pump cavity is not shown.

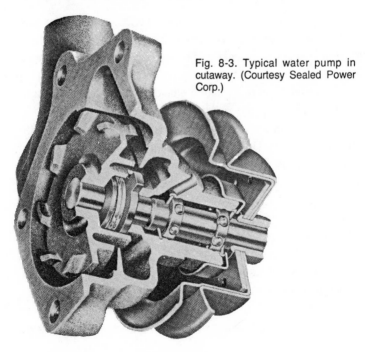

Fig. 8-3. Typical water pump in cutaway. (Courtesy Sealed Power Corp.)

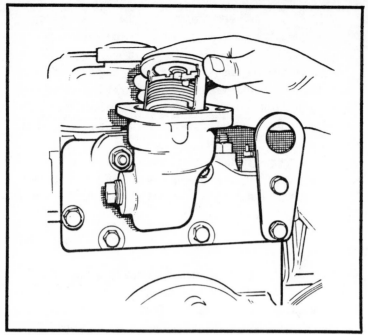

Fig. 8-4. Removing the thermostat on a Lansing Bagnall truck.

Pump failure can have several symptoms, most of them associated with the bearings and seals. Noise is the result of oil seal failure (and subsequent bearing failure) because of lack of lubrication. In an emergency, you can delay further damage by adding water pump lubricant or even brake fluid to the coolant. Eventually the pump will have to be replaced.

Serious water leaks from around the drive pulley mean that the main seal has failed. These leaks may be present when the engine is running or at rest. But a few drops of water at the vent port under the nose of the pump are normal. Some leakage is necessary to lubricate the seal.

Lateral, side-to-side movement of the shaft and fan means that the bearings have gone. In most cases this symptom is accompanied by noise and severe water leaks. But pumps have been known to remain watertight until the shaft wallowed through the bearings and cut into the housing.

Determine pump output by removing the upper radiator hose at the thermostat housing. Water should cascade out of the housing in a steady stream. In addition to pump failure, low output can be caused by a collapsed lower hose or by a stuck thermostat. Remove the thermostat from its housing and check it (Fig. 8-4). It should be in the closed position when cool. (Refer to the section on thermostats later in this chapter.)

It's not practical to rebuild pumps in the field. A press and special fixtures are needed to dismantle the impellor and (in some cases) the hub. Parts are difficult to come by. The choice boils down to a factory-rebuilt or a new pump. Rebuilt pumps can give good service, although there is always something of a gamble involved. Even with the best intentions in the world, a rebuilder cannot match the precision of a new pump. Whenever possible, rebuilders use the original shaft and a new impellor, but the new impellor will not make the same metal-to-metal contact as the original one did. Water seals must be shimmed to allow for the metal lost when flycutting the seats. The quality of parts also depends upon the rebuilder's reputation since there are no national standards for rebuilt parts. The use of new pumps—at least those from the major manufacturers— obviates these difficulties.

When replacing a water pump, scrape the block mounting surface down to bright metal. Use plenty of heavy sealant (3M yellow weatherstripping adhesive is a favorite) on both sides of a new gasket.

Water Jacket

Check the external engine surfaces for leaks, with particular attention paid to the joint between the head and block and to the hose connections. The smallest trickle of rust means trouble, even if the coolant loss is too small to be noticed. Whenever coolant escapes, air enters. And air accelerates corrosion.

According to General Motors, 1 inch of cast iron coated with 1/16 inch of rust and scale has the insulating value of 4 1/2 inches of cast iron. Unless a chemical inhibitor is used, the water passages gradually silt over. After a few years these accumulations become so thick that they break off and collect at the base of the water jacket and across the cored head passages. Local hot spots develop and the coolant breaks into steam.

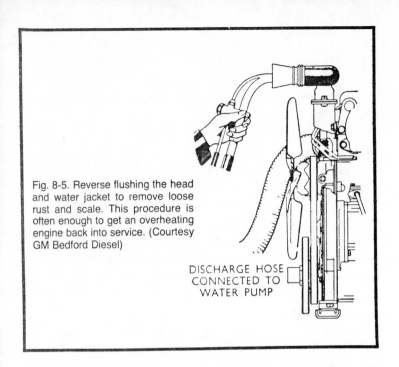

Fig. 8-5. Reverse flushing the head and water jacket to remove loose rust and scale. This procedure is often enough to get an overheating engine back into service. (Courtesy GM Bedford Diesel)

DISCHARGE HOSE
CONNECTED TO
WATER PUMP

The best and surest way to remove rust and scale is to have the block boiled out at an automotive machine shop. All nonferrous parts must be removed, including the camshaft bearings.

Since boiling out is impractical between overhauls, mechanics must use other expedients. Cold chemical cleaners, added to the radiator, can help although you shouldn't expect miracles. This is particularly true if the water in your area has a high mineral content. Follow the instructions on the container package to the letter, since really effective cleaners do not discriminate between rust, scale, and virgin metal. Neutralize the cleaner afterwards.

Every shop should have a flushing gun of the kind shown in Fig. 8-5. The gun is connected to a water hose and to a high-pressure air line. The output—several quarts of water at 100 psi and more—is guaranteed to clear the jacket of loose scale and rust.

For best results, follow this procedure:

- Drain the system.
- Remove the thermostat and replace the housing.
- Disconnect the lower hose and install a discharge hose to the pump inlet fitting.

306

- Mount an adaptor on the hose fitting at the thermostat housing.
- Apply air in short bursts. Continue until the discharge is clear.

Thermostats

Most thermostats are the metal-bellows and wax-pellet type shown in Fig. 8-6. Normally the thermostat is closed, blocking off flow to the radiator. As the coolant warms the wax becomes liquid and expands, forcing the bellows open.

Most faults are readily apparent. The frame members may fatigue and break, and cracks can develop at the folds of the bellows. If it seems mechanically okay, heat it in a pan of water and ethylene glycol. A 50/50 mix will delay the boiling point to 227°F. Support the thermostat with a length of stiff wire so it does not touch the sides of the container. The temperature stamped on the frame is cracking temperature. Full opening should occur some 40 degrees higher.

Radiators

Most radiator cores are made of copper and fitted with brass tanks. The radiator may include a heat exchanger for the oil clutch or

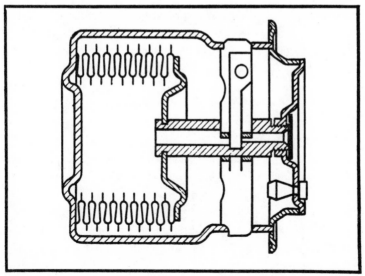

Fig. 8-6. Cross section of a typical thermostat. (Courtesy GM Bedford Diesel)

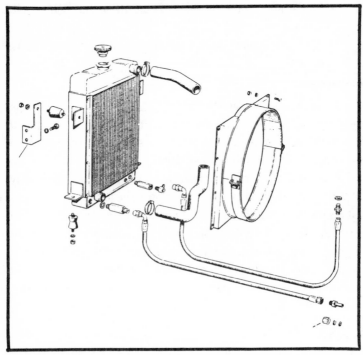

Fig. 8-7. A complete radiator assembly as found on Rubery Owen gasoline and diesel trucks. The high-pressure hoses service the oil cooler in the lower header tank.

transmission (Fig. 8-7). Aluminum cores, although acceptable for automotive systems, are not practical for lift-truck applications because of the difficulty of repair. A few trucks have been built with steel cores, but the use of steel is limited to desert and other highly abrasive environments.

Core configurations are tailored to the application. The canted Z-core is most popular (Fig. 8-8A). Each row of tubes is offset relative to the next to slow the airstream. Some trucks, particularly those intended for construction and textile mill work, are fitted with woods cores (Fig. 8-8B). In this arrangement the tubes are mounted in parallel rows and supported by widely spaced fins to reduce clogging. These cores are nearly always cooled by pusher fans.

The next drawing, Fig. 8-9, illustrates header tank construction. The horizontal baffle reduces turbulence and distributes coolant equally to each of the core tubes. The bleed tube vents air that might be entrapped under the baffle. The upper and lower header

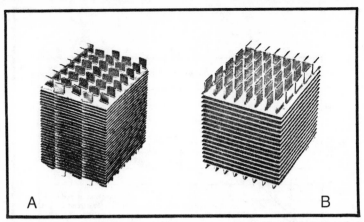

Fig. 8-8. Two popular radiator core constructions. View A is known somewhat cumbersomely as the canted-tube Z-core. It is intended to produce maximum air turbulence and heat transfer. The woods core, shown in View B, is less efficient in terms of heat dissipation, but tends to be self-cleaning. (Courtesy International Harvester Corp.)

tanks are coolant-storage areas. The amount of coolant that can be lost without overheating or excessive air entrapment is known as *drawdown* capacity. The higher the drawdown capacity the better, since the cooling system deteriorates with age. Figure 8-10 shows acceptable drawdown capacities for systems of from 20- to 360-quart capacities.

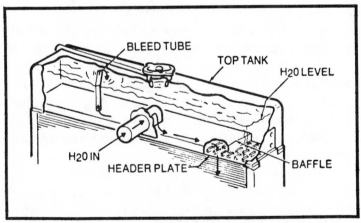

Fig. 8-9. Typical head tank construction. The header plate, a baffle, reduced trubulence and distributes water evenly to the core tubes. The bleed tube vents air that can become entrapped under the baffle. (Courtesy International Harvester Corp.)

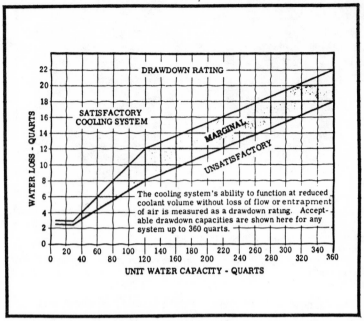

Fig. 8-10. These suggested drawdown ratings were computed by IHC and can be used to test the efficiency of the cooling system.

The coolant level should be kept to within an inch of the bottom of the filler neck or level with a mark on the tank or overflow canister. If the system is depleted, fill and recheck after the engine has run long enough to open the thermostat.

Blow the radiator fins clear as needed. Once a month is enough when handling cartons on a clean floor. Once an hour may not be enough when the machine is handling baled cotton or jute. A three-to four-foot length of steel tubing attached to the blowgun will give the user some dust protection and makes the job easy enough to assure that it is done as often as needed. The air stream should be played rapidly back and forth across the fins and against the direction of fan currents.

Core tubes eventually coat over with rust particles and scale. Reverse flushing can get the machine back into service, although the radiator should be sent to a specialist for chemical cleaning. Drain the system and disconnect both hoses. Fit a throttled-down flushing gun (maximum 30 psi for new radiators and no more than cap pressure for ones that have seen much service) to the lower hose (Fig. 8-11).

Allow the radiator to fill between air bursts. Continue the drill until the discharge flow is clear.

While the average mechanic does not have the time or experience to separate the header tanks, rod out the core tubes, and solder the radiator back together as a watertight assembly, he can cope with small leaks. The trick is in the preparation of the metal for soldering.

Solder forms a molecular bond. When heated, lead and tin molecules interchange with those in the base metal melding the two parts into one. But for this to happen the joint must be chemically clean. Oil, oxidation, or even a fingerprint is enough to block the molecular interchange. Begin by wire brushing the parts to be joined with a dry, clean steel brush. Then sand the area down to bright metal with medium-grit paper. Besides removing whatever residue was left from the brushing, the sandpaper will score the surfaces for a better solder bond. Coat the area lightly with flux, even if you are going to use flux-bearing solder. The traditional flux is a mixture of dilute hydrochloric (muriatic) acid and powdered zinc.

If the crack is very small you can use a pencil-type torch. Otherwise use an ordinary butane torch, but with discretion. Too

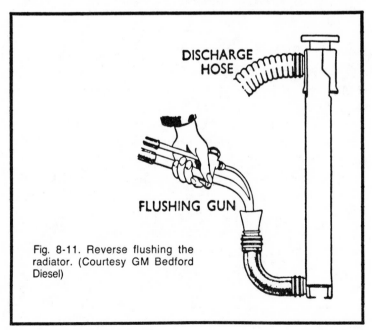

Fig. 8-11. Reverse flushing the radiator. (Courtesy GM Bedford Diesel)

DISCHARGE HOSE

FLUSHING GUN

Fig. 8-12. A one-piece, rivetless hose clamp available from American Parts supply houses.

much heat will weaken the other joints. Apply a light coat of 60/40 solder to the joint. This process is known as tinning. The solder should lie flat and be attracted toward heat. If it bubbles and skates, the joint is not clean and should be sanded and fluxed again. Do not attempt to tame the solder by applying more heat. When the tinning takes, the solder will harden into an almost mirror-like surface.

Test the repair in a water tank. Block off the outlet and pressurize the radiator with compressed air regulated to about 20 psi. A stream of bubbles, as opposed to an occasional bubble that detaches itself from the fins, means a leak.

Hoses and Clamps

Hoses are a necessary evil needed to isolate the radiator from engine vibration. Replace the hoses before they become hardened, heat checked, or soggy at the centers. It is not unusual for a weakened lower hose (one whose wire reinforcement has rusted away) to collapse under pump suction. To remove, loosen the clamp and give the hose a quarter turn to break the seal.

Hose clamps also fail either by becoming so butchered that they cannot be tightened, or by stripping out. Perhaps the most durable clamps are the spring types of the sort fitted to several late-model trucks. Their shortcoming is that a special tool or a pair of pliers slotted to grip the clamp ears are needed. Most mechanics prefer the stainless-steel aircraft clamps because of their convenience. Figure 8-12 illustrates one with a very noteworthy feature—the screw housing is a single-piece casting. They normally outlast several of the riveted types.

Pressure Caps

Modern systems are pressurized to 3 to 15 psi. While pressure stresses the system, and makes Niagaras out of pinhole leaks, it has its advantages. Pressure helps to contain air and steam bubbles, and raises the boiling point of the coolant. At 4 psi, the boiling point of water is raised 15°F. This allows the engine to operate at its most comfortable temperature without danger of coolant loss.

The pressure cap separates the atmospheric vent from the radiator. The pressure relief valve (No. 1 in Fig. 8-13) seals against a flange at the base of the filler pipe, below the overflow port. It opens at the preset pressure stamped on the cap. The vent valve opens after shutdown when the coolant shrinks and cools. Without it, the system would operate at less than atmospheric pressure and the coolant would soon boil off.

The only way to be sure about a pressure cap is to test it under pressure with a tool such as the one shown in Fig. 8-14. Repeat the test on the radiator filler neck, because the pressure developed at the cap is only as good as the integrity of the system.

Fans

Because lift trucks spend almost as much time going backwards as forward, direct-drive, fixed-pitch fans are the only choice. Most

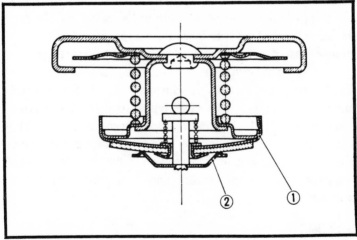

Fig. 8-13. Section of a pressure cap. The relief valve (1) forms a seal against the flange on the filler neck; the vent valve (2) opens to restore atmospheric pressure to the system after shutdown. (Courtesy Chrysler Corp.)

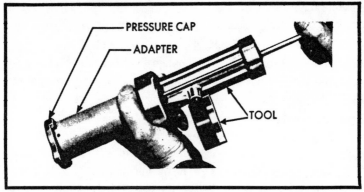

Fig. 8-14. A pressure cap and cooling system tester. (Courtesy Chrysler Corp.)

are pushers, exhausting through the radiator and into the depression formed behind the vehicle as it moves forward.

Inspect the fan carefully. Cracks usually develop at the root of the blades and grow until the blade separates from the hub. Warped blades reduce fan output, load the water pump bearings, and can cause the fan to grenade from a combination of flutter and fatigue.

It is possible to marginally increase cooling capacity by modifications to the fan and the fan drive. In the past, these modifications were made almost as a matter of course, and often in lieu of correcting the problem that caused overheating in the first place. (Today the situation is clouded by OSHA regulations, which take a dim view of any change in the as-delivered state of the machine.) The most common of these fixes is to move the fan closer to the radiator by means of spacers. Purchase a single spacer thick enough to position the fan within a half inch of the radiator. Do *not* stack spacers to get the clearance. Secure the fan with new, high-quality fasteners. Another technique is to fit a venturi-type shroud. Most trucks come from the factory with a box- or ring-type shroud, neither of which is particularly efficient. After-market fans are available in a wide range of diameters, pitch lengths, and blade configurations. Most of these fans deliver more air (and absorb more horsepower) than factory originals.

Drive Belts

Fan and water pump output depends upon the ability of the drive belt to transmit power. A V-belt works by means of the wedging action of its sides against the pulley groove. It requires just enough tension to guide the belt into the groove. More tension wastes power and stresses the bearings, and less allows standing waves to develop that dance the belt off the pulleys. The exact specifications vary with the machine and the power required to operate the fan and pump. As a general rule, the belt should deflect 1/2 inch per 10 inches run between pulleys under 25 pounds force. In other words, if the distance along the belt between the harmonic balancer and the water-pump pulley is 15 inches, the center of the belt should deflect 3/4 inch under moderate thumb pressure (Fig. 8-15).

Examine the belt carefully. It should ride well above the base of the pulley grooves as shown in the left-hand drawing in Fig. 8-16. If it bottoms, the belt and possibly the pulley are worn out. Very little power can be transmitted until this condition is corrected. A belt that is worn on one side and almost like new on the other is running on misaligned pulleys. One that is worn on both sides in a scalloped

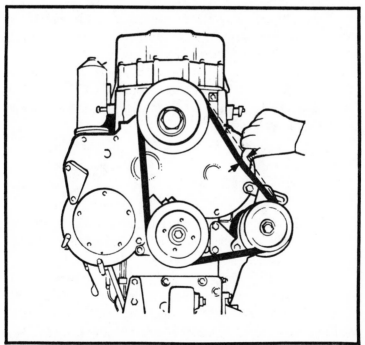

Fig. 8-15. Testing belt tension in the traditional manner on a Lansing Bagnall truck.

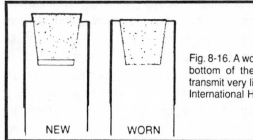

Fig. 8-16. A worn belt will drop to the bottom of the pulley groove and transmit very little power. (Courtesy International Harvester)

NEW   WORN

pattern is slipping because of insufficient tension. Heat checks—a pattern of jagged cracks running across the bottom edge of the belt—are additional evidence of slip.

Replace belts that show any of these symptoms. When dual belts are used (as in the case of some Clark machines), replace them both as a set. Otherwise you will not be able to balance the tension, and one belt will do most of the work.

Coolant

The purity of coolant water is taken for granted by most truck owners. Other users are more particular. For example, ships do not take on boiler water in Houston because of the salinity of the city water supply. If at all practical, you should use water that is relatively free of corrosive sulfates and chlorides and has no more than 20 grains of dissolved solids per gallon. In terms of parts per million (ppm), the allowable limits are:

chlorides	40 ppm
sulfates	100 ppm
dissolved solids	340 ppm
total hardness	170 ppm

Clean and relatively inert water is the first line of defense against rust and scale. A non-chromate rust inhibitor also must be used.

Most lift-truck manufacturers suggest that ethylene glycol permanent-type antifreeze be used year round. Commercial preparations, Prestone, Zerex, etc., include a rust inhibitor. Ethylene glycol raises the boiling point of the coolant. A 30% concentration brings the boiling point up to nearly 220°F in systems operated at atmospheric pressure. A pressure cap boosts the boiling point further. At the same time, the freezing point is lowered to $-18°F$. A 67% ethylene glycol mixture boosts the boiling to 238°F and keeps the coolant liquid at temperatures as low as $-70°F$. Stronger mixtures continue to raise the boiling point, but have little effect on the freezing point. Pure ethylene glycol gives no better freeze protection than a 40% concentration does.

Ethylene glycol is expensive—about $4 a gallon in bulk—and is not as good a medium of heat exchange as water. Adding ethylene glycol will cause the system to run somewhat hotter than on pure water. But the effect is compensated for by the higher boiling point. A more serious objection is the possibility of oil contamination. Should the head gasket fail, coolant can enter the crankcase. When this happens the oil is converted to a species of hard taffy. Unless forced, the engine will slowly bog and stop. If you're lucky, you can flush the system without dropping the pan. Here's how:

1. Drain the oil sump.
2. Remove and discard the oil filter element.
3. Mix two parts Butyl Cellosolve with one part SAE 10 motor oil. (Butyl Cellosolve and equivalent chemicals will attack skin and paint. Handle with care and wash off spillage with clear water.)
4. If the machine is not fitted with an oil-pressure gauge, install one at the oil-pressure sender port.
5. Run the engine for 30 minutes or so at a fast (1200 rpm) idle. Observe the gauge and be ready to shut the engine down instantly if the pressure should drop.
6. Stop the engine and drain the crankcase and filter. Allow adequate time for the thickened oil to drain.
7. Refill with SAE 10 motor oil and run at a fast idle for 10 to 15 minutes.
8. Drain the oil and change the filter element.
9. Fill the sump with the oil recommended for normal service.

As a final check, allow the engine to idle for 30 minutes or so. Then shut it down and restart it immediately. If cranking speed is noticeably slower than it was before, the system is still contaminated. The engine must be torn down for a part-by-part cleaning. Find and correct the cause of the leak before releasing the engine for service.

9

Engine   Overhaul

A truck engine, maintained by conscientious mechanics and operating in a clean environment, should go 6000 hours or more between overhauls. LPG and diesel engines may clock more hours.

OPTIONS

When it's overhaul time, the owner has six options. He can purchase a factory new engine. This choice will assure him another 6000 hours or so of reliable operation, the first few hundred of which are covered by warranty. Or he can economize a bit and purchase a new short-block assembly. A short block includes a new block, crankshaft, connecting rods, pistons, and flywheel. Since the head, alternator, and other accessories are not included in the package, the owner's labor costs include some assembly work as well as installation. Reliability is somewhat compromised, although the short block itself is protected by warranty.

The third choice is to have the engine rebuilt by specialists. A number of firms have earned a good reputation in this field. Repco Industries (11612 Wright Road, Lynwood, CA 90263) specializes in rebuilding Continentals and can supply Allis-Chalmers, Buda, Baker, Chrysler Industrial, GMC, Hercules, and other heavy engines from stock. Or, as is often done, the owner can contract locally for the work. While skillfully rebuilt engines give very good service they do not, in my experience, have quite the durability of new engines. The cost is, of course, lower.

Or the owner may wish to purchase a used engine, particularly if his block is worn so severely that it is useless in trade. There is a kind of gray market in industrial engines but, unless you know the history, a used industrial engine can be a poor bargain. These engines are much more valuable in a machine than on blocks, and are not taken out of service for casual reasons. Automobile engines are, of course, available from wrecking yards and can often be transplanted into lift trucks. American engines are quite inexpensive since there is little demand for Chrysler sixes and the like from hotrodders. But a word of caution—because an engine will bolt up does not mean that it will interchange. There are parts number differences between industrial and automotive versions of the same engine. These differences run the gamut from positive valve rotators to water pumps and can mean the difference between a reliable engine and one that breaks down every few hundred hours. In addition, OSHA must put its stamp of approval on replacement parts. It doesn't do that on junkyard engines.

If you still wish to buy a used engine the first rule is to see it run. Secondly, do not purchase an engine that has been involved in a serious front end crash and don't purchase one that is not protected by some kind of written warranty. Inspect the engine carefully before you accept it. If the proprieter will allow, remove the head and oil pan to measure cylinder-bore and crank-pin wear.

The fifth option is to trade the machine in on a newer model. Unless the truck has been singularly abused, its economic life should end about the same time as the second engine. After this point it costs more to continue to own the truck than it does to replace it.

The last, and by no means always the least desirable, option is for the owner to have the work done by his own crew. This can be the most practical alternative if the mechanics are skilled and if the time required for the job does not interfere with production or shop routine.

FACILITIES

Time will be required. Engine building must be done slowly and methodically if it is to be of much benefit. The work area should be

Table 9-1. Standard Bolt and Nut Torque Specifications
(For Ungasketed Applications). (Courtesy GM Detroit Diesel)

THREAD SIZE	TORQUE (lb-ft)	THREAD SIZE	TORQUE (lb-ft)
1/4 -20	7-9	9/16-12	90-100
1/4 -28	8-10	9/16-18	107-117
5/16-18	13-17	5/8 -11	137-147
5/16-24	15-19	5/8 -18	168-178
3/8 -16	30-35	3/4 -10	240-250
3/8 -24	35-39	3/4 -16	290-300
7/16-14	46-50	7/8 - 9	410-420
7/16-20	57-61	7/8 -14	475-485
1/2 -13	71-75	1 - 8	580-590
1/2 -20	83-93	1 -14	685-695

almost antiseptically clean. All critical fasteners must be torqued (Table 9-1). Parts can be a problem since the dealer may not have full stock. Some engine parts are available from LPM (333 East Touhy Ave., Des Plaines, IL 60018) and from Arrow Fork Lifts (1620 Oakland, Kansas City, MO 64126).

In addition to a well designed, safe engine tackle (Fig. 9-1), the job requires standard engine overhaul tools as well as a number of special items. Standard overhaul tools, available at auto parts stores and other outlets, include piston-ring expanders and compressors, valve spring compressors, torque wrenches, and measuring instruments. Inside and outside micrometers are expensive, and consistent readings require practice. Some mechanics get by with a vernier caliper and send the block out to an automotive machinist for precise dimensioning. In addition to the tools mentioned above, most engines require a few special tools unique to the engine in question. These tools are also expensive and hard to come by. They can, however, generally be fabricated in the shop.

Engine removal goes faster with two or more mechanics. But engine disassembly and assembly—the bench work—should be the province of one man alone. A small story will tell why.

Two of us overhauled a Continental flathead some years back. The engine went together effortlessly—without the false starts, back and filling, and the frustrations associated with assembly errors. Our satisfaction evaporated when we cranked it up and heard the knock. My partner thought that a nut or washer had been left on top of a piston. (We both had the bad habit of using the engine block as a workbench.) He pulled the head and found nothing amiss. It almost had to be a loose connecting rod cap. But both of us had definite memories of torquing the caps. And, sure enough, that was it. The number 3 rod cap was finger tight. Joe thought that I had torqued No. 3 and I was certain that he had. Whose fault? Both of ours for splitting the responsibility on a one-man job.

SYMPTOMS AND TESTS

The usual symptom of engine failure is a gradual loss of power that eventually becomes serious enough to hamper the machine in its work. But this symptom is not definitive. The power the engine delivers depends upon the ignition, fuel, and cooling system as well as upon the condition of the running gear and the hydraulics. If loss of power is the only symptom, do not jump to the conclusion that the engine proper is at fault.

More definitive engine-failure symptoms include blue smoke from the exhaust, loss of oil pressure (often accompanied by bearing knocks), seizure, exhaust gases in the coolant and coolant in the oil sump.

The first order of business is to make a compression test. The procedure has been standardized for spark ignition engines:

- Remove *all* spark plugs.
- Disable the ignition system by grounding the high-tension coil lead to the block.

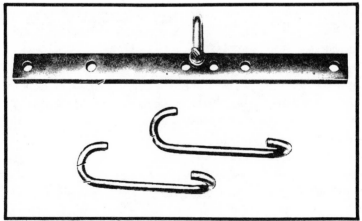

Fig. 9-1. While intended for Peugeot engines, this tackle can be used on all engines.

- Block the choke and throttle plates full open.
- Thread a compression gauge into No. 1 spark-plug port.
- Crank the engine through four compression strokes.
- Note the reading and proceed to No. 2 cylinder.

Taken alone, gauge readings are not entirely meaningful. Compression depends upon a large number of variables. These variables include altitude, temperature, engine compression ratio, starter torque and drive ratio, as well as battery condition. A ballpark figure is 130 psi. The real significance is in the differences between cylinders. For when we compare cylinders readings, we negate all the variables except those that tell something about the condition of the engine itself. Ideally, all cylinders should be within 10—15 psi of each other. A cylinder that generates 25% less compression than the highest of the others is faulty, and this fault should be repaired.

Test procedures for diesel engines vary somewhat. The gauge is fitted with an adapter and installed in place of an injector (Fig. 9-2). The remaining injectors are left in place until their respective cylinders are tested.

With the prominent exception of the GM two-stroke, diesel engines are tested for peak readings while cranking. The control rod is pulled out to the no fuel position and the starter is engaged for approximately 5 seconds to bring the engine up to speed. For best results use a tachometer. Typical readings—and these readings are subject to all of the variables that plague gasoline engines, plus a greater diversity in compression ratios—are in the neighborhood of 275 psi. Again, you are looking for significant differences between cylinders.

Abnormally high readings encountered on either engine type mean that carbon has accumulated in the combustion chamber. While power may be slightly up, sooner or later the carbon will exact a price in the form of detonation. The surest cure is to remove the head and scrape the chambers and piston tops.

Low readings mean that compression is leaking around the piston or the head. Leakage by way of the piston may be caused by worn rings and, more often than not, piston and bore wear. Leakage above the piston usually means valve seal or head gasket problems. Squirting a few teaspoons of oil into the cylinder helps to isolate the

Fig. 9-2. A compression check on a Detroit Diesel. Unlike most other manufacturers, General Motors specifies that the test be made while the engine is running.

leak. If the oil increases compression, the rings are at fault; if not, the problem is above the piston.

A cylinder leakdown test is more accurate than a compression test and only takes a few minutes to make. It amounts to a slow-motion compression test with the engine stationary and compression supplied by an external source.

First remove the spark plugs. Bring the No. 1 cylinder to tdc on the compression stroke. You can do this by feel with your thumb over the spark-plug port, or by trial and error. But the best technique is to use a whistle of the type supplied by Sun Electric for this purpose. The whistle is mounted over the spark-plug port and it goes silent as the piston nears tdc.

Mount the leakdown gauge as shown in Fig. 9-3. Apply 40–200 psi of air pressure to the gauge fitting. Watch the fan. If the engine motors, the piston was not at tdc. Remove the gauge and try again.

Listen for air leaks at the exhaust pipe, radiator filler cap, adjacent cylinders, and at the crankcase breather tube (or PCV fitting) for the following symptoms and cures:

323

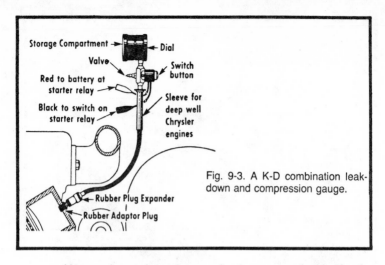

Storage Compartment → Dial

Valve

Red to battery at
starter relay →

Black to switch on
starter relay →

Switch
button

Sleeve for
deep well
Chrysler
engines

Rubber Plug Expander
Rubber Adaptor Plug

Fig. 9-3. A K-D combination leakdown and compression gauge.

- Air escaping at the carburetor intake means a leaking intake valve.
- Air escaping at the exhaust pipe means a leaking exhaust valve.
- Air escaping at the radiator filler cap means a leaking head gasket or cracked casting.
- Air escaping at adjacent cylinders means a blown head gasket or cracked block.

The gauge is calibrated in terms of the percentage of leakdown. In no case should the rate exceed 20%.

A leakdown gauge can also be used to test the integrity of gaskets and seals. This test is particularly meaningful if the engine is operated in a dirty environment, for wherever air leaks, dust enters. Block off the road draft tube or PCV valve connection to seal the crankcase. Remove a spark plug and position the piston a few degrees past tdc on the expansion stroke. Mount the gauge and pressurize the cylinder (the other cylinders should have enough compression to prevent motoring). Listen for air leaks around the sump gasket, front and rear crankshaft oil seals, and valve-cover gaskets.

CYLINDER HEAD OVERHAUL

Unless the engine is up for a complete overhaul, the head is dismounted from the engine, which stays in the vehicle. Drain the coolant at the radiator and block. Remove the upper radiator hose and the thermostat housing, alternator bracket, and manifolds. Remove the spark plugs or injectors.

Rocker Arm Assembly

Remove the rocker-arm cover on overhead valve engines. Plastic sponge gaskets can be reused if intact; cork and composition gaskets should be replaced. Inspect the rocker-arm cover for distortion and bolt-hole pull-down. If the cover bolts have been overtorqued, hammer the edges of the bolt holes level, supporting the lip of the cover on a wood block.

Figure 9-4 illustrates the conventional arrangement with the rocker arms pivoting on a shaft. Remove the pedestal bolts carefully, a few turns at a time. Lift the assembly clear.

Thoroughness requires that the rocker-arm shaft be disassembled for inspection and cleaning. The shaft and rocker-arm bushings

Fig. 9-4. Rocker shaft assembly illustrating the shaft (No. 1), oil feed port (No. 2) and pushrods (No. 3). (Courtesy Ford Industrial Engine & Turbine Operations)

are subject to heavy wear, and together form an important part of the oil circuit. Place the assembly on a clean bench and take a thoughtful look at the parts sequence. If you smoke a pipe, now is the time to light up.

A snap ring or (on older engines) a cotter pin holds the assembly together. Coil springs, usually buffered by washers, separate each rocker arm. The shaft is normally a single length of hardened and polished steel tubing. It is capped and ported to serve as an oil gallery. Oil entry is by way of one of the pedestals (note the oil feed port in Fig. 9-4) or by means of a hollow or relieved hold-down bolt. Each rocker is supplied by a port drilled into the side of the shaft. The oil circuit in the rocker arms may be internal or, as is more often the case, may function by means of spillage through an external port.

Lay the parts out on the bench in their original sequence and position. Rocker arms may have a definite right and left, and are not always interchangeable between banks on V-8 engines.

Give the rocker bushings and shaft careful scrutiny. If the bushings have been oil starved the wear pattern is a series of sharply defined scratches. Should all bushings show this symptom, suspect that the feed port from the pump is clogged. If the symptom is localized at one or two rocker arms, the problem is in the respective shaft ports. Allowable clearance is 0.004 inch.

Clear the shaft oil ports with a drill bit. The end plugs are left in place unless they leak. Replacement plugs and seals can be ordered from the engine builder.

Figure 9-5 illustrates an alternative arrangement. The rocker arm is a simple U-shaped stamping, supported by a stud and pivoting on a slotted ball. Lubrication is via the hollow pushrod. Oil is forced up through the pushrod by the tappet and passes through the small port at the tip of the rocker arm. A second port, not shown, diverts oil to the valve stem.

So long as threaded—not pressed-in—studs are used, this system is completely reliable.

To disassemble, remove the nut and lift the rocker arm and ball clear. Inspect the ball and inner surface of the rocker arm for cracks, pitting, and excessive wear. Replace as necessary. Store ball and rocker assemblies together and in the sequence of removal.

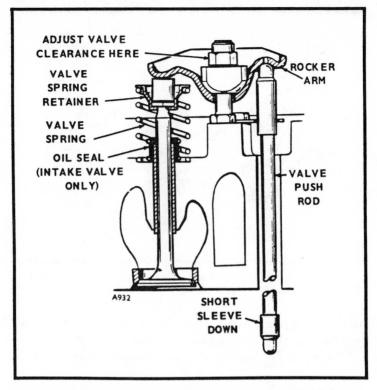

Fig. 9-5. Onan follows modern practice with their stamped rocker arms. In this particular applications the hollow pushrods have a definite up and down.

Withdraw the pushrods one at a time. Chivy the rod a bit to break the hydraulic seal at the tappet. Clean with solvent, blow dry, clear the oil passage, and mount the pushrod on two machinist's V-blocks. Rotate the rod with a dial indicator poised over the center. Deflection should be no more than 0.002 inch (or 0.004 on the dial). If out of tolerance, replace rather than attempt to straighten.

Head Removal

Remove the bolts or studs securing the head to the block. Note their lengths and if any penetrate oil or water passages. Those that do must be coated with sealant before assembly.

The head should lift off. If it is stuck by gasket sealant, gently tap the outer surfaces with a soft-faced mallet. Resist the temptation to pry the head loose at the gasket surface. Rather than take a

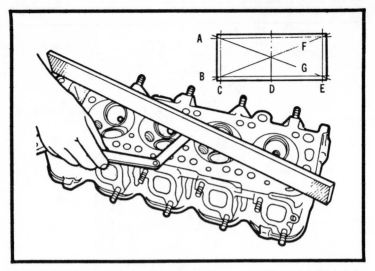

Fig. 9-6. Checking cylinder head distortion with a machinist's straightedge and a feeler gauge. (Courtesy Chrysler Corp.)

chance on warping the head, install the spark plugs or injectors and pop the head off with engine compression.

Place the head, fire deck down, on wooden blocks.

Cleaning

A thorough cleaning is first on the agenda. Every mechanic has a favorite decoking tool. The choice ranges from a dulled screwdriver to a slug of auto body solder. One of the most efficient tools for this purpose is a linoleum knife, ground off square and sharpened. Finish up with a wire brush chucked in a drill motor. Auto-parts suppliers sell a variety of brushes developed for this purpose. They measure about an inch in diameter and have stiff, braided bristles. When you're finished, the chambers, valve heads, piston tops, and gasket surfaces should be bright.

Head Clearances

Use a machinist's straightedge and a set of feeler gauges to determine head distortion. Measure between the points shown on the drawing in Fig. 9-6. Allowable limits vary somewhat between manufacturers, but most mechanics are content if the head is true within 0.00075 times the span length. For example, a 12-inch span that is high or low 0.004 inch is acceptable by this formula. The head would be rejected if the distortion were 0.009 inch (0.00075 × 12). Continental suggests that no more than 0.006 inch be allowed on the long span with 0.003 inch as the maximum on the short dimension.

Heads that fail to measure up can be lightly machined—so long as the compression ratio remains with acceptable limits. For this reason, the amount of cut should be stamped on the head as a guide to mechanics in the future. Typical spark-ignition heads can be taken down 0.015 inch before detonation becomes serious. Diesel heads are much more sensitive and their manufacturers provide a minimum thickness dimension. Detroit Diesel heads must measure no less than 4.376 inches between the fire deck and the upper surface of the casting (Fig. 9-7). If the head is so warped that a deeper cut is necessary, the whole assembly must be replaced.

Head Tests and Repair

Cylinder heads look massive and unyielding. But under thermal and pressure shocks the head moves and crawls between the head bolts. Small cracks become deep chasms. Most shops use some form of magnetic particle detection, such as the Magniflux system. This system involves a power supply, a movable electromagnet, and steel filings. The filings are sprinkled over the inner surface of the head and the magnet is slowly passed over them. Cracks in the metal—even cracks below the surface—act as magnetic poles and attract the filings, and so reveal themselves.

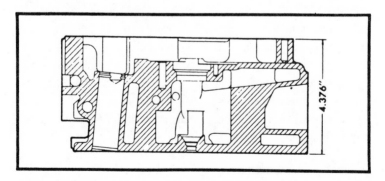

Fig. 9-7. Like all diesel makers, GM publishes minimum head height specifications.

Fig. 9-8. A valve-spring compressor of the type used for Lansing Bagnall trucks.

The next test may seem academic to harried truck mechanics, but it can save an engine—particularly if ethylene glycol is used. Block off all the water ports with steel plates backed by soft rubber gaskets. Diesel engines should have dummy injectors installed to keep the injector sleeves in place. Drill and tap one of the water port covers to accept an air fitting. Pressurize the core at 100 psi and place the head in a tank of water that has been previously heated to near boiling. Allow it to cook for 20 minutes or so and check for air bubbles. Since any leaks discovered at this stage will be deep in the casting, repairs are ruled out. Replace the defective head.

The best advice is to discard a cracked head. But this is not always possible, particularly when you are dealing with an obsolete engine whose parts stock was destroyed in the Johnstown flood. A cold fix can sometimes be made by drilling a row of tiny holes along the path of the fracture. The holes are filled with soft steel pins, peened over to make solid contact. A hot fix can sometimes be made by a good welder, one who knows his way around cast iron, using a high nickel content rod. Nickel has about the same coefficient of expansion as cast iron and will remain in place if the welder can get penetration.

Valves

A simple lever-type compressor is adequate to release over-head valves (Fig. 9-8). Side-valve engines require a plier-like tool capable of exerting and holding pressure on the valve caps. It is always a good idea to plug the oil drain port in the chamber on these engines. Otherwise you may find yourself dropping the pan to recover a valve keeper.

The rocker arm tilts the valve outward as it forces it down. Wear tends to notch the stem at the limits of valve movement. The stem diameter should not be reduced by more than 0.002 inch. Or, by the traditional test, the notches should not be defined enough to snag your thumb nail.

Store the valves, keepers, springs, pushrods, and rocker arms in numbered racks for later assembly.

The valve guides are critical since they assist in valve cooling, and guide the valves into their seats. More than 0.004 inch clearance is excessive and the guide should be reamed for oversize stems or replaced. The most accurate way to check guide wear is with an inside micrometer or a plug gauge. Another method is to measure valve wobble with a dial indicator as shown in Fig. 9-9. The valve is raised to the limit of its working lift and moved into and away from the indicator. You are allowed 0.017 inch.

Most manufacturers stock valves with oversized stems, apparently as a production convenience. Ream the guide to give 0.002 inch running clearance. If it is necessary to replace the guide (no manufacturer supplies valve stems of greater than 0.030 inch oversize and most stop at 0.015 inch), first check its depth in the block. Some guides are bottomed on a flange, but many (e.g., Continental) are

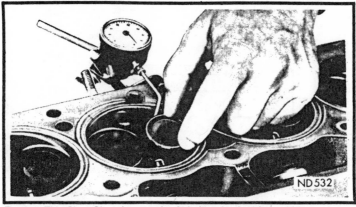

Fig. 9-9. This Slant Six exhaust valve is being checked for wobble.

installed to a predetermined depth. Normally the old guides are knocked out and the new ones pressed home and reamed for a 0.001–0.002 inch stem clearance. Ferroxed guides are distinguished by what appears to be an internal thread. These guides are factory sized and should not be reamed. Installation is delicate; the block should be warmed and the guide chilled in dry ice and gently pushed into place. If the temperature differential is great enough, you will be able to install the guide painlessly, without changing the inside diameter.

Valve Work. Valve lapping is an almost forgotten art. One has visions of coolies grinding valves along the Burma Road. A coolie would work over a "deuce-and-a-half" until he dropped, only to be replaced by another.

In theory, lapping produces a perfect seal. The valve face and seat are ground in together so that they become mirror images of each other. In practice, lapping doesn't work so well. Lapping widens the valve contact area and reduces the unit force applied by the spring. Nor does the perfect seal remain so when the engine gets hot.

If you are going to lap valves, do the job right. First check the eccentricity of the valve face and the stem. More than 0.002 inch eccentricity means that the valve will not seat—no matter how much lapping is done. Replace the valve or have it machine ground. Slip a few turns of coil spring under the valve, between the head and the

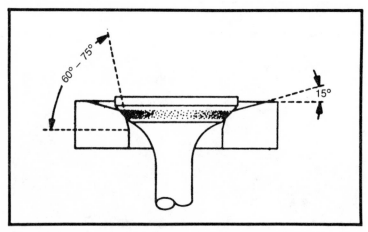

Fig. 9-10. Continental valve seat profiles are typical of most.

guide. The spring should exert just enough force on the valve to unseat it. Valve grinding compound is usually packed in double-sided tins. One side contains coarse compound for fast cutting and the other fine for finishing. Dab a little coarse compound around the periphery of the valve, using no more than necessary. It is important that the compound stays put and does not dribble down into the valve guide. There are special tools for this job, but few mechanics ever see them. Most use a stick and suction cup. Wet the cup and secure it to the valve head. Rotate the stick between your palms, like a Boy Scout making a fire. Occasionally lift the valve and give it a half turn so that the whole seat is ground. Replenish the compound frequently. If the valve runs dry it will score.

You are finished when the valve makes a dull thump as it is dropped on the seat. A valve that rings is not making full contact. Carefully remove every trace of lapping compound.

Machine grinding is superior to lapping in almost every respect. The only hitch is that some discretion must be used. It is easy to get over-enthusiastic with the grinder and change the valve-port profile or bury the valve up in the head. Either event costs horsepower and wasted fuel.

First determine the valve face angle. Most engines require a nominal 45° face angle, and seats are normally 45 degrees. Some makers, in an attempt to improve gas flow, specify that the intake valves be ground to 30 degrees. Flow is not of much concern on the exhaust side and a 45° angle is usually specified. But don't guess at or attempt to discover the angle with a protractor. Check the specs.

Seat width is another variable. It is fixed by undercutting the valve seat insert after the preliminary cut has been made. The entry angles shown in Fig. 9-10 apply to almost all engines. The seat width should be approximately 1/16 inch and the margin, or the vertical edge of the valve head, should be no less than half its original size. This dimension is particularly critical in exhaust valves, since a knife-like margin will overheat and send the cylinder into preignition. Valve height is also critical and especially so with diesel engines. It may be measured from the fire deck or as the assembled height of the valve (Fig. 9-11).

Check the work by coating the insert with Prussian blue. Allow it to dry and give the valve a quarter turn. All of the blue should

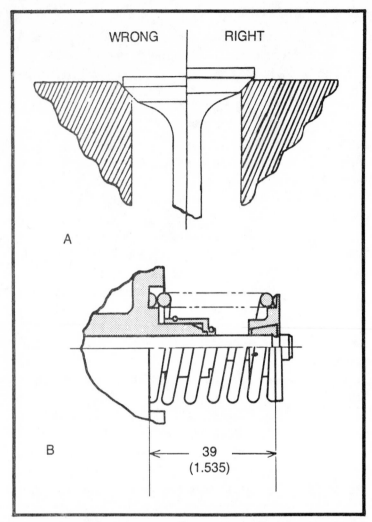

WRONG | RIGHT

A

B

39
(1.535)

Fig. 9-11. The height of the valve is important in terms of compression ratio and gas flow. Continental and other manufacturers think of valve height as the protrusion of the face into the chamber (View A). Chrysler Nissan uses assembled height as the guide (B).

transfer to the valve face. Skips or ragged edges mean that the valve or seat requires more work.

Inserts. Valve seat inserts are standard for most industrial engines. The few that run the valves on cast iron can be counterbored for inserts when the occasion arises. Some Perkins models and many small utility engines are in this group.

Figure 9-12 illustrated an insert puller. These tools are expensive and difficult to find outside of a dealer shop. You can make one up with a short section of channel iron, a large bolt, and a heavy washer. Installing a replacement insert requires a modicum of skill and patience. The shrink fit between the insert and its counterbore is all that holds it in place. Tool marks, metal shavings, or excessive force applied during installation will destroy the fit.

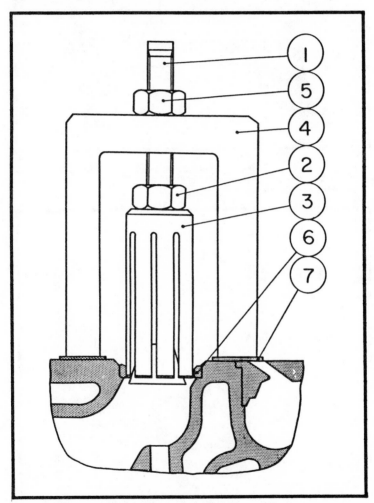

Fig. 9-12. A valve seat insert puller. As the nut (No. 5) is tightened, the shaft (No. 1) draws the cone up and spreads the claw (3) against the valve seat insert (No. 6). The frame (No. 4) is mounted on copper pads (No. 7) to protect the head. (Courtesy Chrysler-Nissan)

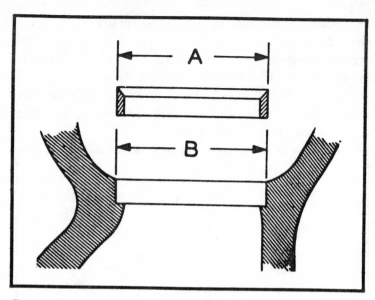

Fig. 9-13. The difference between the insert o.d. (A) and the bore i.d. (B) is the interference fit. Modern designs, like this Continental, depend entirely upon the interference to hold the insert in place.

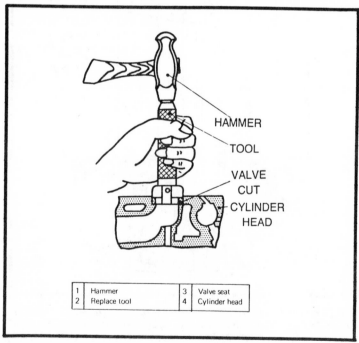

| 1 | Hammer | 3 | Valve seat |
| 2 | Replace tool | 4 | Cylinder head |

Fig. 9-14. Installing the insert on a Chrysler-Nissan engine.

The insert is replaced with an original equipment part, unless the counterbore has been damaged by a floating insert or ham-handed mechanics. Oversizes and reamers to match are available. The interference fit should be on the order of 0.003 inch (Fig. 9-13). Continental's U Series is an exception—experience shows that these engines are happier with an 0.005 inch fit.

The head or block should be heated to expand the counterbore. If you do not have a heat gun, a hot plate is adequate, particularly if the element is in physical contact with the counterbore. It is not suggested that you use a torch. Chill the insert in dry ice and alcohol for 20 minutes or so. Handling the supercooled insert with pliers, place it over its counterbore and drive it home (Fig. 9-14). Work quickly before the temperatures of the parts equalize.

Springs. Examine the valve springs for pitting, flaking, and flattened coils. Compare the freestanding length against a new spring, and discard any that vary by 10% or more. Some manufacturers supply a tilt specification as well (Fig. 9-15). This is checked by placing the spring on a flat surface and measuring the amount of tilt using a square. If at all possible, determine the tension and loaded length with a torque wrench and spring tester.

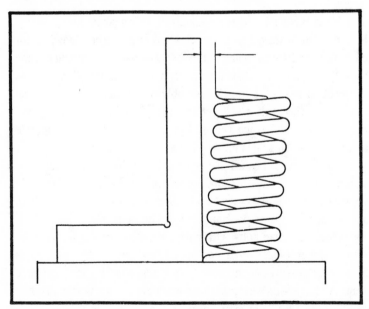

Fig. 9-15. Valve spring tilt is a good index of fatigue. (Courtesy Chrysler-Nissan).

Seals. One problem with overhead-valve engines has never been completely solved. The valve gear needs cascades of oil. It is very possible for oil to be drawn past the valve guides and into the combustion chambers. OEM seals are generally quite primitive and consist of a rubberoid shroud between the valve stem and the guide. A seal of this type is shown back in Fig. 9-5. While the first line of defense is to keep stem and guide clearances within specification, there are times when the original seal should be replaced by something better. Perfect Circle supplies after-market seals that are positively secured by snap rings and made of long-wearing Teflon. In most cases the guide must be counterbored to accept the seals.

Head Installation

Head gaskets are usually marked *Front* or *Top* (Fig. 9-16). Some gaskets are not marked and appear to fit with either side down. If you'll look at the gasket you'll see that one side has heavier crimping than the other. This is the side that goes down on the block. The rationale is that the gasket moves under load and wears the head and block, and the side with the least crimping should cause most erosion. Head resurfacing is an easier proposition than block resurfacing.

Most mechanics apply sealant to the gasket and castings. Kopper-Kote is an old-time favorite and is said to do wonders for mismatched surfaces, filling in the low spots and smoothing out the high. But engine specialists are not always so enthusiastic about this or any other sealant. Later disassembly is difficult and there is a real danger that the sealant will get into the oil and coolant passages.

To assemble, place the gasket on the block, checking once again that the top side is up and that all working passages are open. Carefully lower the head. It is very important that the head go down square without any last minute corrections that could tear or crimp the gasket. While the job can be done by eye, it is not much trouble to use a pair of studs or decapitated head bolts as pilots.

Clean the head bolts with particular attention to the threads. Dab a smear of antiseize compound (available from auto parts houses) on the threads and under the heads. Run the bolts up finger tight, not forgetting wiring-harness brackets, spring tabs, and other miscellaneous bric-a-brac secured by the head bolts.

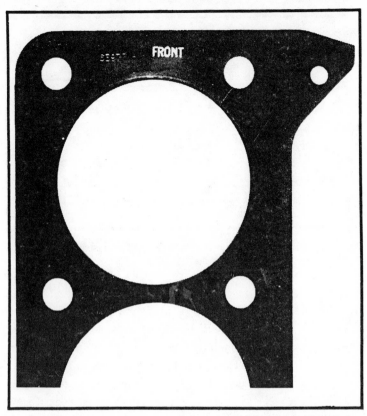

Fig. 9-16. The Bedford practice is to mark the front of the gasket. The lettering should be up.

The torque sequence should be in the owner's manual since the head bolts should be retorqued after the first 50 hours of operation. While the sequence can become a bit complex if three or four rows of fasteners are used, the basic principle is to begin at the middle and work out to the ends (Fig. 9-17). The torque specification varies between engines, but in the absence of factory data, these figures are not far off:

Bolt Diameter (Inches)	Torque (Foot-Pounds)
3/8	35–40
7/16	70–75
1/2	100–110
9/16	130–140
5/8	145–155

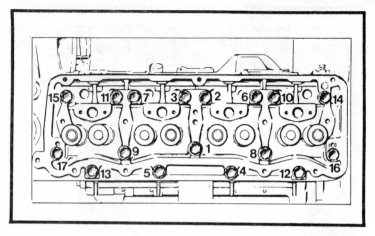

Fig. 9-17. Cylinder head torque sequence on a Ford industrial engine.

Approach final torque in three stages, running through the sequence each time.

Install the pushrods in their respective tappets and position the rocker-shaft assembly. See that each rocker is over a pushrod and that the pushrods remain in their sockets. Tighten the hold-down bolts very slowly, working out from the center in a crisscross fashion. Torque to specification. If valve work has been done, the valves may not seat until the adjustment screws are backed out a few turns. Flood the assembly with oil.

Mount the manifolds (using new gaskets), injectors or spark plugs, and other miscellaneous hardware. Fill the radiator and check the oil level in the sump. The engine is ready to start.

The valve lash or clearance refers to the distance between the toe of the rocker arm and the end of the valve stem when the valve is seated. The specification may be given hot or cold. Hot specifications require that the engine be run up to operating temperature before the valves are adjusted. Cold specifications mean that the adjustment is made at room temperature. The adjustor is at the pushrod end of the rocker arm and generally consists of a screw and locknut (Fig. 9-18). Some modern engines, e.g., Ford and Chrysler, simplify matters by eliminating the locknut. The set screw has an interference thread and, at the moderate engine speeds encountered in lift truck applications, is proof against loosening. The Detroit Diesel, which is a very different engine in so many ways, has the adjustment provision at the pushrods. The rocker-arm end of the pushrods is threaded and secured by a locknut. Lash is set by loosening the nut and turning the pushrods.

Hot lash adjustments are normally made while the engine is ticking over at idle. Cold lash is best done by barring the engine over. Which valves are seated at one time depends upon the number of cylinders, the firing order, and (to a lesser extent) upon the camshaft grind. Without a chart, the surest bet is to successively bring each cylinder up on the compression stroke.

ENGINE BLOCK OVERHAUL

The old-fashioned overhaul, consisting of new rings, main and connecting-rod bearings, and a rear seal, is pretty well obsolete today. Labor costs are such that it is wiser to rebuild the engine—that is, to grind the crankshaft, rebore the cylinders, and to replace

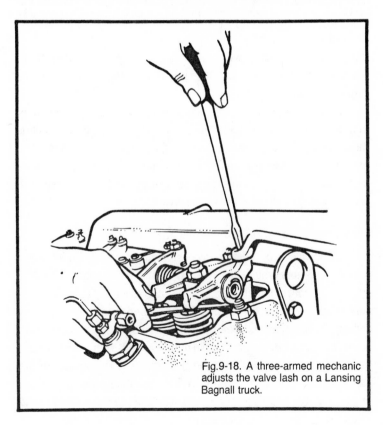

Fig.9-18. A three-armed mechanic adjusts the valve lash on a Lansing Bagnall truck.

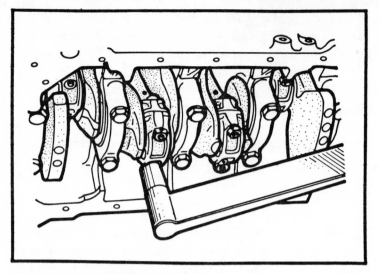

Fig. 9-19. Rod cap bolts. Before disturbing the connecting rods, make note of the numbers on the rods (which should correspond to the cylinders) and the match marks. (Courtesy Chrysler Corp.)

the oil pump, together with all bearings and gaskets—than to attempt short-term repairs. This means that the engine must be removed from the vehicle.

Few shops service a fleet large enough to justify an investment in automotive machine tools. Instead, the stripped-down block is taken to a machinist who specializes in engine rebuilding. The machinist should supply the parts that go into the engine. Otherwise he must depend upon published specifications and tolerances which are not always reflected in the hardware.

Connecting Rods

The connecting rods are accessible after the oil pan has been removed. Before you put a wrench to the rod capnuts, check if cylinder numbers, match marks, and other assembly clues are present (Fig. 9-19). Each rod should be numbered for the cylinder it serves. If the engine has been rebuilt previously, the numbers may be out of sequence. Deface the old numbers and, with a prick punch, make new ones on the base of the rod cap. Note the position of the match marks relative to the crankshaft or some other prominent engine feature. This determines which side of the rod is forward and

Fig. 9-20. This professional quality ridge reamer is available from the Sealed Power Corporation.

can affect oiling. If the cap is reversed upon assembly, the rod will not form a true circle.

Most caps are secured by self-locking nuts. Some Japanese models employ sheet-steel jam nuts as backups against the cap nuts. Jam nuts should be renewed each time the rod is disturbed. Remove one cap at a time, together with its bearing insert. Using a hammer handle, drive the piston and rod up and out of the cylinder bore. Unless the bore is severely worn, the piston will slip out with a minimum of fuss. Otherwise it will be necessary to ream the "lip" that forms at the top of the bore (Fig. 9-20). Once the assembly is free, replace the cap and nuts.

Displace the wrist (gudgeon) pin far enough to disengage the small end of the connecting rod. Most pins are *full-floating*; that is, the pin is free to pivot in the small end and on the piston bosses. The pin is held by circlips or spacers. (See Fig. 9-21.)

While the pin floats on the piston bosses, it only does so at operating temperature. A typical fit is 0.00012 inch cold. Most

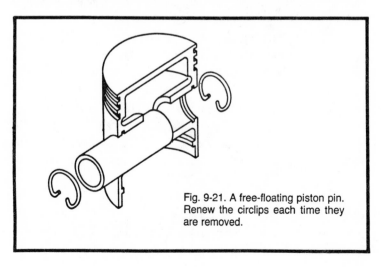

Fig. 9-21. A free-floating piston pin. Renew the circlips each time they are removed.

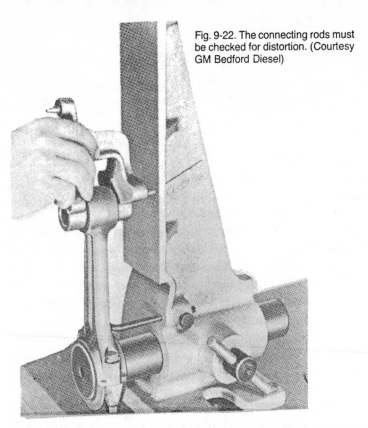

Fig. 9-22. The connecting rods must be checked for distortion. (Courtesy GM Bedford Diesel)

mechanics simply drive the pin out, risking rod and piston damage in the process. A better method is to heat the piston to 150°F or so. Use rags dipped in hot oil or an electric hot plate. Discard the circlips since they are too critical to be reused.

At this point the connecting rod is free and we can begin our examination of it. Assemble the cap, less bearings, and torque to specification. Compare the diameter of the big end against specifications. If it is less than the factory intended, the cap has been filed in an attempt to close up bearing clearances. The rod should be scrapped. The cap bolts should be a light push-fit into both the rod shank and the cap.

Using a jig like the one shown in Fig. 9-22, determine rod parallelism and twist. Out-of-parallelism must not exceed 0.002 inch. Twist must not exceed 0.005 inch per 3 inches of rod length. Corrections can be made by bending the rod with a well-padded monkey wrench. It may be necessary to slightly overcorrect to get the rod back into specificaiton. Do not scratch or burr the surface, since any irregularity acts as a stress riser and encourages fatigue.

Have your machinist inspect the rod for surface cracks. Either the fluorescent or magnetic particle methods can be used, although the former gives a better indication of subterranean cracks. Typical crack formations are shown in Fig. 9-23.

Rod Bearings

The small end bushing should be replaced if wrist-pin clearance exceeds 0.0015 inch. Supporting the eye of the rod, press the old bearing out. Position a new bushing over the eye so that the rod and bushing oil holes align. Press home and ream to size.

All modern engines employ precision insert-type bearings on the big end. The traditional way to check bearing clearance is to torque the rod cap and take several micrometer readings across the inner diameter of the bearing. Do the same for the crankshaft journal. The difference between these two measurements is the running clearance. It should be no less than 0.001 inch and, for an engine that is already apart, no more than 0.002 inch. Another method is to use Plasti-Gage.

A product of the Perfect Circle Corporation, Plasti-Gage is one of the best ideas to come along in years. It gives accuracy comparable to a micrometer and at a tiny fraction of the cost. To use, bar the engine over to bring the connecting rod to its bottom dead center position. (The bearings get most wear at bottom and top dead centers.) Remove the cap and wipe the insert and crankshaft journal dry. Pinch off a length of Plasti-Gage and lay it along the length of the cap as shown in Fig. 9-24. Torque the cap to specifications, exactly as if you were assembling the engine. Remove the cap and compare the compressed width of the Plasti-Gage with the scale on the package. The greater the width, the tighter the bearing clearance.

Bearing inserts are replaced in pairs. The upper half may not be identical with the lower because of oil holes and grooves. Mismatching the two will block off lubrication.

Various undersizes are available. Inserts 0.001 inch and 0.002 inch under stock diameters are used to compensate for journal wear.

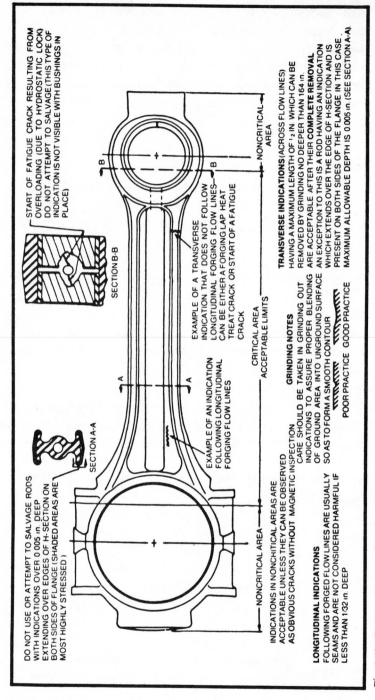

Fig. 9-23. The significance of crack patterns in connecting rods. (Courtesy Detroit Diesel Allison)

Smaller undersizes (available in ten thousandths) require that the crankshaft be reground. Some crankshafts tolerate as much as 0.040 inch under original dimensions; others go soft at 0.020 inch.

Chrysler engines are unique in that they may be delivered with oversized rod or main bearings and crankshafts ground to match. The code is on the numbering pad, located on the right side of the Slant Six block and just aft of the coil. Look for a Maltese cross (the kind painted on the Red Baron's airplane). The codes are:

Cross	One or more rod or main bearings are 0.001 inch under. Bearing numbers are stamped on the center counterweight of the crankshaft.
Cross and X	All connecting rod or main bearings or both are 0.010 inch under.

Fig. 9-24. Since Plasti-Gage is soluble in oil, the cap and journals must be dry. (Courtesy GM-Bedford Diesel)

Cross, X, and R-1, R-2, etc.	Indicated rod bearings are 0.010 inch under.
Cross, X, and M-1, M-2, etc.	Indicated main bearings are 0.010 inch over.

Extreme cleanliness is required when installing new inserts. Remove every trace of oil from the big end and cap. Slip the inserts home with the locking tabs anchored in their respective notches. Flood the bearing surface with clean engine oil. Torque the cap bolts evenly and in several increments, to specification. Do not over-torque since additional strain will only weaken the bolt. Turn the crankshaft over to see that the rod moves freely. If it binds, the first place to check is the match marks. They should be in line with each other and on the same side of the rod as originally installed. Position the rod up against the crankshaft cheek and check the side clearance with a feeler gauge (Fig. 9-25).

Cylinder Bores

Cylinders are classified as *integral* or *sleeved*. Integral cylinders are cast as part of the engine block. This is a standard automotive practice. The best that can be said for this approach is that it is simple

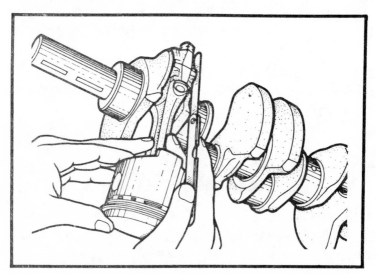

Fig. 9-25. A Chrysler mechanic checks connecting rod side clearance.

and reliable. But the quality of the bore material is compromised by the demands made upon the block as a whole. An engine block must be rigid and pourable. That is, it must be able to withstand the forces generated in the engine and faithfully follow the contours of the mold when cast. The bore, on the other hand, should resist wear and acid attack. The two sets of demands have never been wholly compatible and are more divergent in late model engines.

In recent years, thin-wall castings have become popular. But the precision needed to cast thin water and cylinder jackets demands special irons that don't wear as well as those formerly used. No thin-wall engine can compare with the early Ford V-8s in terms of bore longevity. These engines were cast in a kind of semisteel that poured with the reluctance of cold molasses.

A more obvious disadvantage of cast bores appears at overhaul time. The only way a worn block can be restored is to machine it oversize. Great care must be exercised in this operation. The bore must be at right angles to the crankshaft and finished dead smooth. Pistons for American engines are available in 0.010, 0.020, 0.030, and sometimes up to 0.060 inch oversizes. However, with thin-wall castings, boring the engine much more than 0.040 inch becomes problematic. If the core has shifted, it is not unusual to "strike water" at 0.020 inch.

The results of overboring are marginally more power. The displacement of the engine is increased together with the compression ratio. By the same token, more fuel is consumed and the detonation threshold lowered. Higher octane fuel may be needed, particularly if the head or block has been milled. The engine may be reluctant to operate cold because of the greater surface area exposed to fuel and subsequent condensation.

A more serious problem is the altered balance factor. The crankshaft counterweights match some percentage of piston and upper-connecting rod mass. If the pistons gain a few grams in the transition, engine balance is lost. (This does not apply to Chrysler engines—Mopar pistons weigh the same, regardless of oversize.)

Sleeved bores come in two varieties. *Dry sleeves* (liners) are fitted into recesses in the block. This approach is used to recondition integral bores that have worn past piston availability (or safe operation), and is standard on Perkins and GM Series 110 engines.

The sleeves may be pressed into the block or may be fitted relatively loosely and secured by a flange and counterbore. The fit is critical and must not be guessed at. Nor is the extension of the sleeve above the bore subject to estimate. It must be measured and checked against specification.

Dry sleeves are simple castings and add little or nothing to block rigidity. The alloy used (pearlitic cast iron, rich in phosphides and graphite) gives excellent ring wear. The disadvantage is that the interface between the sleeve and bore recess acts as a heat dam. Most piston cooling is by way of the ring belt and the sleeve. Less than full contact can mean sleeve collapse and piston damage.

Wet sleeves are found on some of the most serious engines, including those built by Cummings and Continental. In this arrangement, the sleeve forms the inner wall of the water jacket. Its upper half is completely surrounded by coolant. While this takes care of matters along the upper bore, it interposes a danger below. The danger is that coolant will slip by the sleeve and enter the crankcase. It is not possible to mate the lower edge of the sleeve and the block in any positive fashion. The sleeve must be allowed to "grow" with heat. Most manufacturers solve the problem by using double or triple rows of sealing rings between the sleeve and the block. An alternative is to mount the sleeve on a pad of synthetic rubber and secure it with the cylinder head.

Bore Inspection. Examine the bore under a strong light. Scuffing (the term means small quantities of metal that have melted and torn loose) is dangerous and the underlying causes must be corrected. Check for:

- Insufficient oil to the cylinder bores. Worn oil pump, clogged pump inlet screen, insufficient connecting rod bearing clearances, low oil level, contaminated oil.
- High combustion temperatures. Detonation, preignition, excessive lugging or overspeeding.
- Cooling system failure. Rust or scale deposits in the water jacket and head core, clogged radiator, worn water pump, loose drive belt, sticking thermostat.

Scuffing can occur in any engine, whether it is sleeved or not. But sleeved engines have special problems of their own. As mentioned earlier, dry sleeves depend upon the fit in the block for proper cooling. For example, V-71 series GM engines call for a sleeve-block clearance of 0.000-0.002 inch, while the in-line 71 and 110 series are set up with a 0.0005–0.0025 inch clearance. Aluminum 71 blocks must be heated to 160–180°F when late-production, press-fit liners are used.

In general, a flanged liner—one that depends upon the cylinder head for security—should enter the block one-half to three-quarters of the way down and require only light tapping on a hardwood block to seat it against the counterbore. A correctly fitted liner is light-straw colored on the outside diameter; one that is too loose will have carbon deposits on the o.d. and may show blue temper marks on the inside diameter. A liner that is too tight in the cylinder can scuff, distort, and even buckle under the stress.

Wet liners are secured in the block by the liner flange and counterbore. Flange breakage may occur if the flange is out-of-parallel with the fire deck, if the inner edge is worn, or if the flange protrudes too far above the fire deck. In addition, this problem can be caused by over- and under-tightening the head bolts or by tightening them out of the specified sequence.

Scuffing on the inside diameter in the seal area is caused by improper assembly techniques. Examination will show that the seal rings twisted or rolled in their grooves. A slight twist in one of these synthetic rubber seals can pinch the sleeve inward and narrow the running clearance.

To avoid this, place the seal in the liner groove with the parting line of the seal centered all the way around the circumference of the groove. This will eliminate twist and center the seal in the groove. Coolant leaks—that mechanic's nightmare—can be eliminated by the use of new seals and careful preparation of the lower-block sealing area. Any trace of rust and scale must be removed (Fig. 9-26). After long service the sealing area will wear egg-shaped. This must be corrected by remachining, or remachining and installing a bushing. While these measures are a bit out of the ordinary routine of engine building, they must be carried through. For if the sealing area is worn, it will leak and may cause the liner to fracture as it moves with the piston.

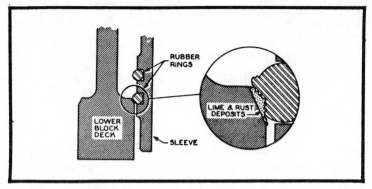

Fig. 9-26. All traces of rust and scale must be removed from the seal contact area if the joint is to be watertight. (Courtesy Sealed Power Corp.)

Regardless of cylinder construction, bore wear has a definite pattern. Greatest wear is at the upper limit of ring travel and shows up as a ridge extending about a half-inch below the fire deck. The depth of the ridge is a rough indication of cylinder condition.

Bore measurement is concerned with the degree to which the bore is worn oversized, the amount of taper, and the amount of eccentricity. Measurements must be taken at several points along the bore and across several diameters. The most convenient tool is a cylinder gauge like the one shown in Fig. 9-27. An inside micrometer may also be used, although accurate readings require a degree of skill that not all mechanics possess.

Bore dimensions are a matter of factory specification and should not be hazarded. Ball-park tolerances are 0.002 inch taper from top to bottom and 0.003 inch out of round. Allowable wear can be as much as 0.008 inch, although most mechanics call for a rebore when wear reaches 0.006 inch.

Reboring requires precision equipment of the type rarely found in a lift-truck maintenance shop; the engine must be taken to an automotive machinist for this work. However, dry or wet sleeves can be replaced without much difficulty. Figure 9-28 illustrates the tool used to remove both types and to install interference-fit (flangeless) dry sleeves. New sleeves and their block mating surfaces should be cleaned with trichloroethylene or the equivalent. Inspect the block sealing area for wet sleeves as detailed previously and the flange areas. The o.d. of interference-fit dry sleeves must be

352

unblemished—the slightest burr can cause block distortion and seal collapse. Some manufacturers employ silicone rubber seals. If this is the case, lubricate the seals only a few seconds before installation, since oil causes silicone to expand. Dry sleeves should be wiped with clean oil along their outside diameters.

Honing. Replacement sleeves are factory honed with an accuracy impossible to match in the field. But honing is necessary for used bores, whether or not they have to be machined oversize.

When viewed under a microscope, a correctly honed bore appears to be broken by a series of sharply defined grooves, running in a crisscross pattern at 22–32 degrees from the vertical. The areas between the grooves, called *plateaus*, account for 50–70% of the cylinder bore surface. The grooves serve as reservoirs for oil and also act as havens for metal and abrasive particles. The plateaus are flooded with oil and in theory the rings should skate on the oil without ever making metal-to-metal contact.

Ideally, honing should be done with automatic machines working through guide plates bolted to the fire deck. However, an acceptable job can be done with a low-speed drill motor (preferably in half-inch capacity) and a spring-loaded hone.

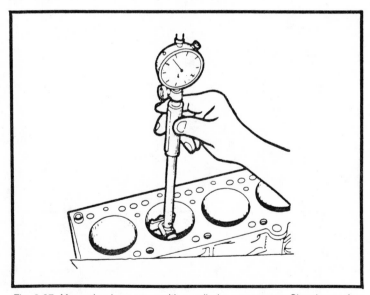

Fig. 9-27. Measuring bore wear with a cylinder gauge on a Chrysler engine. (Courtesy Chrysler Corp.)

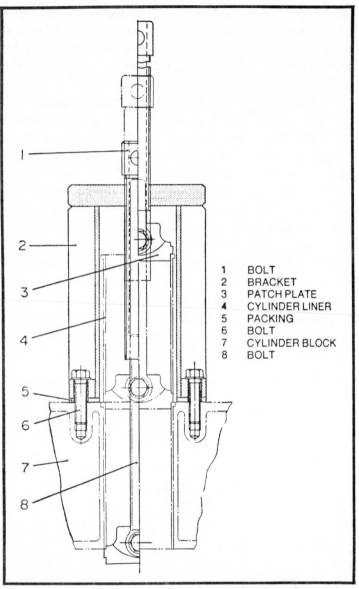

1	BOLT
2	BRACKET
3	PATCH PLATE
4	CYLINDER LINER
5	PACKING
6	BOLT
7	CYLINDER BLOCK
8	BOLT

Fig. 9-28. While this cylinder liner tool is designed for Chrysler-Nissan diesel engines, it can be adapted to others.

Select a 220–280 grit stone with code J or K hardness. Use plenty of cutting oil to flush the bore and hone and to keep temperatures down. The best oil, according to research done by the Sealed

Power Corporation, is straight-run mineral oil with a viscosity of 45 SUV at 100°F. Kerosene and Varsol also may be used.

Match the motor speed and reciprocation speed to obtain the required 22–33 degree diamond pattern. For heavy-duty drill motors this amounts to about 70 strokes a minute. Remember that the hone cuts as it rotates—do not pause at the end of the stroke. Adjust the tension spring for a light drag. Too much pressure increases stone wear to no good end and can cause the hone to oscillate in the bore. Wipe the stones clean before proceeding to the next cylinder and whenever score marks appear on the finish.

When the bores have taken on a uniform burnished appearance, without glaze slicks or deep scores, the job is finished. More metal removal than necessary is wasteful.

Every trace of abrasive dust must be removed from the bore. The crosshatch finish makes this a more difficult chore than is generally realized. Swabbing the bores with kerosene or some other petroleum-based solvent is worse than useless. The particles simply float deeper into the metal. The only way is to scrub the cylinders with hot water—as hot as you can stand—and detergent. Continue to scrub until the suds are white. Flush with clean water, dry, and oil.

Pistons and Rings

The whole history of the engine can be seen in the condition of the pistons and rings. In many cases simple wear is the least of the problems and the underlying cause of failure must be discovered and corrected.

Ring Maladies. The rings should be polished to a mirror-like sheen. Rings that are dull gray have been lapped. Suspect a failed air-filter element or air leaks in the intake tract. Another possibility is that the bores were not scrubbed properly after honing.

Wear on the sides of the rings may be traced to excessive cylinder taper, contaminated oil, or worn piston grooves. Breakage may be the fault of the mechanic who last overhauled the engine, particularly if the edges of the break are worn. Other possibilities include hammered-out piston grooves and improper operation. Lugging the engine under load and overspeeding both generate tremendous vertical pressures on the rings. Detonation can also break rings, although it usually takes out a piston first.

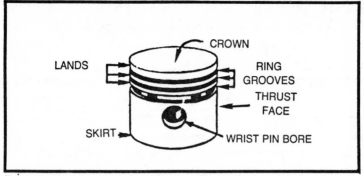

Fig. 9-29. Piston nomenclature. (Courtesy Clinton Engines Corp.)

Piston Faults. The first sign of burning is an irregular depression in the piston crown or top. It appears as if someone had been busy with a chipping hammer. As the crown erodes, temperatures increase. Ultimately the affected area becomes molten and the piston holes. The shape of the hole sometimes allows a mechanic to distinguish between preignition and detonation. A burned-through hole is usually caused by preignition; one that is blasted out, as if by an armor-piercing shell, is the result of detonation. In any event the cause must be corrected before the engine is fit for service.

Most wrist pins are secured by spring clips (circlips). Clip failure is disastrous since it always involves the loss of the piston and may destroy the bore as well. The usual causes are excessive crankshaft end play, tapered connecting rod journals, lock rings that have been overstressed during installation, and misaligned connecting rods. Overstressed lock rings can sometimes be detected by an uneven wear pattern in the pin groove. Rod misalignment leaves its signature on the thrust surfaces (the skirt areas perpendicular to the axis of the wrist pin). Look for a diagonal wear pattern that may be above the pin on one thrust surface and under it on the other.

Piston Fitting. Pistons are cam ground in order to give a greater diameter between the thrust faces than at the wrist pin bores. When the engine is started cold only the thrust faces contact the bore. (See Fig. 9-29 for piston nomenclature.) As the piston heats and expands, it fills out to an approximation of the bore circumference. In addition, most pistons are slightly tapered at the crown. The amount of taper varies with the manufacturer and the

356

piston type, but it is on the order of 0.00125 inch per inch of piston height. In theory, the taper disappears under operating temperatures.

The distance between the thrust faces is normally specified as piston diameter.

Soak the piston in a *noncaustic* chemical cleaner. Sears paint remover seems to work better than most commercial cleaners. Allow as much time as you can spare for the carbon to dissolve and scrape the rest of it out with a grooving tool (Fig. 9-30). Use a drill bit to clear the oil spill ports at the base of the last groove.

Ring groove width is critical—so critical, in fact, that some manufacturers gird their pistons with bands of cast iron for added strength. The difficulty is that the hammering action of the rings widens the grooves. Two factors are at work. As the piston moves up and down, the rings are thrown against the sides of the grooves. But even worse, gas pressures from combustion tends to drive the rings down against the lower edge of the groove. The No. 1 compression ring, the one closest to the action, is affected most by the high-combustion pressures. Eventually, the grooves hammer open wide enough that the rings twist, and, being cast iron, they are brittle and soon break.

It is necessary to accurately determine the width of the groove. For if the groove is too wide, the new rings will break; and if too narrow, the rings will stick. Measure each groove in the following manner:

- Clean the groove to remove any trace of carbon.
- Back a *new* ring into the groove as shown in Fig. 9-31.
- Insert a feeler gauge *above* the ring. If the groove is hammered out, the gauge will enter at a slight downward angle. A clearance of 0.001–0.003 inch is normal. More than 0.004 inch is cause for concern.

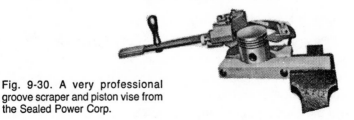

Fig. 9-30. A very professional groove scraper and piston vise from the Sealed Power Corp.

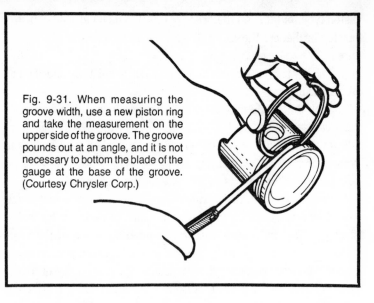

Fig. 9-31. When measuring the groove width, use a new piston ring and take the measurement on the upper side of the groove. The groove pounds out at an angle, and it is not necessary to bottom the blade of the gauge at the base of the groove. (Courtesy Chrysler Corp.)

It's possible to restore pounded out grooves by turning the groove oversize on a lathe. But this takes skill, particularly when dealing with modern, narrow-ring pistons. The sides of the groove must be dead parallel and at right angles to the base. Otherwise the ring will twist and can break under working pressures. Once the groove is cut oversize, a spacer is installed over the ring to restore the original clearance.

Examine the piston-pin boss for cracks and score marks. The most accurate way to determine pin fit is to compare pin and boss diameters. The difference is the cold working clearance and should be between 0.0000 inch and 0.0001 inch on a new engine. The allowable service clearance is 0.003 inch. In practice, this means that the engine is considered safe to assemble if the pin goes into the piston boss with a palm-push fit. If you can mate these parts with a lighter, thumb-push fit, the piston, the pin, or both should be replaced.

Ring Fitting. The ring set the factory specified when the engine was built may not be the best choice for replacement. Original equipment rings are known as *factory sets*. They work fine with tight-fitting pistons and accurately machined cylinder bores. But worn engines respond better to *engineered sets*. These rings are tensioned by springs to conform with worn or tapered bores. In some cases, the ring material is more flexible than originally specified and the ring profile is more tolerant of piston dislocations.

Engineered sets reduce oil consumption in worn engines, but exact a penalty in additional bore friction and higher fuel consumption. They should only be used in worn engines.

The end gap, the distance between the ends of the ring when it is installed on the piston and in the bore, is too important to be left to the factory. An overly wide gap costs power and may increase oil consumption. One that is too narrow leaves insufficient space for ring growth, and under operating temperatures the ends butt together and the ring shatters, destroying the piston and possibly the bore.

There are two theories about where the end-gap measurement should be taken on a worn engine. Some say that the gap should reflect the average diameter of the bore and the measurement should be at the center of ring travel. The ring is in this position in Fig. 9-32. Others opt for the base of the bore where there should be almost zero wear. This position gives a safety margin since errors in ring gap should be on the wide side. In any event, use a piston to seat the ring squarely in the bore. The specification used to be 0.005 inch for each inch of bore diameter. But engines built in the last decade

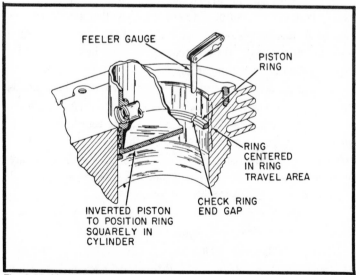

Fig. 9-32. Measuring ring end gap in a Tecumseh engine. Note the way the piston is used as a pilot to square the ring in the bore.

359

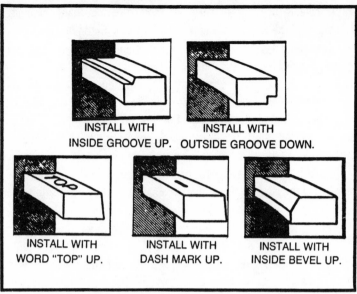

INSTALL WITH
INSIDE GROOVE UP.

INSTALL WITH
OUTSIDE GROOVE DOWN.

INSTALL WITH
WORD "TOP" UP.

INSTALL WITH
DASH MARK UP.

INSTALL WITH
INSIDE BEVEL UP.

Fig. 9-33. Perfect Circle compression rings. Some have their upper sides marked; others must be installed as shown in the drawings.

use a wide variety of ring styles and materials, and the gap specification is not subject to general rule.

Overly wide gaps mean that the ring set has been mislabeled or that the bore is worn out of all tolerance. Gaps that are too narrow must be filed. Special tools exist for this chore, but the average mechanic cannot justify their purchase. Instead, he mounts a flat, single-cut file in a vise and carefully draws the ring over it.

Determine the top side of each compression ring. This sounds elementary, but upside-down rings and subsequent blowby and oil consumption is a major risk in engine work. The top sides on some compression rings are marked, on others they are not. Figure 9-33 shows the lay of the most popular ring styles, but the drawings are not exhaustive and can be misleading. For example, reverse-beveled rings are installed with the groove down.

If you have any doubts whatsoever about the lay of the rings—check with your supplier. A mistake costs a teardown.

Install the rings with the appropriate tool. Prying the ends apart like a wishbone risks splintering the ring. And even if it does not break on installation, it may be weakened enough to fail in service.

360

Various ring expanders are on the market. All of them work to the extent that they keep the ring ends on the same plane. But most concentrate the force they apply on the area of the ring opposite the gap. The K-D tool, shown in Fig. 9-34, employs a spring-steel adaptor to spread the stresses along the whole inner diameter of the ring. Consequently, there is less chance of breaking or fatally weakening the ring.

Fit the bottom or oil ring first. Use an expander with single-piece oil rings. In most cases the ring is symmetrical and has no definite up or down position. Three-piece oil rings consist of a spacer and two steel rails. Install the spacer first. Some are merely butted together; others, such as the Perfect Circle example shown in Fig. 9-35A, have their free ends latched. The ends of both types should meet over a solid portion of the groove. The upper rail is next. Start the rail about 2 inches to the left of the spacer ends and roll it over the piston, doing as little violence to the rail as possible (Fig. 9-35B). The rail seats on a flange at the base of the spacer. Repeat the operation for the lower rail, beginning 2 inches to the right of the spacer ends.

So much for the oil ring. If expander springs are used on the compression rings, install them first, keeping their ends well clear of the ring ends. Place the lower compression ring on the tool. Verify that the top side is up. Expand the ring just enough to clear the piston and drop it into place. Do the same for the upper ring.

Although rings rotate in their bores (at about 90 rpm, according to one study) engine makers agree that the ring ends should be

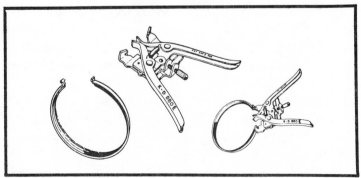

Fig. 9-34. The K-D 880E reduces the chance of ring damage over more conventional expanders.

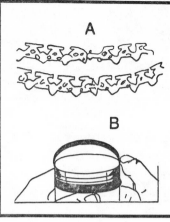

Fig. 9-35. Fitting Perfect Circle oil rings. View A shows the latched spacer; View B shows the way the rail is rolled over the piston.

staggered. The stagger amounts to 90-degree (four ring) or 120-degree (three ring) intervals from each other.

Oil the rings and wrist pin liberally. Some mechanics use the sloppy-but-sure method and immerse the piston, wrist-pin deep, in a container of oil.

Ring compressors come in several varieties. A tapered sleeve that mounts over the cylinder bore is the easiest compressor to use and does least mischief to the rings. The disadvantage of a tapered sleeve is that one must be purchased for each bore diameter. For this reason, most shops use an adjustable compressor of the type shown in Fig. 9-36. To use this tool, follow these steps:

- Cover the ends of the rod bolts with short lengths of fuel line to protect the crankshaft bearing journals.
- Rotate the crankshaft until No. 1 throw is down.
- Check the cylinder number identification on the connecting rod.
- Note the reference mark on the piston. The piston should be installed with the reference mark pointing toward the front of the engine.
- Place the piston and rod assembly in the bore.
- Tighten the compressor enough to overcome ring tension.
- Push the piston down into the bore. Moderate pressure is all that is required.
- Working from the underside of the engine, remove the lengths of fuel line from the rod bolts.

- Oil the bearing inserts and journal.
- Install the cap so that the match marks align.
- Torque the cap bolts to specification.

Main Bearings

The main bearings must form a rigid assembly with the block. The upper bearing halves are machined from the block and buttressed by webs that run across the width of the block. The bearing caps represent a compromise since they must be removable. The most popular approach is to secure the caps with a pair of heavy bolts as shown in Fig. 9-37. In this case, the thrust bearing cap (the cap that takes fore and aft crankshaft loads) is further secured by a dowel pin. The ends of the caps are machined square to index with recesses in the webs. The rear (clutch side) cap is unremarkable in this particular Waukesha engine. But a rear cap may be an interference fit into a block recess. If this is the case, you will need a puller on the order of the one shown in Fig. 9-38 to remove the bearings.

Determine the bearing clearance. If you use the Plasti-Gage method, wipe the journal and cap dry, lay a piece of gauge wire

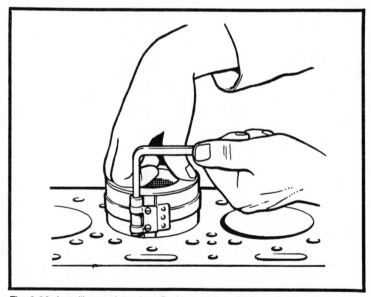

Fig. 9-36. Installing a piston in a Perkins engine. The mechanic adjusts compressor tension at the same time he pushes down on the piston with his other hand. (Courtesy Lansing Bagnall Ltd.)

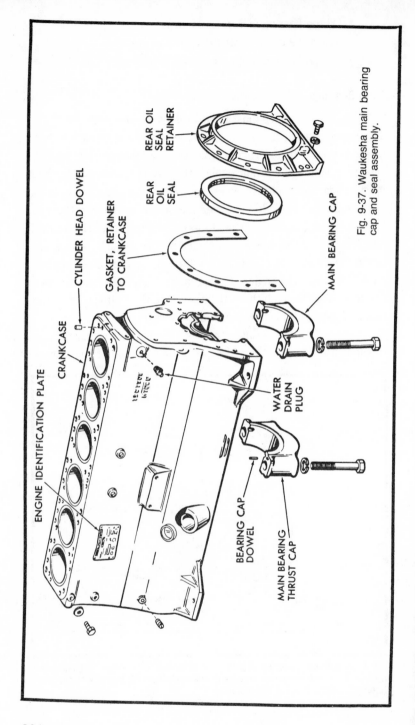

REAR OIL SEAL RETAINER

CYLINDER HEAD DOWEL

REAR OIL SEAL

GASKET, RETAINER TO CRANKCASE

CRANKCASE

ENGINE IDENTIFICATION PLATE

MAIN BEARING CAP

WATER DRAIN PLUG

BEARING CAP DOWEL

MAIN BEARING THRUST CAP

Fig. 9-37. Waukesha main bearing cap and seal assembly.

across the insert, and torque the cap without moving the crankshaft. Remove the cap and compare the width of the gauge to the scale printed on the package. Clearance should be between 0.001 and 0.002 inches.

Bearing inserts are available in 0.001 and 0.002 inch oversizes for use with worn journals. Some engine makers allow, and even encourage, splitting insert shell sizes to obtain optimum clearances. A 0.001 inch oversize can be used with a stock shell or a 0.002 inch oversize with a 0.001 inch. The larger shell is placed on the engine side. Other manufacturers would keelhaul the mechanic who mixed shell sizes. Inserts for reground cranks are available in 0.005, 0.010, 0.020 and sometimes in 0.030 inch undersizes.

Oil Seals

There are two oil seals on the crankshaft, one at the timing gear or chain cover and the other just aft of the rear main bearing. I'll talk about the timing-chain cover seal first.

Remove the accessory-drive pulley and the central bolt that secures the harmonic balancer to the crankshaft. The balancer is pressed over the crankshaft and cannot be jimmied off with a screwdriver or an ordinary gear puller. A special puller, one that threads into tapped holes on the balancer hub, is needed.

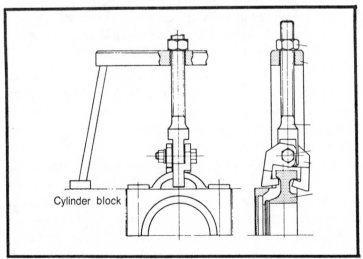

Fig. 9-38. Pressed-in rear main bearing caps always have provision for a puller. (Courtesy Chrysler-Nissan)

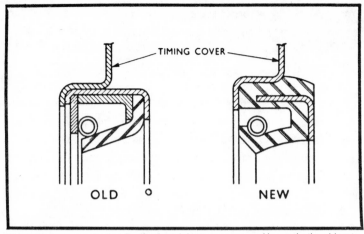

Fig. 9-39. Late-production Bedford seal rings are encased in synthetic rubber to prevent leakage between the ring and timing cover boss.

Once the balancer is off, cam the crankshaft key out of its groove with a pair of side-cutting pliers.

Undo the timing-chain cover fasteners and lift the cover off. Lifting the cover off is easier said than done, particularly if its gasket was assembled with sealant. The safest (and most ineffectual) way of breaking the bond is to tap along the sides of the cover with a mallet. Do not use a hammer.

Should this approach fail, you'll have to pry the cover loose. Force a screwdriver between the cover and the gasket. Confine your efforts to the upper part of the cover. Some warpage is inevitable and it is best to contain it well above the oil level.

The seal is pressed into a boss on the timing cover (Fig. 9-39). In most cases the seal can be pried out with the help of a large screwdriver. If this does not work, deform the seal case (the metal band around the seal) with a hammer and drift. Then remove the seal with a pair of Vise-Grips.

Great care is required to install a seal without damaging the case, boss, or seal lips. The best way to do this is with a press and an arbor sized to exactly match the outer diameter of the case. Without this tool, drive the seal home with a hardwood dowel. Installation pressure must be confined to the outer edge of the case, where the case is strongest. The steep sides of the seal lip are outboard, toward the radiator; the numbered side of the case is toward the engine block. Use enough force to seat the case against the flange at the base of the boss. Use a feeler gauge to verify that the seal makes positive, full-circle contact against the flange (Fig. 9-40). The clearance should be less than 0.0015 inch at any point between the seal case and cover flange.

Mask the crankshaft keyways with tape before mounting the timing cover. The keyway edges are sharp and can cut the seal lips. Wet the seal with oil for lubrication during the initial startup.

Rear seals are available in a variety of styles and materials. Split crankshaft seals are mounted in grooves behind the rear main bearing. One half, known as the upper seal, fits in a groove on the block half of the bearing; the lower seal is mounted in the cap. This construction allows the seal to be replaced without dropping the crankshaft or disconnecting the transmission. These seals may be woven of graphite-impregnated fiber or may be molded in neoprene.

In addition, the rear main bearing cap is flanked by side seals to prevent oil leakage between the cap and block. These seals can be made of fiber or one of the more modern synthetic rubbers, and are usually secured by a cover.

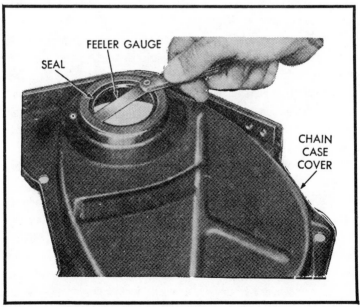

Fig. 9-40. Chrysler Slant-Six seals home on the timing cover. Check the fit with a 0.0015 inch feeler gauge.

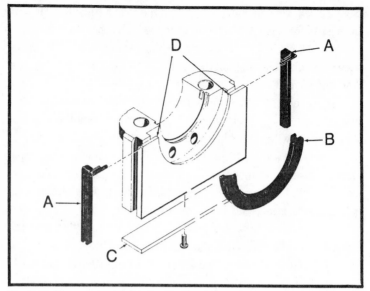

Fig. 9-41. Rear seal assembly for Continental overhead valve engines.

Overhead-valve Continental engines are typical examples of this kind of construction (Fig. 9-41). The side seals are shown at A; the lower crankshaft seal at B; and the side seal cover at C. The upper crankshaft seal is not shown.

Split seals can leak at their rubbing surfaces, through their grooves, or at their ends. Nothing much can be done about the rubbing surfaces, but careful mechanics use gasket sealant (3-M Weatherstripping Adhesive, National Oil Seal cement, or EC-847) on the grooves and seal ends. As further protection, the sharp edges of the crankshaft seal grooves (shown at D in the drawing) should be dulled with a stone.

Chrysler automotive blocks also use a split crankshaft seal. Most blocks are delivered with rope seals, and either rope or molded synthetic can be used as replacements. The side seals are made of a special compound that absorbs oil and swells. Keep the seals dry, protected by their glassine envelope, until a few seconds before installation. Then coat the seals with oil. Secure the seal cover and main bearing cap without delay.

Rope seals are all that are available for many engines. I do not mean that these seals are inferior—on the contrary, they easily accommodate themselves to worn crankshafts and seem to wear

368

longer than molded seals. But installation is complicated by the need to compress the seal halves into their respective grooves. This can be done by guess and by God, but the only sure way is to use a tool such as the one shown in Fig. 9-42. The tool is sized for each engine and matches the diameter of the bearing caps (less the inserts). Once the seal is pressed into place, its ends are cut off flush with the cap.

Without this tool, you'll have to work the seals into their grooves as best you can and trim the ends so that 1/16 inch protrudes above the parting surface of the cap and engine-side bearing boss. Hopefully, the excess will compress the seal when the cap is torqued.

As mentioned earlier, the reason for split seals is to allow the mechanic to replace them without disturbing the crankshaft. To do this, remove the rear main bearing cap and loosen the others. The crankshaft should sag a bit. Remove the seal half from the bearing cap. The upper half is the difficult one, particularly if it is a replacement and was shellacked into its groove. Sometimes it's possible to

Fig. 9-42. GM-Bedford dealers have this seal impaction tool. Once the seal is compressed in the groove, the free ends are cut flush with the bearing parting surface.

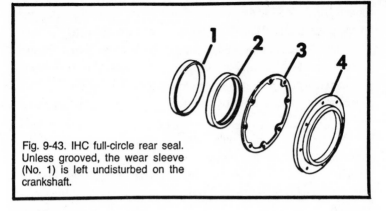

Fig. 9-43. IHC full-circle rear seal. Unless grooved, the wear sleeve (No. 1) is left undisturbed on the crankshaft.

pick the seal out with a small drift and a pair of needlenosed pliers. Stubborn cases require a tool.

The tool is a two-ended affair, one end terminating in a corkscrew and the other in what is known as a Chinese finger trap. The trap is a wire mesh cylinder that shrinks as it is pulled. Work one end of the seal free with the corkscrew and guide it into the trap. Once it is caught, it should pull free.

Carefully feed a new seal into the groove, noting any reference marks. (Chrysler seals, for example, have a paint spot that must be on the clutch side.) If the seal is reluctant to snake its way through, try rotating the crankshaft. You may have to tighten the forward bearing caps to get purchase between the crankshaft and the seal. Place the lower half of the seal into its groove on the bearing cap. Rope seals must be compressed—admittedly a difficult operation when the crankshaft is still in the engine—and their ends trimmed. Leave 1/16 inch standing free above the bearing parting surface.

Full circle rear seals are typical of heavy industrial engines. Figure 9-43 illustrates the seal assembly for IHC 312 and related plants. It is secured to the block just forward of the flywheel and consists of four parts. No. 1 is a replaceable wear sleeve that is pressed over the crankshaft stub; No. 2 is the seal proper, a spring-loaded, lip-type seal of the type used on the timing chain cover; No. 3 is the gasket; and No. 4 the cover. The seal is pressed into the cover and rides on the wear sleeve. No special instructions are needed for removal and installation since the techniques are similar to those discussed in the early paragraphs of this section.

370

Crankshafts

The loving care a mechanic lavishes on a crankshaft is an index of his skill or, perhaps, of his unfortunate experiences. A rebuilt or overhauled engine is no better than its crankshaft. And should the crankshaft fail, the results are catastrophic.

Inspection. The first step is to visually inspect the bearing journals. Wipe them dry of oil and search out any cracks, scores, smears of bearing metal, discolorations, or other signs of distress. Cranks that have seen long service sometimes ridge at the bearing insert grooves. Figure 9-44 shows this ridge in a much exaggerated form. If you plan to install new insert bearings, the ridge must be removed. Minor ridges, those rising less than 0.0005 inch from the journal, can be polished out with crocus cloth wetted in oil. More pronounced ridges call for another technique. Begin with grit No. 120 emery cloth, then go to No. 150. Finish the job with oiled crocus cloth. Emery cloth is a powerful abrasive and can damage the crankshaft unless it is handled with discretion. Tear off enough emery cloth to cover the whole diameter of the journal. Wrap the cloth over the journal and turn it with a loop of rawhide. In this way pressure is applied to the journal evenly. When you're finished, wipe the journal clean and use a pipe cleaner to remove any stray abrasive particles from the oil ports.

Measure the individual journals with a micrometer at several points to determine wear, out-of-round (eccentricity), and taper. Simple wear can be compensated for by 0.001 inch or 0.002 inch oversized inserts. But·no bearing can compensate for taper or

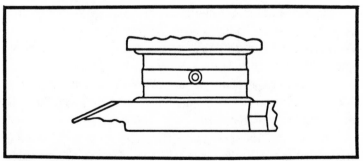

Fig. 9-44. Ridges standing above the journal are caused by the oil grooves in the inserts. These ridges must be removed before installing new inserts. (Courtesy GM Detroit Diesel Allison)

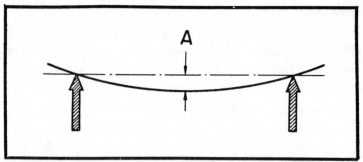

Fig. 9-45. Shaft deflection is measured at the center (point A) with a dial indicator while the ends are turned on precision V-blocks (the arrows). (Courtesy Chrysler-Nissan)

eccentricity. Both of these conditions load the bearing unevenly. Maximum allowable eccentricity is 0.0004 inch and most manufacturers specify something less for taper. Old-line mechanics have been known to reject a crankshaft with any measurable taper.

Further inspection requires that the crankshaft be removed from the engine. It is suggested that you remove the oil gallery plugs and flush out the gallery with solvent. Pay particular attention to the corners. Replace the plugs and peen them over for security.

The crankshaft must be reasonably straight. Otherwise the main bearings wallow and power is wasted. Support the ends of the crankshaft in a pair of accurately cut V-blocks and position a dial indicator over the center journal (Fig. 9-45). Slowly rotate the shaft. The service limit is 0.003 inch (0.006 inch as seen by the dial gauge), but the less deflection the better.

Ordinary crankshafts, whether cast or forged, can be straightened. But crankshafts that have been treated for greater longevity by the Elotherm process will not tolerate press work. These crankshafts are brittle and crack under pressure. By the same token, Elotherm shafts are less likely to bend in the first place.

Magniflux inspection is always a good idea and one that is absolutely necessary after straightening. But, some discretion is required to interpret the results, since crankshafts may be webbed with cracks and still be serviceable. The critical areas are around the oil ports and on the cheeks, just below the pin journals as indicated in Fig. 9-46A. The next drawing, Fig. 9-46B shows typical crack formations as seen with Magniflux equipment.

The location and direction of the cracks has meaning. Those that grow out of the pin fillet and branch off into the connecting rod journal are caused by torsional vibration. Check for a loose flywheel, runaway governor, and unauthorized modifications to the accessory drive system. Cracks that start at the pin fillet and progress through the crank cheek are evidence of crankshaft flex. Check the main bearing bore alignment, the condition of the main bearing inserts, and drive belt tension.

Grinding. "Less is more" should be the crankshaft grinder's motto. Crankshafts are made like hammers—the outside surface is hardened to withstand wear and impact, and the inner core is soft for resiliency. It is possible to grind through the surface hardening, even though bearings are available for that undersize.

It is not wise to grind a single journal and not the others. The reduced diameter of one acts as a stress riser and may be the site of a crankshaft break.

The actual grinding, grit number and hardness wheel, feed, and linear speed are up to the crankshaft grinder and out of the province of this book. But there are ways to insure that the job was done correctly.

In the first palce, the oil-passage plugs should have been removed and the oil gallery flushed. (A reground crankshaft cannot be cleaned by dipping it in solvent and blowing out the oil ports.) The pin fillets should be gently radiused as shown in Fig. 9-47. The exact

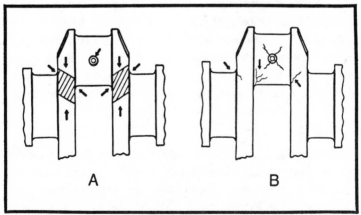

Fig. 9-46. The load-bearing areas of the crankshaft are shown in view A. View B shows typical crack formations. (Courtesy GM Detroit Diesel Allison)

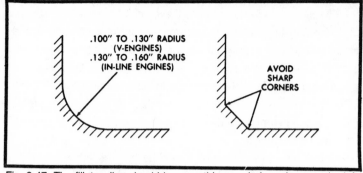

Fig. 9-47. The fillet radius should be smoothly rounded as shown at the left. (Courtesy GM Detroit Diesel Allison)

curve depends upon the engine, but it should be uniform and without sharp edges. The practice of grinding fillets by hand is not acceptable.

Improper grinding techniques can overheat the crankshaft and destroy its temper. The damage is not obvious unless the crankshaft is etched. A number of preparations can be used, but none are so versatile as the Tarasov etch. It will reveal soft as well as re-hardened areas.

Begin by scrubbing the bearing journals with scouring powder and water. Rinse with water and then with alcohol. Apply Tarasov etch No. 1 (4 parts nitric acid, 96 parts water) with a cotton swab and let stand for 15 seconds. Rinse with water and dry. Apply etch No. 2 (2 parts hydrochloric acid, 98 parts acetone) and let this stand for 15 seconds. Rinse with alcohol and blow dry with air.

Undamaged journals are a uniform dark gray. Softened areas are darker and can be coal black if the shaft has been severely damaged. Rehardened areas may be harder than the rest of the shaft and appear white under the etch. Any discoloration is reason to discard the shaft. The grinder should be advised to use a softer wheel, reduce the feed rate, or increase the work-spindle speed.

CAMSHAFTS

The camshaft and its associated hardware deserve careful scrutiny. The camshaft lobes are subject to the greatest pressures developed in the engine. These pressures are on the order of 150,000 psi at idle. In constrast, it is a high-compression engine that generates 600 psi on its pistons.

374

It is hardly surprising that the camshaft, camshaft bearings, tappets (cam followers), and drive train are subject to heavy wear.

Drive Train

In addition to the sheer magnitude of forces developed, the drive train must cope with uneven loads. The drive train tenses with each rise of a tappet and relaxes as the valve spring forces the tappet down and the cam around.

Camshafts for side- and overhead-valve engines are located in the block above the crankshaft. The distance between these two parts is set by the need for a 2 to 1 gear reduction. The camshaft turns at half engine speed since the engine has one power stroke every second shaft revolution. As a practical matter the only drive options are chains and gears. (Overhead-valve engines offer more room for experiment and can employ shafts, Gilmer belts, and even eccentrics to transmit power from the crankshaft to the camshaft.)

Chains are the mark of automotive power plants. They are relatively cheap and silent in operation. The disadvantage is chain stretch caused by wear. As the chain grows longer it rides higher on the sprockets and retards valve timing.

Manufacturers have not been able to devise a universal method for measuring chain stretch. But some idea of stretch can be had by using the engine as a load. Time the engine statically as described in Chapter 7. Then time the engine dynamically with a strobe light. If static and dynamic timing differ by 5 crankshaft degrees or more, the chain is stretched beyond safe limits and should be replaced.

Examine the sprocket teeth profiles. If the teeth appear deformed or if the wear marks show that the chain has ridden up from the roots of the sprocket teeth, replace the sprockets. It is good, but expensive, practice to replace chain and sprockets as a set.

Gear trains are one of the hallmarks of industrial engines. The greater initial expense and the noise are accepted for the better reliability of gears. Inspect the teeth for chips, cracks, irregular wear patterns, and other obvious defects. The clearance between the teeth, or lash, can be determined with a feeler gauge or by means of a piece of solder. The latter approach is preferred. Pinch off a short length of solder and lay it at the base of a crankshaft tooth. Rotate the crankshaft, bringing the solder into mesh with the cam-

Fig. 9-48. This Chrysler mechanic is determining gear lash with Plasti-Gage wire. Solder or a feeler gauge may also be used.

shaft gear (Fig. 9-48). Measure the crushed solder with a micrometer. If the solder is thicker than 0.006 inch, replace the gear set.

Camshaft gears are pressed and bolted to the camshaft hub. Crankshaft gears are pressed on and further secured by a key. An ordinary gear puller removes both (Fig. 9-49). (International Har-

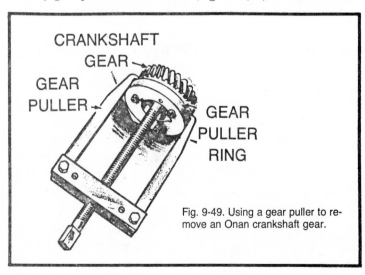

CRANKSHAFT
GEAR

GEAR
PULLER

GEAR
PULLER
RING

Fig. 9-49. Using a gear puller to remove an Onan crankshaft gear.

vester crankshaft gears are split at the pin and removed in two halves.) Press a new crankshaft gear on with an arbor. The camshaft gear can be forced over the camshaft by tightening its central bolt.

Align the timing marks. Most gear drives are simple two-wheel affairs and the timing drill is obvious. Complications arise when the engine is fitted with additional idler gear and accessory drives. The valve drive gears may have multiple marks (Fig. 9-50). Because of the distance between the sprockets, chain-driven engines must be timed with the help of a straightedge (Fig. 9-51).

Camshaft Removal and Installation

Lift the tappets out of their bores while the camshaft is still in place and store them in numbered racks for correct assembly. (Single-cylinder engines, used on the Prime-Move M15BR and

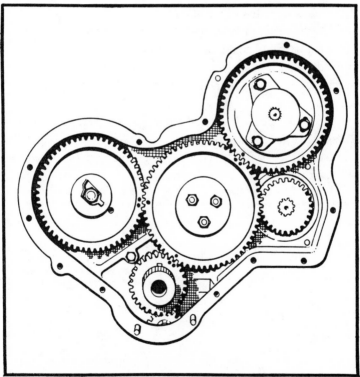

Fig. 9-50. The timing gear train for Lansing Bagnall (Perkins-engined) trucks. The asymmetrical single and double dot system used means that the engine can be timed only one way.

Fig. 9-51. Since real engines do not have imaginary white lines tying the marks together, they must be timed with the help of a straightedge. (Courtesy Chrysler Corp.)

other small trucks, have mushroom tappets that must be held clear of the lobes while the camshaft is withdrawn.)

Use two hands to steady the camshaft. It must not be allowed to strike the bearings or the bearing support webs, since the case-hardened "skin" is only a few thousandths of an inch thick and very vulnerable. A single chip and the tappet pressure peels the lobe like an onion.

Mike the camshaft journals and lobes. The lobe is measured across the larger and smaller diameters as shown in Fig. 9-52. The difference between BD and AC is the lift. This figure should agree with the manufacturer's specification.

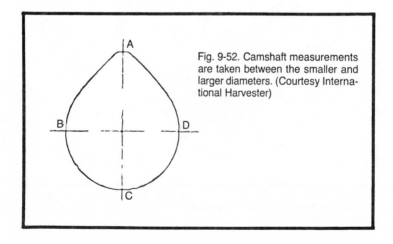

Fig. 9-52. Camshaft measurements are taken between the smaller and larger diameters. (Courtesy International Harvester)

The base of the tappets or the *feet* can be better indicators of camshaft wear than the lobes themselves. At least the wear is easier to see on the feet. New tappets appear flat on the bottom, but are actually convex. The crown or center of the foot is some 0.0005 inch higher than the edges. The individual lobes are ground on a slight angle with one side of the lobe about 0.002 inch higher than the other. This arrangement (Fig. 9-53) causes the tappet to rotate a few degrees during each lift cycle. This rotating motion produces less tappet and tappet bore wear than a simple reciprocation would. As the tappet feet wear, they become concave and dish inwards. At the same time the contact pattern widens and covers the whole lobe. Replace the camshaft and tappets when you observe this condition.

Use the tool shown in Fig. 9-54 to remove and install camshaft bushings. The last bushing in the series, the one on the power

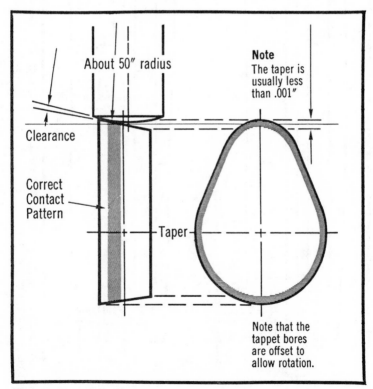

Fig. 9-53. The camshaft/tappet relationship. As the parts wear the tappet foot goes concave and the lobe contact pattern moves to the right. (Courtesy Sealed Power Corp.)

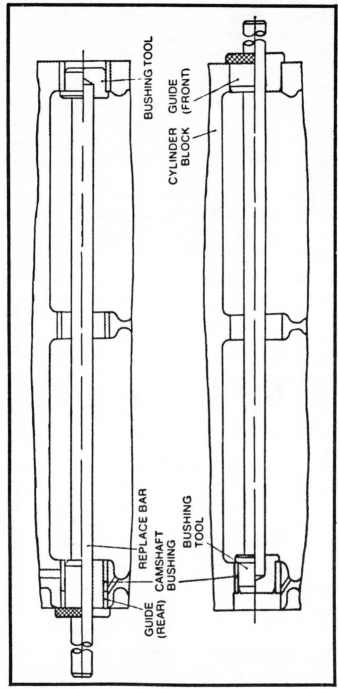

Fig. 9-54. A camshaft bushing tool for Chrysler-Nissan engines. Sized guides allow the bushings to be removed and installed without damage to the bearing webs.

takeoff side, is removed through the camshaft end plug at the rear of the block. Installation is critical in that the oil ports must align with the spillways in the bearing webs (Fig. 9-55). Some trial and error is par for the course.

It is difficult to overemphasize the need for lubricating the camshaft and tappets prior to initial startup. A dry camshaft literally wears itself bald in the few seconds of running before the pump delivers oil. Special extreme pressure camshaft lubricant is available from auto-parts dealers. This lubricant must be used whenever a new camshaft is installed. Used camshafts benefit from it, but can be adequately lubricated if the mechanic takes the precaution of pressurizing the oiling system before startup.

Once the camshaft is home, check the endplay or float (Fig. 9-56). The camshaft needs a minimum of 0.002 inch for heat expansion, but more than 0.006 inch makes for erratic wear patterns and excessive noise. The endplay is controlled by spacer washers or by a renewable thrust plate.

OILING SYSTEM

The oiling system consists of a positive-displacement pump, a pressure-relief valve, single or tandem filters, and a network of

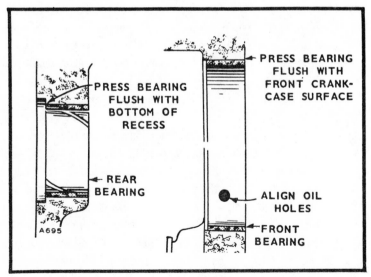

Fig. 9-55. Camshaft bushings must be installed with their oil holes over the bearing web spillways. (Courtesy Onan)

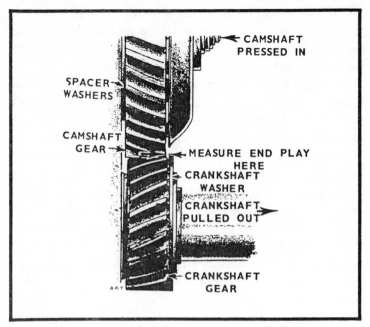

Fig. 9-56. Camshaft endplay is controlled by spacer washers in Onan and most other engines or by a replaceable thrust plate.

galleries, drilled passageways, and spillways. Figure 9-57 illustrates a typical circuit. Oil collects in the sump by virtue of gravity. It is recycled through the pump, passes over a pressure-relief valve, and into the filter. In this case the filter is connected in series and all pump output passes through it. The bypass valve is a failsafe feature. Should the pressure-drop across the filter become excessive, the valve opens and bypasses the filter. Some aftermarket filter elements have a valve to prevent draindown when the engine is stopped. The idea is to keep the filter case full so the bearings receive oil almost immediately upon startup.

The filtered oil goes to the camshaft gallery and through individual passages to each of the main bearings. The crankshaft connecting rod (pin) journals are lubricated by holes drilled from the main bearings. The oil that spills from the crank pins is flung about by centrifugal force. Some of it gets on the lower cylinder bores where it is distributed along the bores by the oil control piston rings.

In this particular engine, the No. 4 camshaft bushing meters oil to the rocker shaft. The relieved head bolt was apparently an

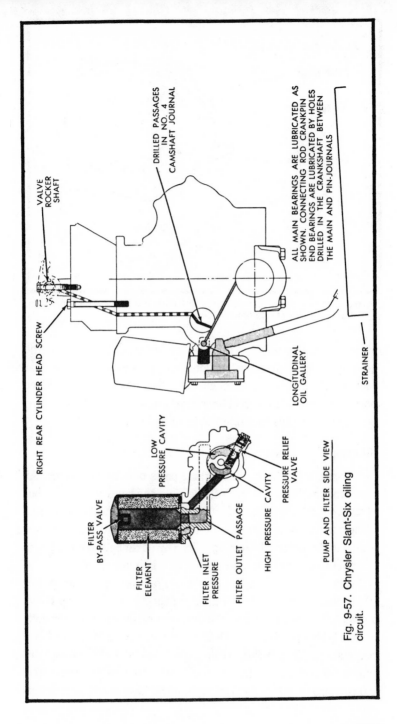

VALVE ROCKER SHAFT

RIGHT REAR CYLINDER HEAD SCREW

DRILLED PASSAGES IN NO. 4 CAMSHAFT JOURNAL

ALL MAIN BEARINGS ARE LUBRICATED AS SHOWN. CONNECTING ROD CRANKPIN END BEARINGS ARE LUBRICATED BY HOLES DRILLED IN THE CRANKSHAFT BETWEEN THE MAIN AND PIN-JOURNALS

STRAINER

LONGITUDINAL OIL GALLERY

LOW PRESSURE CAVITY

PRESSURE RELIEF VALVE

HIGH PRESSURE CAVITY

FILTER OUTLET PASSAGE

FILTER INLET PRESSURE

FILTER ELEMENT

FILTER BY-PASS VALVE

PUMP AND FILTER SIDE VIEW

Fig. 9-57. Chrysler Slant-Six oiling circuit.

383

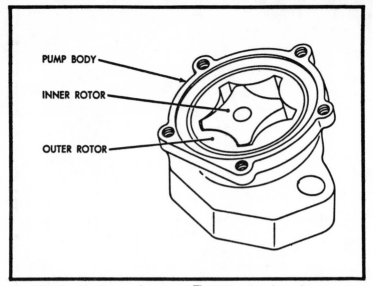

Fig. 9-58. Gerotor oil pump, less cover. The outer rotor always has one more tooth than the inner rotor to provide clearance.

afterthought. Normally the rocker-shaft feed passage is clear of the head bolts and other obstructions. Oil passes around the rear rocker-shaft screw and through the hollow rocker shaft. Drilled ports distribute oil to each of the rocker arms. The overflow returns be way of spillways cast into the head and block.

Oil Pumps

Figure 9-58 shows the working parts of a Gerotor pump. All that is missing is the cover. Both the inner and outer rotors turn, but at different rates and around different centers. The inside diameter of the pump body fixes the axis of the outer rotor, and the inner rotor is mounted eccentrically on a spindle. The offset between the two is compensated for by the extra tooth on the outer rotor.

There are three critical clearances on this type of pump: between the outer rotor and the inner diameter of the pump body, between the inner rotor tips and the outer rotor, and between both rotors and the pump cover. Determine the outer rotor/pump body clearance first (Fig. 9-59A). It should not exceed 0.012 inch with the inner rotor in place. The inner rotor/outer rotor clearance wear limit is 0.010 inch (Fig. 9-59B). The rotor/cover clearance is best determined with Plasti-Gage. Dry the parts thoroughly and lay a length of gauge wire over both rotors. Secure the end cover, remove it, and compare the width of the wire against the gauge printed on its envelope. The reading should be no more than 0.005 inch. Oil the pump before assembly.

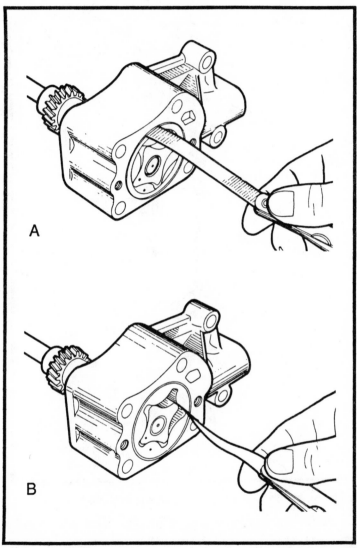

Fig. 9-59. Gerotor pump inspection. In view A the mechanic determines outer rotor/pump body clearance. In view B he establishes clearance between the inner and outer rotors. (Courtesy Chrysler Corp.)

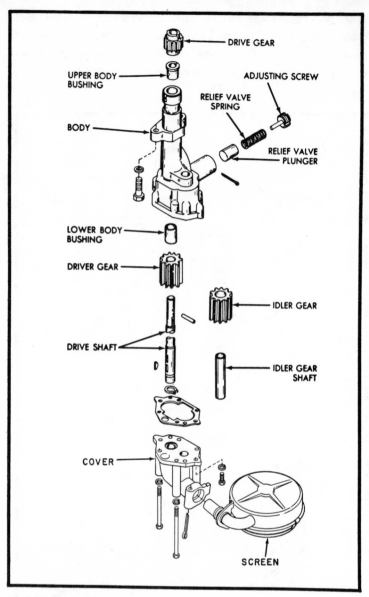

Fig. 9-60. A typical gear-type pump as found on a number of Waukesha models.

Geared pumps remain popular with the more conservative engine makers (Fig. 9-60). The major components are the pump body, cover, driver and idler gears, and the respective gear shafts. Most incorporate an integral relief valve.

Without disturbing the relief valve, disassemble and clean the pump. Inspect the gears and shaft for irregular wear patterns, score marks, chips, and other evidence of distress. Determine the gear lash with solder or Plasti-Gage. The lash should be held under 0.018 inch for all but the largest pumps. Plasti-Gage is also used to determine the clearance between the cover and gear ends. Reject or resurface the cover if the clearance between its inner side and the gear ends exceeds 0.006 inch.

The drive shaft is supported by a bushing along most of its length. The unsupported portion of the shaft is the original diameter. Using a micrometer, compare this diameter with the diameter of the worn area. The difference should not exceed 0.002 inch. If it does, replace the shaft and bushing.

Oil the pump before assembly.

Oil Distribution System Inspection and Troubleshooting

Galleries, passageways, and lines should be filled with solvent and flushed with compressed air. Repeat the process until the solvent blows clean. Pay scrupulous attention to discharge ports. It is by no means unusual to find ports that are incompletely drilled or clogged with chips.

Inspection is a continuous process. As each pressure-lubricated engine part is dismantled, identify and check the allied branch of the oiling circuit. You can discover stoppages and leaks with the help of high-pressure air. Caution: Do not play the discharge stream on your skin. At pressure greater than 30 psi, compressed air can penetrate human skin and send bubbles into the blood stream.

The usual complaint, low oil pressure, can have a number of causes. Look for worn crankshaft bearings, oil leaks on the pressure side of the system, air leaks on the suction side (between the pickup tube and pump body), and a clogged pump pickup screen. Excessive pressure is rare, but should be corrected since it stresses the system and ultimately gutters the bearings. Check the vehicle gauge against a known accurate test gauge. Then change the oil. If the pressure is still high, change the filter element. Should a new filter cause pressure to return to normal, the bypass valve is faulty and should be repaired or replaced.

In both cases, low or excessively high pressure, the relief valve is the last component to be suspected. Turn to it only after the more likely causes have been eliminated.

Relief valve construction is standardized on the pattern shown in Fig. 9-60. Failure involves four possibilities: the valve can be out of adjustment, the spring may be weak or broken, the plunger may be bound by gum and varnish, or the plunger face may be scored.

Tightening the pump adjustment screw increases system pressure; loosening the screw reduces pressure. Small adjustments may be necessary to compensate for wear. If the valve does not respond to a slight tweaking, it should be taken apart and inspected.

Count the number of turns as you unthread the screw. This is the reference for initial adjustment upon assembly. Hold the screw captive with your thumb as you reach the last thead. The screw may, depending upon the pump design, be under considerable spring pressure. Withdraw the spring and plunger and clean the parts in solvent. Compare the free-standing height of the spring with a new one. Replace if the spring is more than 10% short. Inspect the valve end of the plunger and the seat in the relief-valve body. Small irregularities can be removed with valve grinding compound. Oil the parts before assembly.

Running Gear

The running gear consists of the steering-axle assembly, clutch, torque converter, transmission, drive shaft, reduction gears, differential, and braking systems. Transmissions may be manually or automatically shifted.

The running gear is the most diverse area of lift truck technology. With the exception of transmissions and rear-axle assemblies, these parts are built to the truck manufacturer's individual specifications. Dry-plate clutches, not much different from (and sometimes interchangeable with) automobile clutches may be used, although truck builders generally prefer multiplate clutches running in oil and engaged hydraulically. Transmissions may include a reverse gear or may not, according to the designer's whims. If reverse is omitted, a second, reversing transmission is fitted at the differential. Manual boxes may be used in conjunction with a torque converter, although this option is pretty well ancient history today. The rear wheels are almost always driven through a set of reduction gears, but direct-drive trucks have been built in the larger sizes. Automatic transmissions are special types designed for lift-truck applications and no other. These boxes typically offer forward and reverse in two speed ranges. Many feature an "inching" control so the vehicle can creep in restricted quarters.

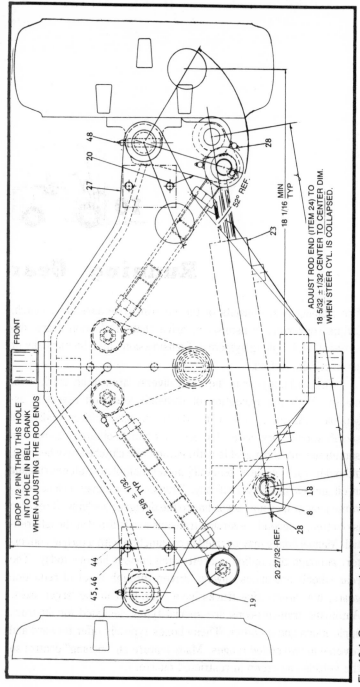

FRONT

DROP 1/2 PIN THRU THIS HOLE
INTO HOLE IN BELL CRANK
WHEN ADJUSTING THE ROD ENDS

45, 46
44

12 5/8 ± 1/32
TYP

19

20 27/32 REF.

8   18

28

23

ADJUST ROD END (ITEM 24) TO
18 5/32 ±1/32 CENTER TO CENTER DIM.
WHEN STEER CYL. IS COLLAPSED.

18 1/16
MIN
TYP

28

52° REF.

27

20

48

Fig. 10-1. One approach to steering with a single power cylinder and two tierods. The axle is hung on two horizontal pins and is free to list a few degrees. (Courtesy Drexel Industries, Inc.)

390

While specific repair procedures vary between makes and models, none of this gear is particularly sophisticated or outrageously demanding. (Automatic transmissions are an exception, and I won't try to talk about them here.) Standard inspection and repair procedures apply.

STEERING AXLE

Figure 10-1 illustrates a steering axle employing a single hydraulic cylinder. The base of the cylinder is secured by a pin. The piston rod connects to the right-hand steering knuckle. As the piston rod extends, the wheel arcs to the left. This motion is transferred through tie rods and a bell crank (sometimes called a "spider") to the left-side wheel.

The next drawing, Fig. 10-2, shows an interesting variation. Two steering cylinders are used. The base ends of the cylinders are mounted on a bell crank while the piston rod ends are fixed to stanchions at the axle ends. The cylinder bodies move, rather than the piston rods. Their movement is relayed through tie rods to the steering knuckles and wheels.

WHEEL BEARINGS

The signs of bearing failure are unmistakable—the machine wobbles as clearances open up and the bearing may groan and

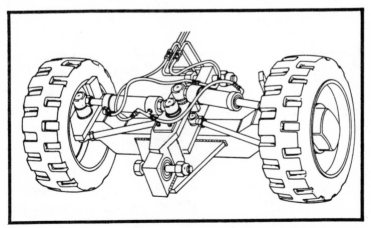

Fig. 10-2. In some respects the Lancer Boss represents a kind of mirror image of the axle in the previous illustration. The power steering cylinders are anchored at their outboard ends and react against the bell crank.

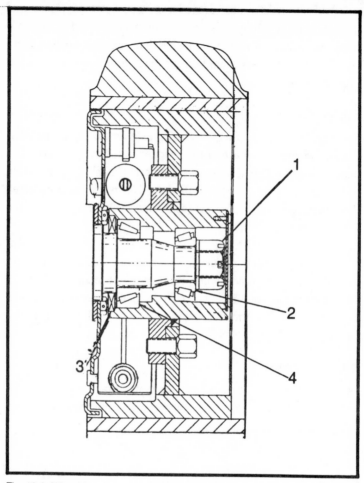

Fig. 10-3. Wheel bearing arrangement in the Drexel. Note the seal behind the inboard bearing.

grumble in protest. Before long the wheel locks solid. Figure 10-3 is our reference drawing. To remove a wheel bearing follow these steps:

1. Block the vehicle up and remove the offending wheel.
2. Remove the cotter pin, nut (No. 1), and thrust washer. Some types dispense with the cotter pin and secure the nut with a tabbed washer.
3. Withdraw the wheel from the spindle.
4. Retrieve the outboard bearing (No. 2) from the wheel.

5. Pry out the dust seal (No. 3). Fiber seals can be reused. The lipped garter-spring variety must be replaced if disturbed.

6. Withdraw the inboard bearing (No. 4).

Wash the bearings in trichloroethylene or the equivalent. The solvent must be potent enough to remove all traces of grease. Dry with filtered compressed air and scrutinize the rollers for flaking, cracks, rust pits, flat spots, and for the discoloration that means overheating. Turn the bearing by hand and be alert for excessive noise (some rattle is normal) and binding. Replace any bearing that is suspect, together with its opposite number on the other wheel.

Pack the bearings with high-temperature bearing grease. (Chassis lube melts and runs.) Tools are available for this chore and are certainly worth the money. Without a special tool, the only way to pack a bearing is the messy way. Place a blob of grease in the palm of one hand and draw the bearing edge down into it. Turn the bearing slightly and repeat the operation until the bearing cage is packed solid.

Wipe off the spindle and flush out the bearing cavity in the wheel. To assemble:

1. Position the inboard bearing (No. 4) in the wheel cavity.

2. Install the dust seal (No. 3). (Garter-spring seals are pressed into place.)

3. Mount the wheel on the spindle.

4. Install the outboard bearing (No. 2) and thrust washer.

5. Tighten the nut just to the point that all end play disappears. Do not overtighten. Turn the wheel and check that the bearings are seated.

6. Back off the nut (No. 1) 1/12–1/6 turn to give 0.0004 inch end play.

7. Install the cotter pin or tab washer.

8. Secure the hub cap.

KINGPINS AND BUSHINGS

The steering knuckles—U-shaped forgings that support the wheels—arc on kingpins and bushings (Fig. 10-4). Wear is signaled

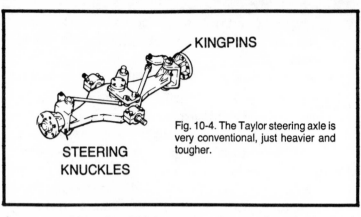

KINGPINS

STEERING
KNUCKLES

Fig. 10-4. The Taylor steering axle is very conventional, just heavier and tougher.

by poor tracking, sluggish response to the steering wheel, and, in extreme cases, by wheel oscillation.

To dismantle:

1. Detach the steering assembly from the vehicle. Cap the hydraulic lines.
2. Disconnect the tie-rod ends at the steering knuckles.
   a. Remove the cotter pins and slotted nuts securing each tie-rod end.
   b. Separate the tie-rod ends from the steering knuckles as detailed in the next paragraph.
3. Remove the necessary steering cylinder(s).
4. Examine the kingpin and steering knuckle to determine if one end of the pin is flanged. If it is, the pin is withdrawn toward the flanged side. The pin is secured to the knuckle by a bolt, compression pin, or setscrew. Remove any fastener.
5. Press out the kingpin. If an arbor press is not available, use a heavy hammer and a drift pin.
6. Retrieve the lower thrust bearings and spacers.
7. Drive out the kingpin bushings. Figure 10-5 shows two typical bushing tools. The dimensions depend upon the machine in question.

To assemble:

1. Press new bushings into the steering knuckle. Figure 10-6 details this procedure.
2. Position the thrust bearings and spacers.

3. Lubricate the kingpins with chassis grease and install.
4. Measure the up-and-down movement of the steering knuckle. Zero lash is ideal, so long as the knuckle arcs without binding. Some manufacturers allow 0.025 inch. Add shims under the upper bushing as required.
5. Secure the kingpins to the steering knuckles with the bolts, compression pins, or setscrews provided.
6. Lubricate the bushings at the grease fittings.

TIE RODS

The tie (or track) rods transmit steering inputs from one wheel to the other. In the neutral, straight-ahead position the tie rods determine the amount of toe-in. The steering wheels must toe-in for tracking stability. The amount of toe-in is expressed in factory specifications as the difference between A and B in Fig. 10-7.

To adjust:

1. Position the vehicle over a service pit.
2. Set the rear wheels dead ahead. Some designs include a reference mark on the bell crank; others must be aligned with the aid of boards or steel channels placed alongside the machine and snugged against the front and rear wheels.
3. Loosen the lock or clamp nuts at the four tie-rod ends (Fig. 10-8).
4. Turn the tie rods with the wrench flats provided. Each tie rod has a left- and right-hand threaded end. Turning the tie

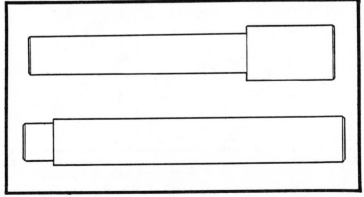

Fig. 10-5. Kingpin bushing tools are usually made up in the shop, dimensioned to fit the machines at hand. (Courtesy Bonser Engineering Ltd.)

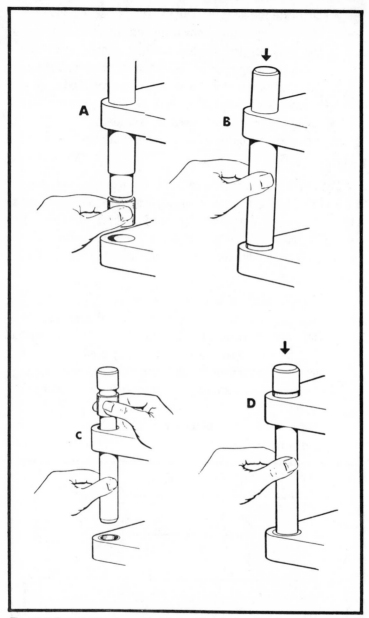

Fig. 10-6. To install the lower kingpin bushing, first position it over the tool (A), then drive the tool home (B). The shank of the tool is the same diameter as the upper bushing boss and assures that the lower bushing is centered. Another tool, with its shank sized to bushing diameter, and its head to bushing boss diameter is used to install the upper bushing (C and D). (Courtesy Bonser Engineering Ltd.)

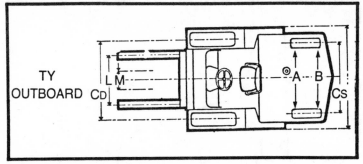

Fig. 10-7. Dimension A should be fractionally smaller than dimension B. (Courtesy Bonser Engineering Ltd.)

rod moves it into or out of the ends and changes its effective length.

5. Measure the distance between the right and left wheel rims at the leading edge. This is measurement A in Fig. 10-7. Compare this measurement with one taken at the trailing edge (measurement B). Adjust the tie rods to specification.

6. Tighten the clamp bolts.

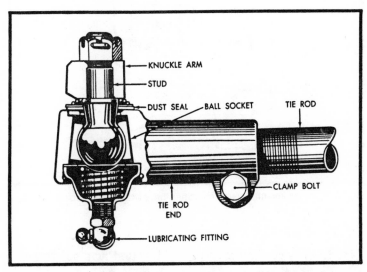

Fig. 10-8. A typical tie-rod in cross section. To remove, undo the slotted nut and insert the business end of a crow's foot tool between the tie-rod end and steering knuckle at the area occupied by the dust seal. Another method is to support the knuckle and drive the stud out with a soft-faced hammer.

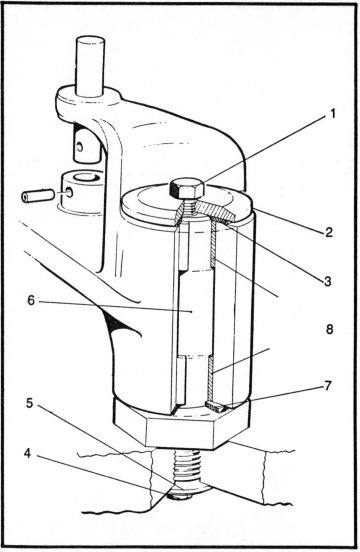

Fig. 10-9. Bonser and many other machines thread the bell crank pin into the top of the axle.

To remove:

1. Remove the cotter pins and slotted nuts securing the tie-rod ends to the steering knuckle and bell crank.

2. Outboard tie-rod studs are always tapered for an interference fit with the steering knuckle. Inboard studs may have

a straight diameter. Remove the tapered studs with a crow's foot tool or with a soft-faced hammer. Take care not to damage the stud threads.

Bell-crank pivot pins are usually threaded into the axle. Figure 10-9 shows an example of this kind of construction. The bushing is subject to severe wear because of road shock and dust. It is not necessary to remove the axle to replace the bushing on most modern machines. (Old models are a different story, and removing the axle usually saves time in the long run.) To replace the bushing:

1. Remove the steering cylinders, tie rods, and other impedimenta.
2. Remove the bolt (No. 1), cover washer (No. 2), and thrust washer (No. 3) from the top.
3. Remove the bolt (No. 4) and washer (No. 5) from below.
4. Using its wrench flats, unscrew the pivot pin (No. 6).
5. Withdraw the pivot pin from the bell crank and remove the thrust washer (No. 7).
6. Drive out the bushings (No. 8) with a suitable drift. Installation is the reverse of the above procedure. Press the bushings to the same depth as they were originally and apply Loctite to the pivot threads before installation.

DRIVE AXLE

The drive axle consists of the final gear reduction and the differential. Two-speed axles are sometimes used with manual transmissions.

Final Reduction

Larger machines incorporate the final stage of gear reduction in a "drop box" ahead of the differential (Fig. 10-10). Small-and

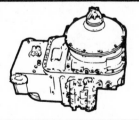

Fig. 10-10. Taylor machines are equipped with Allison transmissions.

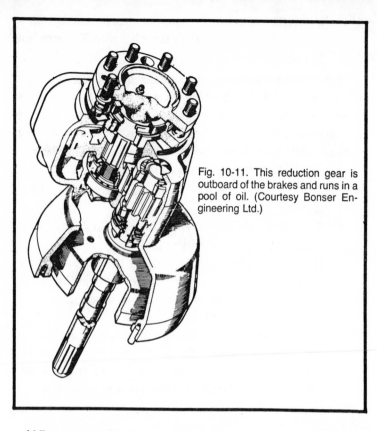

Fig. 10-11. This reduction gear is outboard of the brakes and runs in a pool of oil. (Courtesy Bonser Engineering Ltd.)

middle-range machines mount the reduction gears at or just behind the wheels (Figs. 10-11 and 10-12). In the latter arrangement an internal gear (shown in Fig. 10-12 as No. 60) is integral with the wheel hub. A variant of this approach, used by Towmotor and others, is to mill teeth on the inside diameter of the wheel itself. In any event, gear teeth loadings are high and after a few thousand hours you can expect failures.

While there are detail differences between makes, the Rockwell unit in Fig.10-12 is typical of many and forms the basis of our discussion:

To dismantle:

1. Remove the 12 nuts and lockwasher (Nos. 1 and 2) securing the brake drum and wheel assembly to the gear case (No. 5).
2. Slacken the brake adjustment.

3. Remove the wheel (No. 5) and the brake drum (No. 4).
4. Disconnect the brake line (No. 16).
5. Remove the gear case (No. 51).
6. Remove the oil seal (No. 55), hub cap (No. 56), cotter pin (No. 57), nut (No. 58), washer (No. 59), outer bearing cup (No. 62), outer cone (No. 61) and internal gear (No. 60).
7. Remove the inner cup (No. 64) and cone (No. 63).
8. Remove the bolts (No. 69), nuts (No. 66) and lockwashers from the spindle (No. 71).
9. Withdraw the axle shaft (No. 72).
10. Remove the nut (No. 73), washer (No. 74), lockwasher (No. 77), and dowel (No. 75).
11. Remove the gasket (No. 80), bearing (No. 81), collar (No. 82), cone (No. 83), and cup (No. 84).

Clean the parts in solvent with particular attention paid to the bearings. Inspect the parts for evidence of damage. If the bearings roll rough, are galled, spalled, or pitted, replace them. Replace the gears if they are cracked, scored, or pitted.

Assembly is the reverse of disassembly. Coat inboard face of the wheel spindle (No. 71) and its hold-down bolts (69) with Permatex before mounting. Torque the bolts in increments to 200 ft-lb. Pack the bearings as described under "Wheel Bearings." Tighten the adjusting nut (No. 58) for a light drag as the wheel is turned. Secure with a new cotter pin.

Differential

Figure 10-13 is an exploded view of a differential used with a previous stage of gear reduction. Those used before final reduction are distinguished primarily by the shape of the castings. The principle of operation and the configuration of parts are the same.

The most critical aspect of servicing, and the reason why many mechanics prefer to replace differentials as an assembly, is the matter of gear mesh. Improper adjustment leads to early and catastrophic failure.

Figure 10-14 illustrates the preliminaries. All measurements must fall within factory tolerances for the unit at hand. Check pinion-end float as shown in A while levering the pinion fore and aft.

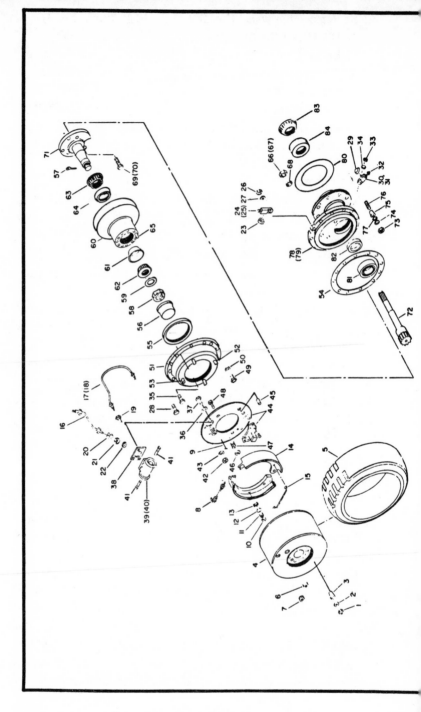

ITEM NO.	DESCRIPTION
1	NUT
2	WASHER, LOCK
3	DOWEL (ROCKWELL)
4	DRUM, BRAKE AND WHEEL
5	WHEEL
6	PLUG
7	PLUG
8	SPRING, RETURN
9	ROD
10	RETAINER
11	SPRING
12	RETAINER
13	NOT USED
14	SHOE AND LINING ASSY LINING, BRAKE
15	SPRING, RETAINER
16	LINE ASSY. BRAKE ACTUATING
17	LINE ASSY. BLEEDER
18	LINE ASSY. BLEEDER
19	ADAPTER, BRAKE BLEEDER SCREW
20	ELBOW
21	ADAPTER, HYD BRAKE CYL
22	GASKET, HYD INLET ADAPTER
23	FITTING, BRAKE LINE
24	ELBOW
25	FITTING, BRAKE LINE
26	NUT JAM
27	WASHER
28	SCREW, CAP
29	ELBOW
30	FITTING
31	FITTING
32	SCREW, BLEEDER
33	NUT JAM
34	WASHER
35	SCREW, CAP
36	WASHER, LOCK
37	SCREW, CAP
38	SPACER
39	CYL ASSY, BRAKE RH
40	CYL ASSY, BRAKE LH
41	PUSHROD, CYL
42	NUT
43	WASHER, LOCK
44	PLATE, BACKING
45	DOWEL
46	CAM, ADJ
47	SPRING
48	BOLT ASSY
49	SCREW, CAP
50	WASHER, LOCK
51	CASE, F.D. GEAR
52	STUD
53	STUD
54	GASKET
55	SEAL, OIL
56	CAP, HUB
57	PIN, COTTER
58	NUT
59	WASHER
60	GEAR, F.D. INTERNAL
61	CUP, OUTER
62	CONE, OUTER
63	INNER
64	CUP, INNER
65	STUD
66	NUT
67	NUT
68	WASHER, LOCK
69	BOLT
70	BOLT
71	SPINDLE, WHEEL
72	SHAFT, AXLE
73	NUT
74	WASHER
75	DOWEL
76	STUD
77	WASHER, LOCK
78	HOUSING, AXLE HL
79	HOUSING, AXLE RH
80	GASKET
81	BEARING
82	COLLAR
83	CONE
84	CUP

Fig. 10-12. Drexel and other American truck builders use the Rockwell drive axle with outboard brakes.

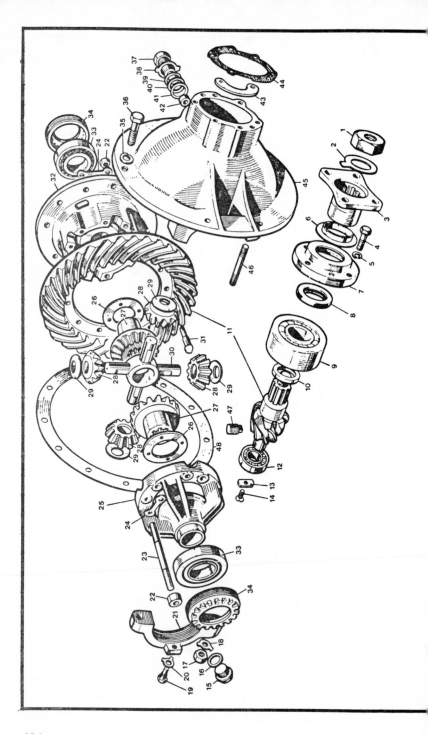

Item No.	Description	Item No.	Description	Item No.	Description
1	Nut – Pinion Flange	17	Nut	33	Bearing – Taper Roller
2	Lockwasher – Bevel Pinion Shaft	18	Lockwasher	34	Collar – Adjusting
3	Flange – Bevel Pinion Shaft	19	Screw	35	Washer
4	Setscrew – Pinion Bearing Cover	20	Lockwasher	36	Setscrew
5	Spring Washer – Setscrew	21	Cap – Bearing	37	Screw – Crown Wheel Kick Pad
6	Dust Shield – Bevel Pinion Shaft	22	Nut	38	Lockwasher
7	Cover – Pinion Bearing	23	Stud – Crown Wheel Carrier	39	Washer
8	Oil Seal – Bevel Pinion	24*	Lockwasher	40	Washer
9	Front Bearing – Bevel Pinion Shaft	25	Cap (Part of 32)	41	Pad for Crown Wheel – Kick
10	Thrust Washer – Bevel Pinion	26	Thrust Washer – Differential Gear	42	Locating Plate – Roller Bearing
11	Crown Wheel and Pinion	27	Wheel – Differential (Sunwheel)	43	Gasket – Pinion Bearing Cover
12	Bearing – Bevel Pinion – Rear (Roller)	28	Pinion Differential (Starwheel)	44	Carrier
13	Retaining Plate – Roller Bearing	29	Thrust Washer – Differential Pinion	45	Stud – Differential Bearing Cap
14	Screw – Retaining Plate	30	Spider – Differential	46	Plug – Drain
15	Plug – Filler	31	Bolt – Crown Wheel	47	Gasket
16	Washer	32	Crown Wheel Carrier (Case Assembly)	48	
				*	Not used with Self Locking Cleveloc Nut

Fig. 10-13. Heavy Conveyancer trucks drive through a BLMC axle.

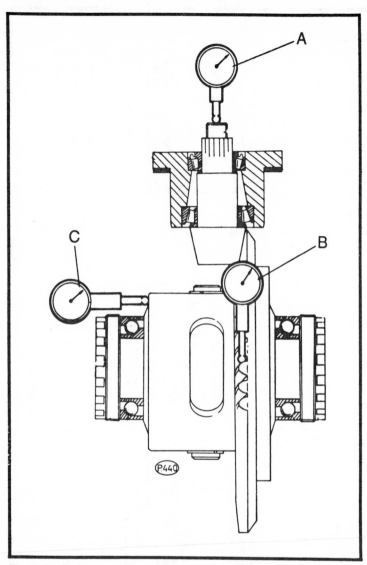

Fig. 10-14. Setting up a differential involves these measurements: pinion end float (A); crown wheel lash (B); and cage float (C). (Courtesy Bonser Engineering Ltd.)

Add or subtract spacers from under the pinion bearing if adjustment is necessary. To determine crown wheel lash, first lock the pinion and the side (spider) gears. Mount a dial indicator at right angles to the crown gear (B) and rock the gear back and forth. Cage-end float may be checked as shown in (C), although most mechanics are content to adjust for zero float and back off the bearing collars one notch.

When these adjustments are completed, coat the crown-gear teeth with Prussian blue or white lead. Apply a slight load to the pinion shaft and rotate the crown gear back and forth. Contact should be slightly toward the outer edge of the crown wheel and cover about 2/3 of the length of the teeth. Correct and incorrect patterns are shown in Fig. 10-15.

TRANSMISSIONS

Figure 10-16 illustrates a two-speed reversing transmission. The drawing provides a view of the major components, but is not accurate as far as shaft centers are concerned. The reverse idler gear No. 4273 is in constant mesh with the cluster gear No. 4266. A pair of input gears rides on roller bearings No. 171 on the input shaft No. 4260. One No. 4261 input gear is in constant mesh with the

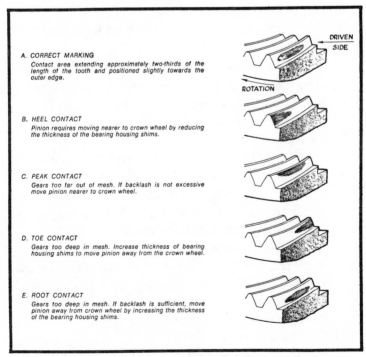

Fig. 10-15. Crown wheel markings. Do not accept anything less than A. (Courtesy Bonser Engineering Ltd.)

reverse idler gear No. 4273. The other is in constant mesh with the cluster gear No. 4266. This arrangement is typical of lift-truck transmissions and distinguishes them from automotive transmissions that carry reverse as an auxiliary gear, to be meshed upon need. Engagement is via the clutch sleeve No. 4262. The sleeve moves fore and aft to mate either of the No. 4261 gears.

A similar mechanism provides low and high speeds. Gears 4270 and 4271 ride on the output shaft. These gears are in constant engagement with the cluster-gear set. Clutch sleeve 4208 is splined to the output shaft and rotates with it. Moving the sleeve to the right clutches it to gear 4270 for low speed; moving it to the left releases low and clutches in 4271 for high speed.

It is futile in a book such as this to give specific repair instructions for this or any other lift-truck transmissions. Other than they all share the constant-mesh principle and shift by means of sliding clutch members, each transmission is a more or less unique proposition. Instructions that apply to one would be misleading in the context of another.

However, in a very general and broad sense, there are certain repair procedures that apply to all.

- Take as much time as you need to understand the workings of the transmission. In some cases you will be able to see the parts by removing a cover plate; otherwise you will have to partly disassemble the box. But you must understand what it is *as a unit*.
- If the box is at all complex, lay the parts out on the bench in the sequence of removal. Clean and inspect one part at a time and return it to its place on the bench. When it's time to put the transmission back together, work through the sequence backwards, beginning with the last part.
- Inspect the gears with a microscopic eye. Any irregularity on the pressure faces of the teeth means that the gear will soon fail. If at all possible, replace gears as meshed pairs.
- Use new gaskets of the same thickness as the originals. The thickness of the gaskets determines end play.
- Test the transmission by hand, before mounting it in the vehicle, shifting the clutches to verify that all speeds are available and turning the input shaft to detect binds

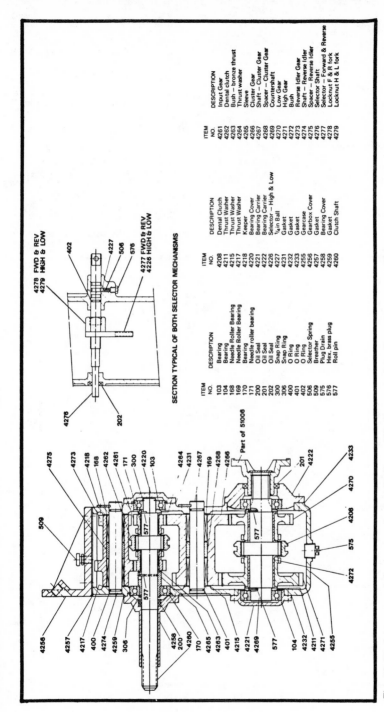

SECTION TYPICAL OF BOTH SELECTOR MECHANISMS

ITEM NO.	DESCRIPTION
103	Bearing
104	Bearing
168	Needle Roller Bearing
169	Needle Roller Bearing
170	Bearing
171	Needle roller bearing
200	Oil Seal
201	Oil Seal
202	Oil Seal
300	Snap Ring
306	Snap Ring
400	O Ring
401	O Ring
402	O Ring
506	Selector Spring
509	Breather
575	Plug Drain
576	Hex. brass plug
577	Roll pin

ITEM NO.	DESCRIPTION
4208	Dental Clutch
4211	Thrust Washer
4215	Thrust Washer
4217	Thrust Washer
4218	Keeper
4220	Bearing Cover
4221	Bearing Carrier
4222	Bearing Carrier
4226	Selector — High & Low
4227	¼ in Ball
4231	Gasket
4232	Gasket
4233	Gasket
4255	Gearcase
4256	Gearbox Cover
4257	Gasket
4258	Bearing Cover
4259	Gasket
4260	Clutch Shaft

ITEM NO.	DESCRIPTION
4261	Input Gear
4262	Dental clutch
4263	Bush — bronze thrust
4264	Thrust washer
4265	Sleeve
4266	Cluster Gear
4267	Shaft — Cluster Gear
4268	Spacer — Cluster Gear
4269	Countershaft
4270	Low Gear
4271	High Gear
4272	Bush
4273	Reverse Idler Gear
4274	Shaft — Reverse Idler
4275	Spacer — Reverse Idler
4276	Selector Shaft
4277	Selector — Forward & Reverse
4278	Locknut F & R fork
4279	Locknut H & L fork

Fig. 10-16. A two-speed, forward and reversing box of the type used on Conveyancer machines.

409

CLUTCHES

Heat is the enemy of clutches. Dry or air-cooled clutches work fine in automobiles, tow tractors, and other vehicles designed to spend most of their working lives running in one direction. But the ordinary dry clutch is inadequate for lift trucks that are reversed almost continuously. For this kind of service we need some sort of positively cooled clutch.

Wet clutches use oil as the cooling medium. Oil circulates over the pressure plate and disc, and out to the heat sink at the radiator.

Figure 10-17 illustrates one popular wet clutch in cross section. The clutch disc or plate No. 4194A is splined to the transmission input shaft. Coil springs in the pressure plate hold the disc securely

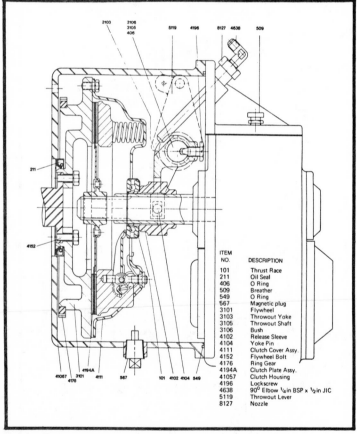

ITEM NO.	DESCRIPTION
101	Thrust Race
211	Oil Seal
406	O Ring
509	Breather
549	O Ring
567	Magnetic plug
3101	Flywheel
3103	Throwout Yoke
3105	Throwout Shaft
3106	Bush
4102	Release Sleeve
4104	Yoke Pin
4111	Clutch Cover Assy.
4152	Flywheel Bolt
4176	Ring Gear
4194A	Clutch Plate Assy.
41057	Clutch Housing
4196	Lockscrew
4638	90° Elbow 1/4 in BSP x 1/2 in JIC
5119	Throwout Lever
8127	Nozzle

Fig. 10-17. Conveyancer trucks employ oil clutches.

against the machined face of the flywheel. So long as the disc and flywheel are in intimate contact, power flows out of the flywheel and into the transmission. The clutch is disengaged by means of the throwout lever No. 5119 acting against the throwout bearing No. 101. Leftward pressure on the bearing releases the pressure plate and the clutch disc moves away from the flywheel. Power stops at the clutch.

Special features of this clutch (and of wet clutches in general) are the oil discharge nozzle No. 8127, the use of cork rather than asbestos disc linings, and the oil seals. The main seal No. 211 is at the flywheel hub. Additional seals prevent leakage around the throwout-lever shaft. The transmission case is sealed by an O-ring at the transmission housing.

Observe these precautions when servicing clutches:

- Torque the pressure plate to the flywheel with the utmost care. Run up the fasteners in a crisscross pattern, tightening each a few revolutions at a time. Failure to do this will distort the pressure plate.
- Do not attempt to adjust the pressure-plate fingers (shown in the lower half of the drawing).
- Replace the throwout bearing as a matter of course.

BRAKE SYSTEMS

The brake system consists of a master cylinder, slave cylinders at each wheel, and shoe and drum assemblies. Larger machines feature a vacuum-operated booster to reduce pedal effort.

The plumbing should offer no difficulty for an experienced truck mechanic. If he can cope with lift and tilt cylinder hydraulics, he can certainly handle the simple systems used to engage the shoes against the drums.

But lift-truck brake systems have some special characteristics that should be taken into account. In the first place, brake systems are not self-bleeding. The only way to remove air from the system is by opening a line or wheel-cylinder bleeder screws and purging the system with brake fluid. The quick and dirty approach is to open the connection and have a helper press the brake pedal. The connection must be closed before the pedal is released to prevent air from backing into the system.

The rubber seals or cups do not tolerate petroleum. *Never* clean a master or wheel cylinder in petroleum-based solvent. Use alcohol or brake fluid.

And finally you should realize that brake fluid is hydroscopic—that is, it has an affinity for water. Keep fluid containers tightly capped and store out of the weather. Since the reservoir is vented to the atmosphere, the fluid is exposed to air and draws some water from it. Water plays havoc with seals and aluminum parts, so a wise mechanic will drain and flush the system with alcohol once a year or so.

Index

Index

416